Practice and Procedure for the
Quantity Surveyor

By the same Authors
SPECIFICATION WRITING FOR ARCHITECTS AND SURVEYORS
ELEMENTS OF QUANTITY SURVEYING
MORE ADVANCED QUANTITY SURVEYING
and in collaboration with W. N. B. GEORGE and H. P. SCHER
THE ARCHITECT IN PRACTICE

Also by Arthur J. Willis
AN EXAMPLE IN QUANTITY SURVEYING
INTRODUCING GENEALOGY
CANTERBURY MARRIAGE LICENCES 1751-1780
CANTERBURY MARRIAGE LICENCES 1781-1809
CANTERBURY MARRIAGE LICENCES 1810-1837
CANTERBURY LICENCES (GENERAL) 1568-1646
HAMPSHIRE MARRIAGE LICENCES 1607-1640
HAMPSHIRE MARRIAGE LICENCES 1669-1680
HAMPSHIRE MARRIAGE ALLEGATIONS 1689-1837 (SUPPLEMENT)
WILLS, ADMINISTRATIONS AND INVENTORIES WITH THE
WINCHESTER DIOCESAN RECORDS
WINCHESTER SETTLEMENT PAPERS 1667-1842
WINCHESTER GUARDIANSHIPS after 1700
WINCHESTER ORDINATIONS
I Ordinands' Papers 1734-1827
II Bishops' Registers, Subscription Books and Exhibition of Orders 1660-1829
A HAMPSHIRE MISCELLANY
I   Metropolitical Visitation 1607-8
II Laymens' Licences of the Diocese of Winchester 1675-1834
III Dissenters' Meeting House Certificates 1702-1844
IV Exhibit Books, Terriers and Episcopatus Redivivus
WINCHESTER CONSISTORY COURT DEPOSITIONS (Selections 1561-1602)
CHURCH LIFE IN KENT, 1559-1565

in collaboration with A. L. Merson
A CALENDAR OF SOUTHAMPTON APPRENTICESHIP REGISTERS
1609-1740
(*Southampton Records Series*)

in collaboration with Margaret J. Hoad and Robert P. Grime
BOROUGH SESSIONS PAPERS 1653-1688
(*Portsmouth Record Series*)

in collaboration with Molly Tatchell
GENEALOGY FOR BEGINNERS

Arthur J. Willis, F.R.I.C.S., Hon. F.I.Q.S. and
Christopher J. Willis, F.R.I.C.S., F.C.I.Arb.

Practice and Procedure for the Quantity Surveyor

Eighth edition

GRANADA
London Toronto Sydney New York

Granada Publishing Limited – Technical Books Division
Frogmore, St Albans, Herts AL2 2NF
and
3 Upper James Street, London W1R 4BP
866 United Nations Plaza, New York, NY 10017, USA
117 York Street, Sydney, NSW 2000, Australia
100 Skyway Avenue, Rexdale, Ontario M9W 3A6, Canada
PO Box 84165, Greenside, 2034 Johannesburg, South Africa
CML Centre, Queen & Wyndham, Auckland 1, New Zealand

British Library Cataloguing in Publication Data
Willis, Arthur James
Practice and procedure for the quantity surveyor. –
8th ed.
1. Building – Estimates – Great Britain
I. Title   II. Willis, Christopher James
624'.1   TH435

ISBN 0-246-11172-0
ISBN 0-246-11242-5 Pbk

First published in Great Britain 1951 by Crosby Lockwood and Son Ltd
Second edition 1957
Third edition 1963
Fourth edition 1966
Fifth edition (metric) 1969
Sixth edition 1972
Seventh edition 1975 by Crosby Lockwood Staples
Eighth edition 1980 by Granada Publishing Limited, Technical Books Division

Printed in Great Britain by W & J Mackay Ltd., Chatham, Kent.

To
THE QUANTITY SURVEYORS OF THE FUTURE

I hold every man a debtor to his profession, from the which as men do of course seek to
receive countenance and profit, so ought they of duty to endeavour themselves, by way of
amends, to be a help and ornament thereto.
BACON: *Maxims of the Common Law* (Preface).

D
, 624.1
WIL

PREFACE

The preface to the seventh edition of this book suggested that the changes facing the profession were such that changes in any further edition would have to be extensive. This has indeed proved to be the case, hardly a week has gone by without a so-called Quango coming or going, a practice note being issued or some other change which affects Practice and Procedure.

The 1980 form of contract is to be published early next year and the publication of this edition has been held back so that the fundamental changes in the main and sub-contract conditions can be referred to and comment made where appropriate. At first glance the new contract looks much better ordered and set out, if somewhat more detailed in parts. It is to be hoped that it will go a long way towards answering the criticisms levelled at its predecessors.

Detailed reference is made in Chapter 11 to the recommendations contained in the report by the Monopolies and Mergers Commission on the Supply of Surveyor's Services with reference to Scale Fees. This report suggests fundamental changes and even in some cases the abandonment of fee scales completely. Whether or not by the time this edition is published these recommendations will have been implemented remains to be seen. Whilst quantity surveyors in the main are quite ready and willing to compete on performance, they are reluctant to compete on fees. Professional services are not sold like cans of beans in a supermarket and costed accordingly.

It has been suggested from time to time that the content of the chapters on Policy, Office Organisation and Finance are too elementary to be included in a text book. Any success that we may have had with our books over the years has been, we think, due to the fact that the reader has been assumed to know little or nothing of the subject. It was with the intention of explaining some of the fundamentals of practice to someone just starting out, that these chapters were originally included. Today, despite the gloomy economic situation, there are still people setting up in practice and for this reason the chapters in question have been left in and brought up to date. Moreover, there are those starting practice who, as assistants, have not had to consider matters that only affect the principal. Whilst we are reluctant to recommend anyone not to read what we have written, our reply to these erstwhile critics must be "skip it".

There has been much talk recently about "broadening the base" of the profession. Despite having two of the broadest bases in quantity surveying we have made only passing reference to the new fields in which the profession is now operating: heavy engineering, petrochemicals, coal mining and, of course, work abroad. These are all specialist areas which demand more space than is available in a text book of this nature. However, if the bounds of the profession are like the Land of Hope and Glory to be "wider still and wider", then the practitioner will need a sound technical base from which to move forward and we hope that this book will help to clarify the Practice and Procedure element of that base.

September, 1979

A.J.W.
C.J.W.

ACKNOWLEDGMENTS

WE are also most grateful to Mr. Richard Seymour, barrister-at-law, for giving us most useful help on Chapters 11 and 12.

We have had the invaluable help of Mr. H. S. Page, F.R.I.C.S., and Mr. Kenneth Lindsell, F.R.I.C.S., for the chapter on Public Service, naturally largely outside our direct experience.

The forms etc. in Appendix 1 are reproduced by permission of their respective publishers and the paragraph on the Price Adjustment formula on page 75 is reproduced from "The Chartered Surveyor" with the permission of the Royal Institution of Chartered Surveyors.

PREFACE TO THE FIRST EDITION

THE first thought of a writer putting pen to paper is (or should be): who will be my readers? It is only by constantly bearing them in mind, their requirements and their limitations, that one can so focus the writing that it becomes a readable book. The mere exposition of one's thoughts without this concentration on the reader produces a blurred image so often exemplified by dreary writing.

Who then is likely to be interested in the subject on which I have embarked? Not, I think, the established quantity surveyor in practice. He has explored the subject himself in the development of his practice, not in theory but by thought and experience. Not that any amount of reading will dispense with the need of both thought and experience for the successful practitioner. However, just as it is easier to make one's way through thick undergrowth in a wood if one can follow where someone has been before, so the path may be made easier for the practitioner of the future if he can follow footsteps: if he can see two or more tracks all the better; he can pick his way by whichever seems at the moment the most suitable, and it may be that in places the tracks will coincide and make the path still easier.

I have, therefore, visualised as my readers the student in his fourth or fifth year working for his Final examination who has an interest beyond the limits of his syllabus, the surveyor who, having passed his Final, may feel that he never wants to see another text-book, yet sees the need to extend his knowledge of the profession, and the practitioner in embryo or new-born, who has during his employment seen little of "how it works."

Offices vary considerably in size, type and even quality, and practice differs accordingly, as well as with the ideas (and idiosyncrasies) of the individual surveyor. Bearing in mind my probable readers, I have concentrated on the smaller office and the requirements of the younger man. Other readers must not mind if they find the picture a little out of focus from their own standpoint.

Some of the subjects touched on—office organisation, finance, partnership—are not peculiar to quantity surveying, but, as in most cases the young surveyor will not have made any particular study of them, I felt that it was essential to outline something of their principles.

It is, perhaps, obvious to say when speaking of practice that what I have found, chosen or decided is not necessarily the experience, choice or decision of others. I must not, therefore, be read as laying down rules, but rather as putting forward suggestions.

PREFACE TO THE FIRST EDITION

Having started my professional training late, thanks to a little matter of a war, and practice rather early because opportunity knocked at the door, I felt that I lacked the variety of experience necessary to write authoritatively on professional practice. I am, therefore, particularly grateful for the help I have received from Mr. E. W. Leaning, M.A., F.R.I.C.S., and Colonel J. B. Marks, O.B.E., F.R.I.C.S., who have both made valuable suggestions for amendments, alternatives or additions, the latter being of particular assistance on the subject of public service. Further, without legal support I would not have dared to write on law, and I have to thank Mr. D. A. Grant, D.S.O., barrister-at-law, for reading my first effort, correcting my misconceptions and giving me his most helpful advice. I must add thanks to my partner, Mr. D. T. C. Thompson, F.R.I.C.S., and several members of our staff, who have also pointed out errors and made numerous suggestions.

One cannot acknowledge all the sources of one's knowledge of practice, but I should particularly like to mention the value to me of those two text-books on which I was brought up—Leaning's "Quantity Surveying" and Fletcher's "Quantities." Between them they did much to lay the foundation of the two chapters on law.

I shall welcome any suggestions for improving the book, and incidentally widening my knowledge of how others do things.

October, 1950   A.J.W.

CONTENTS

PREFACE...v
ACKNOWLEDGMENTS vi
PREFACE TO THE FIRST EDITION vii
INTRODUCTION xi
1. THE WORK OF THE QUANTITY SURVEYOR..............1
2. PUBLIC RELATIONS 9
3. PRE-CONTRACT COST CONTROL..............................17
4. PREPARATION OF THE BILL OF QUANTITIES..........25
5. BUILDING CONTRACTS...43
6. RECEIPT OF TENDERS 51
7. VALUATIONS FOR INTERIM CERTIFICATES 59
8. VARIATION ACCOUNTS 67
9. OCCASIONAL SERVICES 83
10. STRUCTURE OF THE BUILDING INDUSTRY 91
11. LAW—THE QUANTITY SURVEYOR AND HIS
    CLIENT...103
12. LAW (*continued*)—THE QUANTITY SURVEYOR AND
    THE BUILDING CONTRACT 121
13. POLICY...131
14. OFFICE ORGANISATION—PROVISION AND
    EQUIPMENT OF THE OFFICE 145
15. OFFICE ORGANISATION (*continued*)—
    MANAGEMENT 151
16. FINANCE...165
17. PARTNERSHIP 177
18. PUBLIC SERVICE 183

APPENDICES

1. FORMS & PRECEDENTS 193
2. BIBLIOGRAPHY 227
   INDEX 233

Abbreviations used:

A.C.	Appeal Case
All E.R.	All England Reports
B.R.E.	Building Research Establishment
B.S.I.	British Standards Institution
D.O.E.	Department of the Environment
E.E.C.	European Economic Community
G.L.C.	Greater London Council
H.M.S.O.	Her Majesty's Stationery Office
I.Q.S.	Institute of Quantity Surveyors
J.C.T.	Joint Contracts Tribunal
L.G.R.	Local Government Reports
N.F.B.T.E.	National Federation of Building Trades Employers
N.J.C.B.I.	National Joint Council for the Building Industry
N.J.C.C.	National Joint Consultative Committee of Architects, Quantity Surveyors and Builders
P.S.A.	Property Services Agency
R.I.B.A.	Royal Institute of British Architects
R.I.C.S.	Royal Institution of Chartered Surveyors
S.I.	Statutory Instrument
S.M.M.	Standard Method of Measurement of Building Works
S.R. & O.	Statutory Rule & Order (the former name of S.I.)
S.S.T.	Society of Surveying Technicians
V.A.T.	Value Added Tax
W.L.R.	Weekly Law Reports

Note: The Journals of professional Institutions have been described as such for easy identification by non-members, rather than by their titles.

Since from time to time inaccuracies have been pointed out in this book, it should be emphasised that the reader must have regard to the date of publication, the last date given on the back of the title page. He must remember, too, that probably some nine months elapsed between passing of final proof and publication. Every effort will be made to keep the book up to date.

INTRODUCTION

To define "Practice & Procedure" is a little difficult. A negative definition has been adopted for the purposes of this book. What it is *not* is the technical knowledge of the processes involved in preparing a bill of quantities or pricing it. Everything else which might be of professional interest to the quantity surveyor has been regarded as a possible subject for treatment.

There is, perhaps, no hard and fast dividing line between "practice" and "procedure". Generally speaking, "procedure" may be regarded as being governed by rules over which we have little or no control, but by which we must learn to do our work correctly. "Practice" is more the way we do it, representing decisions which are left (more or less) to our own choice. That a quantity surveyor must give notice to the contractor before beginning the measurement of variations is a matter of procedure laid down by both the Standard and Government Conditions of Contract; how he does so, e.g. by telephone or letter and the wording of any letter are matters of practice.

Being written by quantity surveyors in private practice the subject is looked at principally from that angle, but the viewpoints of the official surveyor and the contractor's surveyor are not forgotten.

In treating of building contracts the "Standard form" has been the one principally considered, but references are also made to the Government from "GC/Works/1," on which many Government contracts are based. Both are published documents* and are referred to throughout by the above-mentioned short titles.

After an outline of the work which may properly be called quantity surveyor's work and some explanation of his relationship with the various personalities of the building industry, the services rendered by the quantity surveyor are considered in turn and notes are made on procedure to be followed and difficulties likely to be met. A sketch of the structure of the building industry follows and some legal notes and rulings. The book concludes with chapters on policy, office organisation, finance and partnership and a special chapter on the outlook of the surveyor in public employment.

---

* *Standard Form of Contract:* Joint Contracts Tribunal (in two forms for use with and without quantities), 1980 edition. Referred to as the Standard form (the form for use with quantities unless otherwise stated). The forms are also available adapted for use by Local Authorities.

General Conditions of Government Contracts for Building and Civil Engineering Works (Form GC/Works/1). Edition 2: H.M.S.O., referred to as GC/Works/1.

INTRODUCTION

In the Appendices will be found a number of forms, typical letters &c., which may be of interest and use to the student who does not come into contact with them in his office. These must not be regarded as fixed forms. They are only offered to help those who may have difficulty and to emphasise the essential points in each case. An effort has also been made to prepare a list of books, official publications &c., which may be of value to the quantity surveyor.

THE WORK OF THE QUANTITY SURVEYOR

THE work of the quantity surveyor in connection with building contracts cannot be better summarised than is done in "The Services of the Chartered Quantity Surveyor," published by the Royal Institution of Chartered Surveyors, as follows:—

> A construction cost adviser who, by virtue of his specialist training and experience, has developed a knowledge of construction economics which enables him to:—
> 1. Advise on what a project would cost.
> 2. Advise on what size and standard of structure can be erected for any given expenditure.
> 3. Advise on the economics of a project and the preparation of a budget.
> 4. Co-operate with the designers to ensure that a building can be erected within an approved expenditure.
> 5. Advise on tendering procedures and contractual arrangements. Prepare documents for obtaining tenders and arranging a contract.
> 6. Exercise control during the construction so that the cost is not exceeded without authority.
> 7. Act with the Architect or Engineer to ensure that the financial provisions of the contract are properly interpreted and applied so that the Client's financial interest is safeguarded and that the builder is paid a proper price for the work.

ACCURATE BILL OF QUANTITIES.—A large part of the work of the quantity surveyor is the preparation of the bill of quantities, dependent for its accuracy on the availability of full particulars of the work required. The fuller and more detailed the architect's drawings the better the chance of an accurate bill, with a minimum of "extras" arising during the progress of the works. The great majority of building contracts over £50,000 or so are let on this basis.[1]

APPROXIMATE BILL OF QUANTITIES.—There are, however, times when sufficiently full information cannot be given to enable an accurate bill of quantities to be prepared. It may be a foundation contract, in which depths of excavation and even thickness of concrete cannot be ascertained until the bearing surfaces are exposed. Nevertheless, it may

[1] See page 25.

be known fairly accurately in advance what items are likely to occur in measurement. A bill can therefore be prepared which, though with only approximate quantities, can be used for tender, subject to a complete measurement of the work as executed and revaluation at the tender rates. The quantities will be sufficiently accurate to show which is the lowest tenderer, and according to the extent of information available they may or may not be a reliable approximate guide to the final cost. In fact, an approximate bill can be very near an accurate bill, or little more than the schedule of prices referred to in the next paragraph. A form of contract for use with approximate quantities was first published in 1976.[2]

SCHEDULE OF PRICES.—Information may be so scanty or time so short that not even approximate quantities can be given. In such a case a schedule of probable or possible items can be prepared, giving descriptions similar to those in a bill of quantities, but without any quantities. There is difficulty in making comparison of tenders with such schedules, as there are no totals available. Comparison must, of course, be mainly between the major items, as the minor ones would probably have little effect on the result.

Alternatively, the schedule can be priced by the surveyor and each contractor tendering can be asked to quote a percentage on or off the schedule prices, the whole work being measured as it proceeds and priced accordingly. Whilst such a method of tendering enables the tenders to be compared more satisfactorily than if the contractors price a schedule themselves, the decision of contractors on a percentage is apt to be difficult, as their own pricing would not throughout be related directly to the schedule. They might, for instance, have their own joinery shops, and so be able to price joinery very advantageously: they would have to balance a lower percentage in this trade against a higher one in others, and the mean which they strike would vary according to the anticipated proportion of joinery. It is, of course, possible to allow tenderers to quote different percentages for each trade: though this would help with the above-mentioned problem, it increases the difficulty of judging which tender is the lowest.

There are standardised schedules which could be used, such as that of the Department of Environment,[3] which contains a comprehensive list of items in each trade with prices against them. The difficulty with any standardised schedule is that it is almost certain not to contain some items which it may be known will be required for the particular job. This procedure is, perhaps, most suitable for the purpose of which this particular Schedule was originally prepared, viz. the letting of term contracts for maintenance, i.e. contracts by which the builder

[2] *Standard Form of Building Contract for use with Approximate Quantities.*
[3] *Department of Environment Schedule of Rates for Building Works:* H.M.S.O.

2

undertakes to carry out all repair work within a certain area for a specified term at the quoted percentage on or off the schedule.

PRIME COST CONTRACTS.—Information may be so lacking that an *ad hoc* Schedule of Prices could not be prepared, and no standardised schedule may be considered suitable. In that case a form of prime cost contract would be used, i.e. one under which the contractor is reimbursed his proved cost and paid in addition, to cover his overheads and profit, either a percentage on that cost or a fixed fee. The important thing in a contract of this nature is to be quite clear as to what is to be considered cost for reimbursement and what an overhead charge covered by the percentage or fixed fee. A form of contract is published by the R.I.B.A. for prime cost plus fixed fee contracts.[4] This gives in a schedule a full definition of prime cost under headings of labour, materials, plant, &c. and sub-contracts.

The disadvantage of the prime cost contract is its lack of incentive to economy on the part of the builder. He gets his fixed fee whatever he pays for his materials (if a percentage, then the more he spends the more he gets), but in certain circumstances there is no other satisfactory way of placing the contract. With a selected list of contractors of good standing, well known to the architect and in whom he has complete confidence, this form of contract is perfectly fair.

In the case of prime cost contracts the surveyor has no form of bill of quantities to prepare. Instead, his services are made use of in checking the contractor's records of prime cost, reporting from them the value of work done from time to time for interim payments and agreeing the final cost on conclusion of the work.

ALL-IN CONTRACT.[5]—A development of recent years is the all-in contract sometimes referred to as a "package deal" (generally by those inclined to disparage it). With this form of contract the building contractor undertakes the whole of the services required for the erection of the building from the first designs, so dispensing with the independent architect, consultant and quantity surveyor. Their technical work is, of course, required, but is provided by the contractor's own staff, permanent or specially commissioned. It is suggested that the unity of control speeds up administration, but, on the other hand, such a contract is not normally on a competitive basis, and may, therefore, be at a higher price than if it were let in the normal way. Price, however, is not always the primary consideration of the building owner.

A modification of this procedure allows the building owner's own appointed architect to be employed, giving him the advantage of consultation with the contractor from the very start.

[4] *Fixed Fee Form of Prime Cost Contract:* R.I.B.A.
[5] For the conditions in which chartered quantity surveyors may be engaged in such schemes, see *The Chartered Quantity Surveyor and "Package" Contracts:* R.I.C.S.

The services of the quantity surveyor in this type of contract will, therefore, be under the direction of the contractor, though a building owner's quantity surveyor may have either a watching brief or a more definite share in control.

CONSORTIUM.—The term "consortium" has recently appeared in connection with the Building Industry and its technical meaning does not seem to have been authoritatively defined (the Shorter Oxford Dictionary just says "partnership: association"). The word seems to be applied to the association of a number of contractors to carry out particularly large contracts. They may give a joint tender under normal procedure, or they may adopt the all-in contract principles referred to above. Sometimes a development group is formed for large projects with parent, holding and development companies incorporated. The intricacies of company law are not our concern here, but the outlook of the quantity surveyor may vary according to the organisation of the consortium.

The consortium may be extended to comprise architect, consultants, quantity surveyor and contractor, a kind of partnership, but unlike a normal one in which all partners are responsible for all the acts of the partnership. In the consortium each has responsibility for his own sphere as individually employed. The important thing is that all are in the project from the first, a price being negotiated with the contractor and the other parties each having agreed remuneration from the client.

CIVIL ENGINEERING WORK.—Some quantity surveyors have a practice to a greater or lesser extent in work which is properly civil engineering rather than building, and others may meet such work occasionally. Though civil engineering contracts have bills of quantities, the rules governing their preparation are different.[6] The efficient and economical carrying out of civil engineering work very much depends on the way the contractor organises and sets about his work and on his use of mechanical plant, and the bill usually consists of large quantities of comparatively few items. The minor labours measured in building work are included in the general rates and such precautionary work as timbering of excavations is also so included, leaving the contractor more freedom to devise his own methods. Owing to the usually unforeseeable nature of many things, civil engineering work is normally based on either an approximate bill or a schedule of prices.

It is impossible to define an exact border line between civil engineering and building work, as there are many composite contracts which are usually treated according to which of the two industries is predominant. Though civil engineering work is concerned with

[6] *The Civil Engineering Standard Method of Measurement:* The Institution of Civil Engineers.

railways, docks, canals, roads, reservoirs, water mains, sewers and other large scale undertakings such as airports, hydro-electric schemes, sea defences, &c., an engineering contract may have normal buildings, e.g. an administration block, as part of it. A factory or office building may well have a substantial part, such as excavation, foundations, reinforced concrete frame and floors, carried out under the supervision of a consulting engineer and by a civil engineering contractor as a sub-contractor under a building contract.

The quantity surveyor who may be concerned with civil engineering work must, besides making himself familiar with the method of measurement referred to above, acquaint himself with the conditions of contract, working rules, daywork rates and other such matters which are different from those applying to the Building Industry. Most of these will be found conveniently together in the Handbook of the Federation of Civil Engineering Contractors, or they may be obtained separately.[7] The study of a booklet on engineering contracts issued by the Institution of Civil Engineers[8] will emphasise the marked resemblances in practice as well as show up the important differences.

Quantity Surveyors who find themselves working in the civil engineering field will be providing similar services to those traditionally given in connection with building. They will be employed in different roles, some in the professional team advising the engineer, others in providing a post-tender service to the contractor or in his direct employment. What is expected will depend on the nature of employment.

Quantity surveyors are likely to be called upon at pre-tender stage to assist in the provision of a financial budget prior to detailed design, preliminary cost studies, to monitor and evaluate the design as it evolves and to advise on contractual arrangements and the preparation of documents.

Civil engineering projects require a design solution of physical and geological problems. These problems will dictate the cost of the solution and the engineer must be able to provide an acceptable one within the confines of a predetermined budget in the same way that buildings can be cost planned within cost limits.

The quantity surveyor is an expert in financial appraisal, whereas this can only represent a small part of the training of designers. The promoter has to know the likely cost of the project in advance of construction and the quantity surveyor's experience can be usefully employed to provide the engineer with comparative costs of alternative solutions. After tender, the quantity surveyor may be asked to analyse and report on tenders and, after the contract is awarded, called upon to

[7] See page 227.
[8] *Civil Engineering Procedure:* The Institution of Civil Engineers.

evaluate the final cost including re-measurement, variations and assistance in claims adjudication.

STRUCTURAL ENGINEERING WORK.—Closely akin to civil engineering work is that of structural engineering, mainly concerned with the fabrication and fixing of structural steel, either in engineering contracts proper, such as bridges, or in building contracts, such as a structural steel frame. The initiative and ingenuity of the individual contractor not having the same importance as in civil engineering work, the structural engineering side of building work is rather a specialised form of building construction, with which the quantity surveyor should be acquainted and for which he should be able to prepare bills of quantities.

HEAVY ENGINEERING WORK.—This work encompasses the petro chemical industry, oil and coal fields, steel works, cement plants, energy centres and other such heavy engineering work. The professional quantity surveyor has been involved for a comparatively short time, but because of the changing circumstances within the industries and the accent being placed on value for money, he is now being accepted by many clients and contractors as a very valuable member of the project team.

The basic methods employed are not very different from those used by many other quantity surveying practices. Bills of approximate quantities are produced for all elements of work including building; civil engineering; steelwork; piping and mechanical and electrical installations; instrumentation installations; fabrication of modules for offshore production platforms; rig conversion works; offshore hook-up work, and so on.

Bills are prepared from drawings and sketches provided by one of the design departments or from a take off prepared by a specialist department for the purpose of purchasing bulk materials.

In an industry which employs a large number of specialists, the quantity surveyor has a lot to offer, there is the need for more all-rounders capable of bridging the gap between the thinkers and the doers. The quantity surveyor, with his practical background, commercial sense and legal understanding, is such an all-rounder.

OVERSEAS WORK.—The economic recession which strikes this country from time to time at seemingly shorter and shorter intervals has caused quantity surveyors to look to wider areas than they have traditionally been used to. These have included involvement in Heavy Engineering and Civil Engineering work, described here, and also in work overseas. This may mean either working in this country on projects abroad, with visits as necessary, or the much more costly enterprise of setting up abroad to provide an on-the-spot service with all the problems, political and financial, that this involves. Opportunities abroad, like all opportunities, are there to be taken and it must be up to the practitioner to make his decision, all that can be said is that many are the occasions when the failure to take up an opportunity has afterwards been regretted. The actual work differs only in the respect that professional ethics traditional in this country do not necessarily apply abroad, in fact the reverse is often the case and a quantity surveyor must be prepared to proceed in a much more competitive way not only on the question of fees but in some of the short cuts he may be forced to take.

DISPUTES AND ARBITRATION.—In many cases building work is embarked on without clear conditions being agreed between the parties, sometimes, indeed, on a very vague basis. This naturally leads to disputes which somebody is called in to settle, often the quantity surveyor, owing to his special knowledge of building construction, measurement and costs. If not appointed as arbitrator to settle the dispute, he may be consulted by either side and required to give expert evidence before an arbitrator or Court.

PARTY WALL AWARDS.—A particular form of dispute sometimes dealt with by quantity surveyors is any difference between adjoining owners in London over the repairs to or erection of a party wall or party fence wall, procedure for the settlement of which is laid down by statute.[9] A building owner is required to serve notices in certain events on all owners of land adjoining his building and provision is made for each party to appoint a surveyor to negotiate a settlement.[10] Outside London there is no such statutory control, but, of course, adjoining owners have their Common Law rights and negotiation may be necessary to get them waived or modified.

SCHEDULE OF DILAPIDATIONS.—The preparation or checking of a schedule of dilapidations, being very similar to the preparation of a bill of quantities, often falls to the lot of the quantity surveyor, as well as being embraced in the more general practice of a building surveyor. Instead of being supplied with drawings and specification, the surveyor will measure on the premises and make up his specification according to the view of what is necessary to comply with the repairing covenants of the lease. His measurements must be worked up into a bill and priced.[11]

FIRE DAMAGE ASSESSMENT.—As in the case of a schedule of dilapidations the surveyor in assessing the value of damage by fire must

[9] London Building Acts (Amendment) Act, 1939, Sections 44-59.
[10] See page 84.
[11] See page 86.

7

measure from the remains of the premises and any drawings available and price his bill. The main difference—sometimes a serious difficulty—is that in the case of fire the evidence of what was there before may have been destroyed, and the occasions when drawings are available are comparatively few.[12]

[12] See page 87.

2

PUBLIC RELATIONS

THE ARCHITECT.—The first contact which a quantity surveyor makes with a future job for a private client (as distinct from a public authority) may well be through the architect. As the building owner's adviser he is very often in a position to recommend a quantity surveyor for appointment, and the building owner, knowing little or nothing of the profession, or having no individual in mind, is likely to accept the recommendation. The architect relies on the efficiency and co-operation of the man he recommends, and a mutual understanding of each other's problems will go a long way towards ensuring a satisfactory financial statement when the contract is completed. The advice of the quantity surveyor should be available on matters of cost before and during the progress of the building work, and, though sometimes it may not be specifically paid for, this is an auxiliary service which he should render willingly. The architect as manager and co-ordinator of the building project is concerned with a diversity of matters, and the knowledge that in one of the directions in which he may need support the quantity surveyor stands ready to help is usually much valued.

In the case of a public authority, such as a Government Department, Local Authority or large corporation there is usually constant need for the services of a quantity surveyor. Such bodies will either have a permanent quantity surveying staff directly in their employ or will appoint one or more firms in private practice to do their work as and when instructed. They may combine the two systems. In such cases the architect often has no say in the appointment of the quantity surveyor, but he should nevertheless be able to rely on his ready assistance in matters within his sphere.

The architect will deal with all necessary official approvals in accordance with the various statutory and other controls binding on him. These include the Building Regulations[1] which lay down certain requirements on materials and workmanship.

THE BUILDING OWNER.—There was a time when the quantity surveyor rarely met the building owner, who often did not even know of his existence. If he did, he probably considered him an unnecessary

[1] *The Building Regulations 1972*
The Building Standard (Scotland) Regulations 1963.

luxury in which his architect had somehow persuaded him to indulge. In recent years, with the increase of direct appointment and direct payment referred to later, the value of the quantity surveyor has been brought more and more to the notice of the building owner, who is realising the service that he gets, and that the consequent fee is not just an addition to the general bill without any return. Though much of his contact with the building owner may be through the architect, the quantity surveyor will very often be brought in to give any explanation on matters of account which may be required. In many cases, of course, such as the public authorities referred to above, the work of the quantity surveyor is well understood.

The surveyor must remember that the building owner normally has no technical knowledge and that he himself is, like the architect, a technical adviser to watch the building owner's interests. He must not, however, allow such a watching brief to interfere with strict impartiality, when, as in the case of the Standard form of contract, he is appointed by both parties to the contract to prepare the account.

CONSULTANTS.—A hundred years ago buildings were constructed almost entirely of brick and timber, with stone for embellishment and perhaps some cast iron columns or girders to solve occasional problems of big spans. The need for many-storeyed buildings had not yet been forced on us by the congestion of the cities; electric lighting of buildings was unknown, central heating was in a very rudimentary stage. The development of building construction has since introduced structural steelwork and reinforced and prestressed concrete. Some years ago there was a limit of 80 feet for height of buildings in London (with certain limited relaxation for storeys in the roof)—a limit which looks silly now when one sees the "tower blocks" that have been built, but these have only been made possible by the developments in structural design.

One of the difficulties of an architect is to combine the artistic sense in design with the practical aspects of construction in a specialised form, such as reinforced concrete. Except in a few cases, he cannot be expected to master the detailed calculations involved by these forms of construction, work which requires a temperament just the opposite to that of the artist. Accordingly the consulting engineer has come to the fore, who takes from the architect responsibility for the detailed design of steel or reinforced concrete members required by his plans. This consultant is probably a civil engineer, some of whose practice might be concerned with roads, sewers, railways, bridges, docks and the like. The design of steel or reinforced concrete in buildings will quite possibly be only one branch of his work.

In the same way has grown up the practice of the consulting mechanical and electrical engineer, who specialises in the design of central heating, hot water services, ventilation, electric lighting and power systems, lifts, &c. The science of designing these in a building of any size needs so much specialised knowledge that few architects are qualified to practise it.

There are other specialists to whom an architect may refer, e.g. on sanitary work, acoustics and other branches which have been the subject of special study.

The work of all these specialists is co-ordinated by the architect and the quantity surveyor's approach to them will often be through him. They will supply the quantity surveyor with particulars of builder's work required in connection with their schemes, either by means of drawings from which he can measure or schedules which he can adapt and incorporate in his bill.

In certain cases the quantity surveyor may be employed to prepare quantities for purely engineering contracts, in which case the engineer takes the place of the architect. Engineering works are tendered for on rather different conditions from those ruling in building contracts, allowing the ingenuity of the contractor scope to devise the best method of carrying out his work.

CONTROLLING AUTHORITIES.—Contact with the authorities controlling building is a matter for the architect, but the quantity surveyor will have to represent their requirements in his bill of quantities. The Building Inspector is the representative of the Local Authority to see that the regulations or conditions made on approval of the plans are adhered to. He is normally a member of the staff of the Authority's Surveyor or Engineer, through whom plans submitted for approval pass with a recommendation to the Buildings Committee of the Council. In London the control of the Inner Boroughs over building is qualified by the London Building Acts, which give authority over structural matters to the Greater London Council through their District Surveyors.

THE CONTRACTOR.—The contractor to be invited to tender will be selected as described in Chapter 4.[2] When a tender is considered for acceptance the quantity surveyor will make contact with the tenderer. After acceptance of a tender he will have a good deal to do with him during the progress of the contract, and may in turn have to show tact, firmness or ready agreement. The decision of the quantity surveyor will often affect the contractor financially, sometimes seriously, and it is important that he should maintain a fairness and reasonableness in all his dealings with him. Contractors will, of course, vary from the small man, possibly working himself and with only a small staff, to the big corporation with a number of autonomous divisions. Though the contractor can usually look after himself technically, some of the small

[2] See page 39.

firms, unused to contract work, may need guidance in the keeping of those records and production of information required for the preparation of the final account.

THE CONTRACTOR'S SURVEYOR.—Special mention should be made of the contractor's surveyor, with whom the quantity surveyor will be mainly in contact during the progress of the contract. His work is very much akin to that of the contract quantity surveyor, the preparation and pricing of whose bills he must understand. Of recent years his academic training has become nearer to being identified with that of the contract quantity surveyor, as, after all, their work is very similar, the measurement and valuation of every element that builds up the cost of building work; indeed today, providing he or she has the necessary training, a contractor's surveyor can qualify as a Chartered Quantity Surveyor without, as was previously the case, experience of a professional office. His main duty is estimating for tender and watching the contractor's interest in preparation of the final account. However, in the smaller firms he may have to help in planning, budgeting and co-ordinating the various branches, such as ordering materials, costing of work being done or passing accounts for payment. From this it will be seen that he has a position of great responsibility in his firm, as bad estimating or lack of ability, foresight or firmness in negotiation may lead to serious financial loss.

The quantity surveyor's first contact with the contractor's surveyor will probably be on raising any queries on the priced bill delivered with or following the tender. The man who priced it may be the man to reply, and he may also later meet the quantity surveyor for interim certificate valuations, measurement of variations and settlement of the final account. In the larger contracting firms the estimating and site surveyors will be in different departments.

SUB-CONTRACTORS.—Just as the architect, with the development of building science, has had to delegate some of his work to consultants, so the builder often does not undertake all branches of work necessary in the erection of a building, and sub-lets certain parts of his work accordingly. The extent of such sub-letting varies with the locality and the builder, but such services as central heating or electrical work will mostly, and highly specialised services such as lifts, telephones, &c. always, be sub-let. In many cases builders will sub-let trades which are normally within their sphere, either because they do not have the staff or because the management by a specialist is considered an advantage.

In view of the fact that certain services are normally sub-let, the building owner, through the architect, often takes the opportunity of selecting the specialists concerned, so exercising more direct control. Such sub-contractors are, under the normal forms of contract, called "nominated sub-contractors" (Standard form, 35; GC/Works/1. 31 and 38) and special provisions are contained in the building contract controlling their employment. Where, however, the builder decides on his own account to sub-let part of the work for which he has made himself responsible, the sub-contracts are entirely a matter between builder and sub-contractor, except that the architect's approval of the firm is usually required. In both cases, however, it is the essence of a sub-contract that the general contractor retains supervision and control of the work and is responsible to the building owner through the architect for its proper execution.

STATUTORY AUTHORITIES.—There are certain authorities which have statutory powers to control building work affecting their particular service and the exclusive right to carry out certain work themselves. Such are the Electricity and Gas Boards and the Water Undertakings that supply electricity, gas and water respectively, and the extent of their work will be found to vary. The two first usually themselves bring their mains into a building, whereas a Water Authority will probably only bring the supply to a point close to the boundary of the site. The Local Authority also has statutory powers in regard to the connection of drains to a public sewer and other work disturbing a public road. Clause 6.3 of the Standard form makes it clear that statutory authorities carrying out work solely in pursuance of their statutory obligations are not sub-contractors within the terms of the contract. Provision must therefore be made in the bill of quantities for including sums for this work making it clear that they are nett i.e. do not include 2½% discount. If the work to be done is clear cut such sums can be followed by provision to price profit, general and, if applicable, other attendance, otherwise they will be included as provisional sums which will include these items. Delay by Statutory Authorities is recognised as a 'relevant event' when it comes to granting extensions of time (clause 25.4.11) but it should be noted that it does not appear in the 'list of matters' in clause 26.2 as a ground for reimbursement of any loss or expense incurred by the contractor.

Some authorities, such as the Electricity and Gas Boards, besides carrying out the work which they are bound to do, will tender in competition for other work to the building, such as the electric wiring or gas services and the supply of fittings for each. In such circumstances, if the tender is accepted, they are, for that part of their work, in the same position as nominated sub-contractors.

MERCHANTS.—The quantity surveyor will not normally have much direct contact with merchants, the dealings with them being mostly a matter for the builder. The usual contracts, however, provide for suppliers being nominated in some cases by the architect (Standard form, 36; GC/Works/1, 38). The quantity surveyor will have to deal with these suppliers on paper—see their estimates and check invoices. Other merchants he will on occasion communicate with to satisfy himself as to the description of a material that he must specify or to make enquiry as to prices for comparative purposes.

CLERK OF WORKS.—The clerk of works acts for the architect on the building site to inspect and approve the materials and workmanship. He has the authority to reject what is not in accordance with the specification. He sometimes acts in other ways as the architect's agent, when special authority for this is given him. Also, being constantly on the site, he has an opportunity of seeing all work before it is covered up, and can therefore keep records which will be required by the quantity surveyor in adjusting variations on the contract. The quantity surveyor obviously cannot be on the site on all necessary occasions to make these records (except in large contracts when he may have a resident surveyor), and if the clerk of works agrees his records with the builder's site representative, there should be no dispute on fact.

The clerk of works keeps a record of the progress of the job and renders reports, usually weekly, to the architect. He provides information as to the numbers working, state of weather on the site, any delay in delivery of materials, further drawings or instructions required and generally anything that will help the architect in his administration of the job.

The architect is not relieved of responsibility by the actions of the clerk of works, whose primary duty is that of an inspector to see that materials and workmanship are in accordance with the specification.

AGENT AND HIS STAFF.—The quantity surveyor will probably have some contact with the builder's agent, i.e. the builder's site manager. Though usually the clerk of works will have agreed questions of fact with the agent, it may happen that there are differences, so that the surveyor will have to hear what the agent has to say at first hand. On small contracts where there is no clerk of works the quantity surveyor may have to rely on the agent's statements on work which has been covered up.

In some cases the works may not even be big enough to justify a full-time agent, and the builder will appoint one of his workmen to take charge. Just as a small builder may need some guidance in the quantity surveyor's requirements on the administration side, so a working agent may not understand the methods of the surveyor and the site records he requires. The surveyor will have to judge in each particular case how far he can rely on the ability of the agent to give him the information he needs and on the accuracy of his statements.

On the other hand, on the larger contracts the agent may have sub-foremen and clerical staff.[3]

In the same way the quantity surveyor may on occasion have to deal with the foremen of sub-contractors, though in view of the general contractor's responsibility this should only be done with the approval of his representative.

TRADE REPRESENTATIVES.—The manufacturers of building materials have their representatives who travel round collecting orders for their firm. They know, of course, that in most cases the builder decides from whom he will order, and that sometimes the architect selects the particular firm. They must, therefore, look in these two directions principally to fill their order books. But they also know that the surveyor often advises the architect on materials, particularly from the cost angle, and that he has to convey to the builder tendering the precise nature of the work required. They, therefore, sometimes include him in their list of calls.

The quantity surveyor, particularly if young and inexperienced, can learn a lot from the manufacturer's or merchant's representative. He must remember that the salesman's job is to sell, and therefore take "with a pinch of salt" any high-sounding praise of the material and all its capabilities. Setting that aside, the representative is in possession of many facts about the materials which are of use to the quantity surveyor, and can supplement the information with his firm's advertising matter to meet the particular needs of the case. He can also supply or obtain prices, which owing to present day fluctuations are very often kept out of catalogues and leaflets, but are invaluable to augment the quantity surveyor's knowledge.

The surveyor should, therefore, take the opportunity of seeing representatives, when possible, though in some cases to see everybody would make too heavy a call on his time.

[3] Page 93.

3
PRE-CONTRACT COST CONTROL

WHOEVER proposes to erect a building, whether an individual having a house built for himself or a large Company, Corporation or Department of the Public Service spending in six or seven figures, they must control their expenditure. In order to be able to finance the building they will either state how much they have to spend or they will ask how much the building will cost. In either case, a figure being arrived at, it is the duty of the building owner's professional advisers—architect, consultants and quantity surveyor—to do their best to suit the building to the client's pocket, both at the tender and final account stages.

The rising costs of building in recent years have emphasised the need for careful control of cost. The Quantity Surveyors' Research and Development Committee of the R.I.C.S. has over the years studied the subject and a number of their Papers have been published by the R.I.C.S., from whom a list of those available can be obtained. In addition, the publications of the Building Cost Information Service and the Building Maintenance Cost Information Service of the same Institution are of the greatest help in dealing with this subject.

DEFINITIONS.—The term *cost control* is here used to cover the whole service required to meet this end. In the first instance, an *approximate estimate* must be given based on the client's stated requirements. This will be conveyed to the client as his advisers' considered opinion from the information they have. Much has to be done to develop the scheme from that stage, and it is important that a careful watch should be kept to see that the progress of designing will not upset the estimate and the client's budget. In his design the architect will consider alternative solutions to the various aspects of his problem, and may require information from the quantity surveyor on *comparative costs* of alternative materials or construction. This stage has now been developed in more detail, the specialised elaboration of this aspect being given the name of *cost planning*. This may be described as

> a system of relating the design of buildings to their cost, so that, whilst taking full account of quality, utility and appearance, the cost is planned to be within the economic limit of expenditure.

To enable any form of cost planning to be undertaken there must be a

17

cost analysis of the scheme, a splitting up of the approximate estimate into subdivisions, whether of the various trades and trade sections or of the constructional elements of the building, a combination of these or of some other classification. These subdivisions are then available for comparison with other records.

The traditional practice of dividing the bill of quantities into trades has been largely abandoned in favour of a division by constructional sections, following the headings of the S.M.M. This can be adapted to the rather different classification into the elements above-mentioned, there being separate bills under such headings as Floors, Roofs, Windows, &c. instead of Concrete Work, Carpentry, Joinery, Finishings, &c. This type of bill is called an *elemental bill,* useful for cost analysis by elements, but not essential for that purpose, since the cost analysis can be prepared from the normal sectional bills.

APPROXIMATE ESTIMATE, SQUARE METRE BASIS.—The first requirement of the client, an approximate estimate before the scheme has been developed at all, is, perhaps, the most difficult part of cost control. There may be little in the way of drawings, but the architect must have converted the client's floor space requirements into some kind of outline plan. It has been found that the cost of buildings bears a relation (*more or less*) to their floor area (expressed in square metres) with the qualification that user, site conditions, construction and type of finish must also be considered. In other words, if a building is to be erected similar in these respects to one built, it should be possible to relate its price to that of the first one in proportion to the floor area, also bearing in mind fluctuation in cost of labour and materials which may have occurred in the interval. The more dissimilar the buildings are in their character, the more difficult comparison becomes. It is obvious, therefore, that in order to give an approximate estimate on this basis there must be records available as a guide.

The best records for the purpose are those which the surveyor has himself prepared from his own experience. He will remember something of the job and probably have drawings and priced bill of quantities to refresh his memory. It is obviously important, therefore, to keep cost records of every job.[1] Difficulty, of course, faces the newly established practitioner who may have few or no records of his own. The R.I.C.S. has established a cost information service for members which supplies data from time to time, and the technical Press when they report and illustrate new buildings often provide not only overall costs according to floor area but an analysis of such cost. The figures in price books and published articles must, however, be treated with great caution. Whatever research the surveyor may undertake, there can be no records as useful as his own.

[1] See page 161.

The reference to user as affecting price means that buildings having the same use, e.g. schools, civic offices, &c. have an obvious basic similarity which should enable costs within each category to be more comparable than those of buildings in different categories.

Site conditions are obviously an important factor. A steeply sloping site must make the cost of a building higher than it would be for the same building on a flat site. The nature of the sub-soil too may have serious effect, e.g. if it necessitates piling.

Construction, of course, has an important influence. A single storey garage of normal height will merit a different rate per square metre from that of one constructed for double-decker buses. Again, a requirement for, say, a 20 m clear span is a different matter from allowing stanchions at 5 m or 7 m intervals. Further, an overall price per square metre will be affected by the number of storeys. A two-storey building of the same plan area has the same roof and probably much the same foundations and drains as a single-storey on that area, but has double the floor area. On the other hand the prices for high buildings are increased by the extra time in hoisting materials to the upper floors and the use of expensive plant, such as tower cranes.

The shape of a building on plan also has an important bearing on cost. A little experimental comparison of length of enclosing walls for different shapes of the same floor area will show that a square plan is more economical than a long and narrow rectangle, and that such a rectangle is cheaper than an L-shaped plan.

Standard of finish naturally affects price. There will be the client who wants a block of offices with the simplest finish and there will be another to whom, perhaps, more lavish treatment has advertisement value: he may want expensive murals or sculpture.

To measure floor area, the usual practice is to take measurements of all usable floor space within external walls but over internal partitions, the areas of all floors being added together. Deduction is not made for stair or lift wells, &c. Detailed rules are laid down by various authorities such as those responsible for Housing, Schools and Hospitals, which must be followed in their particular cases.

APPROXIMATE ESTIMATE, CUBE BASIS.—For very many years the basis of approximate estimates was the cube rather than the square. The idea behind this was probably that the cube reflects variations in the height of storeys, which a square unit does not. In fact, this qualification is not as marked as may at first appear. The difference per square metre for differing storey heights can always be estimated by comparing approximate quantities of the material items in each case.

If used, measurements of cubic contents for approximate estimates are taken, for length and width between the outer faces of external walls, and for height from top of concrete foundation to half way up a pitched roof, or in the case of flat roofs to 600 mm above the flat. The full volume is taken for a mansard roof. Projections such as porches, dormers, roof lights, chimney stacks, &c. are added. Such projections may in some cases need to be priced at a different rate or separately assessed as a lump sum. A boiler chimney stack cannot be priced at the same rate per cubic metre as the building. In the case of a raft foundation or a basement it is best to measure from underside of slab and bear in mind the circumstances when assessing the rate per cubic metre. Large ducts should be added to the cube and again remembered in assessment. Approximate estimates for building work are rarely prepared on this basis today.

APPROXIMATE ESTIMATE, UNIT RATE BASIS.—Certain types of building lend themselves to estimates based on a price per place, seat, &c. Primary Schools might work out at, say, x per place; churches, theatres, &c. could be rated at so much per seat, hospitals at so much per bed. Such estimates must be very approximate and vary according to the type of construction and standard of finish, but they might in the very earliest stages give a guide to a board or building committee as to whether their expenditure is likely to be £200,000 or £500,000. They must be understood to be subject to a subsequent proper estimate for the particular scheme.

THE STOREY-ENCLOSURE SYSTEM.—Some years ago a study group evolved a system of estimating based on the area of all enclosing surfaces of each storey of a building.[2] The areas were given certain "weightings" and then added together and priced at a single rate. This, it was maintained, represented more accurately the varying heights of the storeys, and made better comparison between single-storey and multi-storeyed buildings, than an over-all cube price could do. To use such a system needs the analysis of a number of completed jobs on this basis to provide necessary data as a guide for the future.

COST PLANNING.—An approximate estimate being established and reported to the client, the ideal of cost planning is to see not only that design is so controlled that the tender figure agrees with the estimate, but that (what is sometimes overlooked), if possible, it shows a saving through finding reasonable economy without detriment to the client's requirements.

One way recommended for doing this is to prepare a cost analysis according to the elements of the building. This is prepared from data in records to split up the over-all price per square metre already arrived at in the approximate estimate into separate rates for each element. Then, as each element is designed, approximate quantities are prepared and

[2] R.I.C.S. Journal, May 1954, page 810.

priced to check the rate against each. Differences are adjusted either in the design or by transferring the surplus or deficit to other elements. Those who find this nutshell hard to crack may refer to the prolific supply of articles and papers on the subject and text books recently available, particulars of which are given in Appendix 2. The subject cannot be mastered without study, experiment and practice, and its detail must be left as outside the scope of this book.

It is noteworthy that the leading advocates of such cost planning have been officers of Public Authorities carrying out building work, for the most part of a particular type—schools, barracks, &c. Such Authorities have the advantage of a large staff on which to draw for research and a correspondingly large quantity of available data for analysis. Seeing that it has been more than once emphasised that cost data are mainly of value to the firm or Department who prepare them, such Authorities naturally start with an advantage. What is suited to their problems may not suit everybody's.

A variation to the above system of cost analysis was one used by the former Ministry of Public Building and Works.[3] In this, the square unit of floor area not being considered suitable for analysis of all elements, some were priced on a unit of their measurement, e.g. the general structure by the cube, internal partitions by an over-all area, plumbing at so much per sanitary fitting, and so on.

The carrying out of this full cost planning necessarily needs the ready and willing co-operation of the architect. Here, again, perhaps Public Authorities have an advantage in having the architect and quantity surveyor mostly in the same building and both subject to a common discipline. But this is no reason why the private architect and quantity surveyor should not be able to work together in the same way, if they both give their time willingly to achieve the end aimed at.

Apart from a full system of cost planning the surveyor can be of use to the architect on the cost aspect by assisting with comparative costs for alternative systems of construction or finish. It may be a question of comparing different shapes of plan or different forms of internal partition or external cladding. The particular problem must be examined and, in the case of materials, investigation made into their cost and methods of fixing, where these are not already known. A useful table of some comparable costs can be expressed in the form of ratios, an example of which appears in the article referred to above.

APPROXIMATE QUANTITIES.—Until recent developments the main check on a first approximate estimate was made when the architect's schemes had been developed and probably drawings were available in pencil form. The surveyor could then take off approximate quantities

---

[3] *Cost Information:* C. A. Wales, F.R.I.C.S.: R.I.C.S. Journal, April 1962, page 517.

leaving out all the minor items and grouping items together where practicable. This, of course, is still a useful practice. Normal foundations would be measured per lineal metre, to include excavation, concrete and brickwork, a unit rate for which is fairly easily built up. Walls would include internal and external finish and windows be measured as extra over walls to include glass, paint, &c. With such a system an approximate bill of quantities can be prepared and priced. The whole thing can normally be done either on dimension paper, using the left hand group of columns for measurements and pricing out across the right hand group or using special paper having the right hand half ruled for rate and cash columns.

The disadvantage of this system of cost control is that it comes too late. By the time the drawings have reached the required stage, many matters of principle have been settled, which cannot be altered without a major disturbance of the whole scheme. For this reason there was a tendency to avoid preparing approximate quantities, the tender stage being so near, and just to hope for the best. The test of the tender may still be sufficient if the client is determined on what he wants and the architect gives him that, in other words if the client says "I want so and so: find out what it will cost" and asks for the best evidence—a tender.

RELIABILITY OF APPROXIMATE ESTIMATES.—It will be realised that, whether the check of cost planning at the design stage is used or not, cost analysis of tenders is of value as a more reliable guide in future approximate estimates than an over-all price per square unit of floor area or per cube unit. But however carefully such estimates are prepared, there will often be considerations that one cannot anticipate two or three years before. One must, of course, watch the tendency to fluctuation in the cost of labour and materials and make reasonable provision according to the prospect at the time of the estimate. One cannot forecast future legislation nor exceptional swings in existing tendencies. The introduction of National Insurance and the Holidays with Pay Schemes caused major disturbances in costs, and such an increase as the former Selective Employment Tax could not have been anticipated before the announcement. However, the surveyor should be alive to current developments which he will find referred to in the Journal of his Institution or the subscription service of a builders' Federation. Any serious qualification of an estimate should be reported promptly and not left to contribute to an explanation of an unexpectedly high tender.

One thing may be found to affect estimates seriously where a series of contracts is planned on the same site. There is sometimes reluctance on the part of tenderers to submit a really competitive tender when there is a contractor already working on the site, which that contractor knows well. The result is obvious. If, therefore, a scheme so develops that these circumstances arise, the approximate estimate may need qualification.

The continuation of cost control after the tender stage is referred to in Chapter 8.[4]

---

[4] Page 67.

4

PREPARATION OF THE BILL OF QUANTITIES

APPOINTMENT OF QUANTITY SURVEYOR.—As already mentioned the appointment of the quantity surveyor may have been made at an early stage when approximate estimates were under consideration, but when the architect has his working drawings ready the appointment will have to be settled, or in the case of small contracts a decision made as to whether a quantity surveyor is required at all. The building employers' federations had a rule that members should not tender in competition for work estimated to cost more than £8,000, with certain limited exceptions, unless bills of quantities were provided, but such a rule has been declared contrary to the public interest by the Restrictive Practices Court[1] and has been dropped. Nevertheless, the figure (brought up to date, about £50,000) gives architects and surveyors a good guide to a reasonable limit of contract size, beyond which in normal circumstances builders should not be asked to tender in competition without bills of quantities. There may, of course, be special considerations that would justify such invitations for a larger contract. The work involved if six or eight builders are each asked to prepare their own quantities for estimating, when only one can be successful (and even then the job might be abandoned), is very heavy and obviously uneconomical. Certain public authorities are required by their standing orders to advertise publicly for tenders.

Following entry into the E.E.C., public sector construction contracts over 1 million European units of account (approximately £660,000) must be invited and awarded in accordance with the procedures laid down in E.E.C. Directive 78/669. The Directive provides for a "Restricted Tendering Procedure" which permits the selection of technically competent and financially competent contractors following advertisement in the official journal of the European Community circulating throughout member states. In such cases there might be 5, 10 or more contractors tendering, and the sum total of increased overheads if they had to prepare their own quantities would be impossible, to say nothing of the scarcity of qualified staff to do it. The different interpretations which, if the quantities are left to him, each builder may put on the same

---

[1] (1964) 3 A.E.R. 577.

drawings and specification, if there is cause for doubt, are a further disadvantage and a possible cause of differences at a later stage.

TAKING-OVER OF DRAWINGS, &c.—The drawings may be sent to the quantity surveyor with specification notes or a complete specification, or he may be asked to go to the architect's office to collect them and discuss the job. He should on such a visit make notes of any verbal instructions given, but it would be unwise to ask too many questions until some examination has been made of the documents. The questions in mind may be answered by detailed examination of the drawings or perusal of the specification. The surveyor should ascertain whether it is proposed to supply any further drawings. It may happen that drawings of some section of the work are not complete, and a good deal of time may be wasted if the taking-off of that section is begun on the drawings available. A 1:20 detail to follow may quite likely alter the 1:100 drawing, and an alteration, however slight, may affect a lot of items in the dimensions. If further drawings are to follow, it is helpful if the order in which they are to come can be agreed, having regard both to the architect's office procedure and the surveyor's requirements. If there will be many, a programme with dates should be drawn up to enable the surveyor to organise his work.

STUDY OF DOCUMENTS.—The drawings received should be stamped with the surveyor's name and date of receipt, except, of course, in the case of originals which have to be returned, and, on a job of any size, a list of drawings should be prepared, giving their reference number, scale and brief particulars (see specimen list in Appendix 1[2]). Alternatively, a book may be kept for this purpose in which the record is kept for all jobs. The advantage of separate sheets is that each taker-off can have a copy which will assist quick reference until he is thoroughly acquainted with the drawings. Particulars of any further drawings received should be added to the list when they come in. It will be found of value in the case of a job of any size to have the main key drawings, usually 1:100 or 1:50 sheets, bound on the edges. A useful machine is obtainable to bind edges with a linen or plastic tape and such binding will prevent drawings which are much handled from becoming easily torn.

The documents will then be examined by a principal or senior assistant in charge of the job and the takers-off to be employed. One of the first things to be done is to see that all the necessary figured dimensions are given, both on plans and sections, to see that the figured dimensions are checked with over-all dimensions given and to insert any dimensions which can be calculated and may be useful in the measurement. Any errors in figured dimensions, which are easily made

[2] Page 193.

in a final tracing, should be confirmed with the architect, so that he can correct his originals accordingly.

Except in the smallest jobs the drawings should be supplied in duplicate, and in the larger jobs there may be three or more copies. It is advisable to number the sets, so that it can be seen at a glance to which set a drawing belongs. This can easily be done by numbering each set 1, 2 or 3 in coloured pencil in the bottom right hand corner. If these markings, as well as surveyor's name, date, &c., are kept in this corner they will be easily visible, when drawings are in a drawer of a plan chest, as the sheets are turned up. It will make the rooms stand out clearly if the walls are coloured in on plan and section in the surveyor's office; moreover, the act of colouring them will give an early indication of the general construction. This can be done quickly with coloured pencil and will be found well worth while. There may also be manuscript notes, or even alterations in plan, made by the architect at the last moment on one copy, and these should be transferred to the other copies. It sometimes happens that plans and sections are only hatched as a labour-saving device (as hatching will be continually printed on all copies) but the surveyor should superimpose his colouring.

It will also be found useful in a job of any size to mark on the general plan (usually 1:100) the position of the parts which are detailed. A cross reference in coloured ink in both cases will stand out. There may, for instance, be a number of 1:20 details spread over several sheets, e.g. entrance doors, bay windows, particular points of construction, &c. Sections can be referenced by normal section lines superimposed on the plan in a distinctive colour with the drawing number and section reference given thus,

B ———————————— 24 ———————————— B

meaning that a detail on this line will be found on drawing No. 24, section B—B. Elevations can be referenced in a similar way.

The extent of detail plans can be marked in the same colour with the number of the drawing to be referred to and arrows showing the approximate extent covered, thus:—

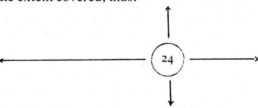

It may be found frequently that sections on detail sheets are not given a letter reference by the architect, but have such a title as "Section through Kitchen.'' The surveyor can give them a letter reference for the special purpose. The marking of the general plans in this way makes them serve as a key, so that a taker-off working on some particular part of the building can see at a glance what details are available.

A careful perusal should then be made of the specification or specification notes. By following through systematically in one's mind the sections of the taking-off one may find gaps in the specification which need filling. These may be quite numerous when only notes are supplied, as "notes" vary considerably in quality, thoroughness and extent.

SCHEDULES.—Schedules are very useful, both for quick reference by the taker-off and for eventual incorporation in the specification for the information of clerk of works and site agent. They may be supplied by the architect with the drawings, or it may be necessary for the surveyor to draft his own. Internal finishings should certainly be scheduled in a tabulated form, so that the finishes of each room for ceiling, walls and floors can be seen at a glance, with particulars of any skirtings, dadoes or other special features. Schedules for windows and doors would include frames, architraves, ironmongery, &c., those for manholes would give a clear size, invert, thickness of walls, type of cover and any other suitable particulars. Some of the material on schedules may be otherwise shown on drawings, but the schedule brings the parts together and gives a bird's-eye view of the whole. The schedule of finishings if not supplied in the form of a drawing should be typed and given to each taker-off, as each will at some time want to know what finish comes in a particular place, when he has to take for deductions or making good.

QUERIES.—As a result of the examination of drawings and specification a first list of queries for the architect will be prepared. These should be written on foolscap sheets on the left hand half of the sheet and numbered serially, each batch also bearing a date (see specimen in Appendix 1[3]). Ruled and headed sheets can be printed for the purpose at small expense. When a sufficient batch of queries has been collected, they can be typed and sent to the architect in duplicate, asking for the return of one copy with replies. It may be more convenient for the surveyor to call on the archiect to discuss the queries, in which case he can jot down the replies on his copy, and on return to the office send another copy with replies filled in to the architect as confirmation of his decisions. This procedure can be repeated from time to time as necessary. The queries should be given serial numbers, carried from one set to another, and the sets pinned together as they are received, so that the series is complete. Each taker-off should, if possible, have a copy and mark off those points he has dealt with, a final check being made in

[3] Page 193.

conference, when taking-off is finished, to see that there are no gaps or overlapping.

It will often happen that some proprietary material, of which the surveyor has never heard, is mentioned in the specification. If the name and address of maker are not given the surveyor should find them out and send for particulars of the material, which the makers are usually only too pleased to supply. At the same time he should ask the approximate price as an addition to his general knowledge and to have this available should the question of cost of the material arise in his discussions with the architect. In suitable cases he might ask for a small sample, as the sight and handling of a piece of the material is often helpful in disposing of difficulties which may arise in describing the fixing. In London a telephone enquiry to "The Building Centre"[4] will almost always provide the name and address of maker when only the trade name of a proprietary article is known. Lists of trade names with the names and addresses of manufacturer will be found in the following reference books:—

Laxton's Price Book

Specification

The Architects' and Contractors' Year Book

The surveyor should *never* accept an unknown name without investigation. A material specified has, before now, been found to be obsolete, and to require it in the bill of quantities not only looks silly and reveals ignorance but involves the raising of queries by tenderers. Even when the surveyor knows a material, if he has not had occasion to refer to it for some time he should obtain up-to-date particulars. Specifications for use sometimes vary and new developments, and prices, on which he must keep an eye, will fairly certainly have changed.

References to merchants' catalogue numbers, or number of British Standards, Codes of Practice, &c. should be verified. A wrong figure may appear in the specification either by a typing error or through not realising that the reference is obsolete.

DIVISION OF TAKING-OFF.—In the case of a small building it is most satisfactory if one man does the whole of the taking-off. For larger buildings how much sub-division is made will depend on the time allotted for the job and the availability of takers-off. Where two are made available a sub-division might be

A. Carcase of the building.

B. Internal finish, windows, door and fittings.

Such sections as Sanitary Plumbing, Drainage, Roads, &c., being more or less independent of other sections, could be allotted as one or other of the takers-off becomes available. When three-takers-off are available C

---

[4] Also in certain provincial towns. See page 95.

29

could start on these sections and it may be found, with certain types of building involving a lot of joinery fittings, that he might take over fittings from B. There are few jobs except the very large ones in which it would be practicable to use more than four takers-off, and for the smaller jobs two or three would be normal. The measurement of carcase of a building would not normally be divided; one possible division would be into foundations and superstructure, and this might be done if foundations are elaborate, complicated by basements, pipe ducts, &c. The superstructure might be sub-divided in the case of a steel or reinforced concrete frame building, the frame with floor and roof slabs, beam casings, &c. being the charge of one man, the brick "clothing," roof coverings, &c. being dealt with by another. Such a section as Roofs could, if necessary, be separated. If possible, however, one person should see the whole structure through. In the same way windows and external doors can hardly be divided, as they are sometimes structurally combined and have similar finishings, and it would be preferable for internal doors to be done by the same man, as many items such as lintels, plaster reveals, &c. will occur in both sections. Internal Finishings can be given to somebody else if a careful schedule has been prepared and there is close co-operation between the takers-off measuring Finishings and Openings.

The more the taking-off is sub-divided the greater risk of A thinking incorrectly that B has measured something, or C & D both measuring the same thing without each other realising it. There are certain items in which practice differs with different offices. Some surveyors take skirtings with floor finish, others with wall finish. Some measure them net, others adjust for openings in the Doors section. Rough rendering brick flues in roof space, eaves filling to brickwork are other items in which it will be found that practice varies. It is important, therefore, that a specific rule should be adopted on such items in the office, and care is necessary to see that new or temporary takers-off not used to the office custom are informed.

A set of the 1:100 and 1:20 or other general drawings should be available for each taker-off, and it is worth the surveyor paying for the extra prints, if they are not supplied. Single copies would probably be sufficient of special drawings, e.g. details of joinery fittings, lay-out of plumbing services, drainage, &c., as they would each in the main concern only one taker-off. If a second copy of the specification can be supplied it will be found to save a lot of time when two or more takers-off are engaged. On a large contract it may be well worth while to spend £5 or more to have copies of the specification or substantial extracts typed or photographed, particularly when, as may be the case, it is supplied in draft. The time saved reading from type instead of handwriting is considerable, and if each taker-off has a copy further time in lending from one to the other is saved.

The amount of supervision of the taking-off necessary varies, of course, with the experience of the individual. The junior taker-off just starting to do this work will need a good deal of watching, answering of queries, &c. Cases have been known where one could almost do the work oneself in the time spent in supervision. However, the beginner must learn, and it must not be at the expense of serious mistakes. Quite a casual query may reveal unexpected ignorance and with the inexperienced one must always be on the alert.

BUILDINGS ERECTED IN STAGES.—When buildings are to be erected in stages, separate prices may be required for each stage. If so, each stage will require an entirely separate bill or set of bills. It may, however, be that the division into stages is only for organisation of the work, e.g. when part of a building must be completed before another part can start. So far as the building owner is concerned only one price would be necessary, but it would be found of great convenience, both for certificate valuations and variation account, if each section is separately billed, provisional sums for specialist work being split up accordingly.

Rather similar circumstances arise in the case of housing estates where houses are completed and handed over one at a time or in batches. Though it is not necessary to have a separate bill for each type, this does help. In any case, some idea of the value of each type must be arrived at, both for certificate valuations and for the release of retention which is usually proportionally released for each house or batch of houses.[5]

TRADE-BY-TRADE TAKING-OFF.—In some parts of the country, particularly in the North, it has been the custom to take-off by trades instead of by sections of the building, the idea being that the dimensions are more or less in an order ready for billing, can be squared out and reduced on the dimension sheets and billed without an abstract.[6] The change in the S.M.M. to a classification by constructional sections does not affect this general principle.

"CUT AND SHUFFLE."—Difficulty in recruiting working-up staff was probably the urge which developed the "cut and shuffle" system. This eliminates the abstract, so saving time and much of the labour of working up. On the other hand, more taker-off's time is necessary, as he must aim at writing all his descriptions in their final form, as he is in fact writing the draft bill. Moreover, the reconciliation of the descriptions of different takers-off must be done in the final editing instead of being partly done by the worker-up.

[5] See page 65.
[6] *Principles of the Trade-by-Trade System of Taking-Off:* R.I.C.S. Journal, February 1958, page 448.

31

The detail of the process is a technical matter outside the definition of "practice" adopted here and is dealt with elsewhere.[7]

TAKING-OFF FOR ELEMENTAL BILLS.—Where the billing is to be by "elements" instead of by "trades," the taking-off must be sub-divided accordingly. If the surveyor is not himself concerned with the cost analysis and cost planning, he will probably be given a more or less standard list of elements to adopt, so far as he can. The peculiar character of the job may mean that all in the list cannot be used, and it may be that a new one must be introduced. In the interest of more accurate cost analysis the standard list should be adhered to so far as possible. If it is found practicable to make the sections of the taking-off correspond with the elements, it will probably be possible to save some abstracting; if, however, billing direct is overdone, a point comes where it would be quicker and clearer to prepare an abstract than to do a lot of transferring and collecting of figures on the dimension sheets. Until one is used to taking-off by elements there is also the risk of something being missed. There is nothing to prevent the normal order and classification of taking-off being followed, so long as it is clear to the worker-up to which element each item is assigned. Each taker-off and worker-up on the job should have the list of elements and it will be found useful to give code letters to each element, such as FDN for foundations, W EXTL for external walls or P for partitions. Dimensions can be marked up with these code letters in red before working-up begins.

OPERATIONAL BILLS.[8]—A development made some years ago was the division of the bill of quantities in such a way that the materials required for each of a predetermined series of operations are given separately with space provided for the estimator to price the relative labour. Each operation is given a serial number and the bill sections are arranged in the same order. Specimen arrangements are shown in the articles referred to in the footnote.

How far this arrangement suits the needs of the estimator is questionable. The quantity surveyor is there to provide the data required by tenderers for competitive estimates, not to dictate to them what he thinks they ought to want. It may be that this system suits large contractors and large contracts but would only be confusing to the smaller contractor.

The preparation of an operational bill is dependent, as will be seen from the articles, on a pre-arranged order of operations. In a negotiated

[7] *Elements of Quantity Surveying:* 7th Edition 1978, page 198, and *The Modernisation of Techniques in Quantity Surveyors' Offices:* R.I.C.S. Journal, September 1961, page 152.

[8] See *The Operational Bill:* R.I.C.S. Journal, February 1963, page 429 and *Introduction to Operational Bills:* I.Q.S. Journal, September/October 1964, page 27. Reprinted by the Building Research Station (D 1 and D 32).

contract this can be settled in consultation with the contractor, but on whom does the responsibility fall to decide the order in the case of competitive tenders? If the successful contractor does not want to follow the order on which the bill is based, his estimating may well be upset. It has always been drilled into us that we give the tenderers facts and that it is not for us to decide *how* the contractor is to do the job.

Operational bills have been used in practice, but not generally adopted.

NUMBERING DIMENSION SHEETS.—It is advisable to mark every page at the top with the section of the dimensions to which it belongs and the serial number of the page, e.g. Roofs 24, Windows 38, &c. On reference to any sheet one can then see quickly to what section it belongs. Sheets are also usually numbered serially right through, either on each page or each column. If this latter can be done before abstracting is begun such numbering can be used for referencing in the abstract. If not, the sectional reference will have to be given. In either case it is important to ensure that sheets do not go astray, and it is advisable to keep a running index to the dimension sheets as a check, giving at the same time, whenever referred to, a bird's-eye view of what has been done of the taking-off. It need not at this stage be prepared in the full detail which is advisable in an index to be used for looking up dimensions, but it can form an outline for the fuller index. A specimen index is given in Appendix 1.[9]

NUMBERING ROOMS, &c. ON DRAWINGS.—In a domestic building it may be practicable to describe each room by its name, e.g. Dining Room, Kitchen, &c., when referring to it in the dimensions, but in a building of any size it will be difficult to do so. Each room should then be given a serial number marked on all copies of the plans, and references made in the dimensions accordingly. In the same way, windows, doors and other openings can be given numbers in one or more series, so that a reference to the opening number in the dimensions will identify the window or door at once. The same references will be used in the schedules referred to above.[10]

ALTERATIONS IN TAKING-OFF.—It often happens that alterations are made by the taker-off after his dimensions have been squared and perhaps at even a later stage when they have been carried through to the draft bill. It is most important that such alterations should be taken through all the stages of working-up done. If the taker-off marks his alterations with a pencil cross and hands it personally to whoever is responsible for the working-up this should ensure the correction being

[9] Page 194.
[10] Page 28.

33

made. If the working-up has been checked the pencil cross will not be rubbed out until the alteration has been checked, but it should then be erased, as otherwise every time it is seen it will raise a query as to whether something is left undone. If the taker-off has made a number of alterations he can hand a list of the page references on which the crosses appear. Where the dimensions have not been worked-up when altered, no further step will be necessary, except to cross out any relative squaring which has been done.

No alteration should be made to the taking-off, by a worker-up, supervisor or even the principal without reference to the taker-off, unless he is necessarily not available in time. There may be a reason behind the apparent error. It often happens that after making a correction it turns out that the dimension was right the first time.

ABSTRACTING.—Where abstracts are still being used dimension sheets should be squared and checked to be ready for abstracting, but the starting of abstracting work will probably be deferred until there is a substantial number of dimension sheets ready and a prospect of sufficient being available to keep the abstractor going continuously. But this must be qualified by the state of work in the office. If it happens that an abstractor is available earlier than really needed, he may be able to make a start which will fill in his time and leave that much less to be done later. On larger contracts, if pressed for time, the abstract may be divided, one taking say the first part up to Carpentry, and the other the last part. This method takes more manhours, as one abstractor instead of going straight ahead has to look at items which he will not be abstracting in order to decide that he will not.

There is a tendency to avoid what appears to be unproductive work, but on a large contract it will be found useful to have some sort of chart to indicate the stage the work has reached. The above-mentioned Index to the dimensions could be used, each batch of dimensions being marked off as they are abstracted and again in red as they are checked on the abstract.

In a large office there would be a chief worker-up responsible for allocating all working-up to the staff available, but in a small office the organisation would be in the hands of the principal or senior assistant.

BILLING.—The ideal is for the worker-up to finish his job, hand over the complete abstract for checking, casting, checking of casts and reducing, and then have it returned to him to write the bill. The time factor often interferes with the ideal of organisation, and short cuts must be looked for. The greatest part of the biller's time is taken in arranging the items and writing the descriptions. If, therefore, part of the abstract, still uncast, can be made available, the bill can be written in blank, i.e. without any quantities inserted. The filling in of quantities is quickly done when the abstract is finally ready. Another way of catching up with time is to have any items which can be billed direct done in advance. Manholes, joinery fittings, &c., which have to be kept under separate headings can be billed any time after they are taken-off. The sheets should be fastened together and kept in a folder. It is important that no part of the bill should be checked until it has taken its place in the finished draft and the pages have been numbered accordingly. Otherwise, if a page went astray after checking it might never be missed.

SPECIALIST BILLS.—If for the purpose of prime cost sums it is required to get specialists' estimates based on the quantities measured, bills for this specialist work must be prepared first, to enable tenders to be obtained by the time the main bill goes to the printers, or at any rate by the time the proof is passed.

Such bills should state that the specialist will be a nominated sub-contractor and the form of main contract to be used. It is as well to mention the amount of cash discount to be allowed, as it may not agree with the specialist's normal practice. Similar bills can be prepared for the materials of nominated suppliers. Specimen bills are given in Appendix 1.[11]

Bills should be sent in duplicate, so that the specialists have a copy of their instructions. They will sometimes quote on their own form, but it is advisable to ask for a copy of the bill to be signed and returned as confirmation of the terms of enquiry.

It is worth having extra thin typing paper with bill ruling, so that six copies or so can be typed at a time: it is not usually worth while having these bills duplicated, as it is unusual to invite more than three specialists to tender. Additional copies can always be made by photographing the original.

PRELIMINARY BILL AND PREAMBLES.—If possible before billing of the measured work starts, the preambles to each section covering materials and workmanship should be drafted from the specification, amplified if necessary by reference to previous bills. This should be done by one of the takers-off, who will by then have a comprehensive knowledge of the job. It is advisable to have before one, as each section is being done, the abstract sheets of that section, in order to see what items occur and therefore what materials and workmanship need description. These preambles being written first, the biller can see how far the descriptions before him are already covered and make notes of any clauses which he thinks should be added.

The Preliminary Bill must also be drafted. If for a public authority the surveyor may be supplied with their typical clauses. Otherwise he will probably follow one of his own past bills. Care is necessary when using

[11] See pages 195 and 196.

35

other bills to see that everything is applicable to the particular case. There may be clauses, parts of clauses, or even single words which were inserted specially for the previous job, and which, being in type like the rest, are not now evident as insertions. In the same way, owing to some particular circumstances, omissions may have been made previously which now need reinstatement.

As everything which concerns price must be in the bill of quantities, the unnecessary duplication of descriptions in specification and bill can be avoided by reference in the bill to clause numbers and headings of the specification, where there is a full specification prepared and issued with the bills. Where, however, the specification is not part of the contract, it is more satisfactory for the tenderer to have everything in the bill and save the extra time spent in cross-reference. Reference can then be made to the bill item numbers in the specification which can be in a shortened form.[12]

P.C. SUMS.—A check should be made of all p.c. items with the sub-contractors' or merchants' estimates, with an eye to seeing that they include the proper cash discounts. Where the proper cash discounts are not provided for, adjustment should be made so that the prime cost sum complies with the requirements of the contract. It may be noted:—

> For converting net estimate to estimate subject to 2½% add $^1/_{39}$
> For converting net estimate to estimate subject to 5% add $^1/_{19}$
> For converting net estimate subject
> to 2½% to estimate subject to 5% add $^1/_{38}$

Any incorrect discounts should be pointed out to the architect, so that the position may be regularised when he instructs acceptance. If the point is left and overlooked by the contractor, there may be difficulty with auditors if the adjustment is made in the variation account. Their view will be that the contractor should have examined the estimate and had it corrected before accepting it.

The surveyor must also ensure that provision is made for any materials to be supplied by the builder (e.g. cement and sand for tiling). There may be other special conditions accompanying a specialist's estimate, often set out in small print on his standard form. These must be examined to ensure that they are acceptable. For instance, there may be a requirement from steelwork or structural floor contractor for a hard standing alongside the new building to enable him to hoist direct from his lorries into the final position. Requirements as to unloading vary and these must be made clear.

It is advisable to mark the estimate with any adjustments made, so that the build-up of the sum given in the bill can be traced. As the estimate may not be retained it will be found useful to note on the

[12] See page 56.

dimensions against the provisional sum the name of the firm, date and reference of estimate, amount, discount, &c. If there are any blanks in p.c. prices, provisional sums, quantities, &c. on the draft they should be marked in with a pencil cross so that they are not overlooked. A schedule of all p.c. provisional sums should be prepared showing how all the figures have been arrived at, and a copy should be sent to the architect. A specimen of such a schedule is given in Appendix 1.[13]

NUMBERING ITEMS.—Items in the bill can be serially numbered from beginning to end, when a numbering machine will be found a useful item of office equipment. Alternatively, each page can have items referenced from A onwards through the alphabet, so that an item can be quoted as page 50 G, 94 B, &c. The advantage of this is that there is less risk of confusing item number and quantity, when quantity is on the left-hand side, but if the paper is ruled with an item column between double rules or in the form referred to below there should be little danger. On the other hand the page number and lettering cannot be settled until the draft is in the typist's hands, so cross-referencing, often very useful to clarify the bill and help the estimator, is made more difficult. If a serial number is given in the draft which will be the same in the finished copy, the references can be finally filled in on the draft bill.

A form of ruling of bill paper which eliminates any confusion between quantity and item number is now quite general. The exact ruling can be varied to taste, but there is a British Standard.[14] Items with this type of ruling read:—

					£
363	100 × 19 mm Moulded skirting	m	100	0·45	45·00
364	Mitres	Nr	16	0·10	1·60

Another advantage of this ruling is that since the quantity and rate are next to each other, the distance the eye has to travel in pricing-out is much reduced.

SCHEDULE OF BASIC RATES.—If the contract contains a clause covering fluctuations in prices of materials, an appendix will be required to the bill in which the contractor can set out the rates on which the tender is based. The appendix can contain a list of the principal materials (which the contractor can supplement if he wishes), or it can be left to the contractor to prepare his list. Alternatively, a fixed priced list could be given of the principal materials, but it is preferable to let the contractor put his own rates, as one contractor may be better placed than another through being a large buyer or for some other reason.

[13] Page 198.
[14] See page 152.

If the priced bill is not being returned with the tender, it is advisable to reprint the schedule of basic rates of materials as an appendix to the form of tender as well, so that it can be considered when tenders are compared.

SCHEDULE OF ALLOCATION.—When the Price Adjustment Formula for calculating variation of price claims is to be used it is necessary when the bill of quantities is complete and before it is sent out to tender to prepare an allocation of all the items in the bill. This is done by preparing a schedule of all 48 work categories and then going through the bill allocating the items to the work sections or, as in the case of preliminaries and certain provisional sums, into a balance of adjustable items section. When this allocation is complete it is bound in the back of the bill and in submitting a tender a prospective contractor is deemed to have agreed to the allocation chosen by the quantity surveyor. It is unlikely that a tendering contractor will challenge the allocation, but if he does he must do so when submitting his tender. When the tender has been accepted it is a straightforward exercise to complete the schedule by filling in the money, the whole thing being self-checking in that the end result must be the contract sum.

DESPATCH TO PRINTERS.—The draft bill should receive a final careful reading through and editing before being sent to the printers, and an examination made to see that all blanks have been filled in, e.g. cross-references to item numbers or summary pages, &c. If possible it should also be looked through by the principal or a senior assistant other than the takers-off, who at that stage quite possibly cannot "see the wood for the trees." An outsider will often be able to put his finger on something wrong.

Careful examination should also be made of the drawings and specification. All notes on the drawings should be looked over in case any have been missed. "Of course you've taken this," may get an answer "No, I thought *you* had!" The specification can be run through in pencil clause by clause in confirmation that each has been covered, either by the taker-off measuring or by whoever drafted the Preliminary Bill or Preambles.

At some stage between completion of the draft bill and passing of the proof the whole of the dimensions and abstract should be looked through to see that

(*a*) all squaring is checked.

(*b*) all items are run through in the dimensions by both abstractor and checker.

(*c*) all casts and reducing on abstract or cut slips are checked.

(*d*) all items are run through on the abstract by both biller and checker.

(*e*) all items in the draft bill or cut slips are checked.

If the surveyor is arranging for printing, the printers' instructions as to number of copies, binding, &c. should be clearly made in writing. To decide the number of copies the architect, if he has not already supplied a list of tenderers, will be asked how many are tendering, and allowance must be made for additional copies, varying with circumstances, but say:—

Contract 2
Building Owner 1
Architect 1
Quantity Surveyor 2
Successful Contractor 2
Clerk of Works 1
Spare .... 2 or more

"Spare" may be required for a last minute addition to the list of builders, or for, perhaps, the freeholder or other person to whose approval the work is to be carried out.

INVITATIONS TO TENDER.—The architect will usually prepare, often in consultation with the surveyor, a list of firms to be invited to tender. He will send the firms a letter of invitation and on receipt of replies give the surveyor a list of those who have accepted. Sometimes the architect asks the surveyor to send the invitations for him. Such a letter should include at least

name of client and architect,
title and location of the job,
approximate date when bills of quantities will be issued,
time to be allowed for tender,
where the drawings may be seen or some description of the works,
the form of contract to be used.

A typical letter for such a case is given in Appendix 1 based on the example published in the recommended code of procedure.[15] Occasionally some of the requirements of the code of procedure are not always necessary; the requirement, for instance, that tenderers should have two copies of the bill is important if they must send a priced copy with their tender or even forward it on advice that their tender is under consideration. If, however, a blank copy is sent after receipt of tenders (two or three days being allowed for filling in the prices), the extra expense of two copies to all tenderers does not seem justified.

The offer of additional copies of the bill, or of sections of it, which the above-mentioned code stipulates is only likely to be necessary in large contracts.

FORM OF TENDER AND ENVELOPES.—Except in the case of public authorities who have their own standard tender forms, the surveyor will probably be required to draft one (see Appendix 1[16]) to go to the printers with the draft bill. Envelopes of suitable size to hold the tender form will

[15] *Code of Procedure for Selective Tendering:* N.J.C.C. (obtainable from R.I.C.S.).
[16] Page 194 and Appendix B of the above-mentioned Code.

also be required, addressed to the architect or building owner according to the arrangements made for delivery of tenders, and marked with the name of the job so that they can be put aside on receipt and all opened together. A draft of the address should accompany the tender form to the printers, who will supply the number of envelopes required. The number of tender forms will be twice the number of tenderers (if each is being sent two copies) with, say, two or three extra copies, one of which should be sent to the architect for his reference.

If the contractor is to be given the option to tender for work covered by prime cost sums, in accordance with clause 35.2 of the Standard form of contract, it is advisable to make provision in the form of tender for tenderers to state what work (if any) they would like to tender for. With the present day emphasis on early planning, the architect may want to settle some of his specialists provisionally when he is preparing his drawings, and so obtain the benefit of consultation with them. Since this contract clause leaves the matter entirely to the discretion of the architect, it has little practical value in such cases.

Some public authorities require the priced bill returned with the tender, but this is not usual, though sometimes done, in private practice. If it is required, a separate addressed envelope for return should be provided, of suitable size and strength to hold the bill. The priced bill will be delivered sealed, and only opened if to be considered for acceptance: its envelope must, therefore, be marked with the name of the job in the same way as that enclosing the tender form, and the tenderers should be instructed that each must put his name clearly on the outside.

READING PROOFS.—The various methods of duplicating available are discussed in Chapter 15.[17] In any case a proof should be required. The reading through of a proof is a laborious task. One person comparing draft and proof will very easily miss differences, and probably the best way is for two to check, one reading from the draft and the other following in the proof. Periodically the duties and documents should be changed to avoid the soporific effect of listening to the reading for too long. A good way to simplify the reading through is to go through the quantities columns first to ensure

(a) correctness of figures, both of item numbers and quantities.

(b) that they are in the right column.

(c) that the "m" or "m²" or "m³" is correct.

Descriptions can then be read through separately. This method is particularly valuable if only one person is reading through the proof, as in the usual way one is apt to relax concentration on the three above-mentioned points which are all-important. In all cases reading

[17] Page 160.

should be from the draft, as being slower than reading from type: otherwise the reading would be too fast to follow properly.

ISSUE OF DRAWINGS.—It is necessary to issue to tenderers a copy of each of the location drawings, i.e. the site plan and the general 1:100 sheets and certain of the component details in accordance with the requirements of S.M.M.6 Clause B.3. Sufficient copies of these should be obtained from the architect in time for issue with the bills.

It often happens that in preparation of the bill of quantities errors are found in the architect's drawings, which should be corrected. He should be advised of these in time to correct his originals before prints are taken for issue to tenderers.

DESPATCH OF FINISHED BILLS.—A covering letter (see Appendix 1[18]) must be drafted to go to tenderers with the bills and this should state:—

(*a*) what documents are enclosed.

(*b*) date, time and place for delivery of tenders, and that tenders are to be delivered in the envelope supplied.

(*c*) what drawings are enclosed and where and when further drawings can be seen.

(*d*) what arrangements the tenderer must make for visiting the site, e.g. with whom appointment should be made, or where the key can be obtained. If the site is open for inspection this should be stated.

(*e*) a request for acknowledgement.

Care must be taken in arranging the documents for each contractor, so that all have them complete and correct. They are probably best laid out in piles with their envelope and checked as they are put into it.

CORRECTION OF ERRORS.—The bills despatched, a copy should be looked through, as mistakes, made perhaps in the rush to get the bill off to time, may catch the eye. If the surveyor is preparing the specification after the bill is finished, mistakes in the taking-off may come to light as he works through the bill and looks up the dimensions. Queries may arise, too, from contractors tendering. Unless errors are of a very minor nature, they should be circulated to contractors in time for them to correct their copies before tenders are made up. An acknowledgement should be asked for to ensure that all tenderers have had the opportunity of making the corrections. Even so, when the priced bill of the successful contractor is being examined, it should be verified that the corrections have been made. A typical letter will be found in Appendix 1.[19]

[18] See page 200.
[19] See page 203.

5
BUILDING CONTRACTS

GENERALLY.—The detailed study of the law of contract and of building contracts in particular is a separate subject for the student and cannot be given anything like full treatment within the scope of a book of this type. In this chapter the principal forms in use are noted and some attention is drawn to those clauses which most affect the practice of the quantity surveyor and deserve his special study. Some text books and reference books will be found quoted in Appendix 2.

PROCEDURE.—Recommended procedure for the placing and management of building contracts is set out in the official report of a Committee appointed by the Minister of Public Building and Works, popularly known as the Banwell Report.[1] The National Economic Development Office has published a working party report described as a "survey of the implementation" of its recommendations.[2] In both these will be found useful information and advice.

DIFFERING FORMS OF CONTRACT.—Broadly speaking there is a distinction between forms of building contract used in private practice and for public authorities. For private practice the Standard forms[3] prepared by the Joint Contracts Tribunal are in general use. There are separate forms for use with and without bills of quantities. Local Authorities and nationalised organisations generally use a specially adapted version of the Standard form, the main difference in which is the inclusion of a special "fair wages clause" which is required in all Local Authority contracts.

Government Departments use an entirely different form of contract, usually that known as GC/Works/1.[3] Government contracts are the responsibility of the Contracts Co-ordinating Committee which deals with forms of contract for the purchase of all goods and services required by Government Departments. Building contracts are handled by a sub-committee, the Works Sub-Committee, which consists of representatives from each Department concerned, mostly non-

---

[1] *The Placing and Management of Contracts for Building and Civil Engineering Works:* H.M.S.O. 1964.

[2] *Action on the Banwell Report:* H.M.S.O. 1967.

[3] See footnote on page xi.

technical. Although it is consulted, the Construction Industry is not represented and consequently Government contracts are not jointly agreed documents as is the Standard form.

Government Departments also make considerable use for maintenance work of term contracts. These are contracts, let competitively by which a builder undertakes to carry out all repair and maintenance work on Government buildings within a stated area for a particular period or term, usually two or three years. Competing contractors state a percentage on or off a published schedule of prices. Many other Departments use the D.O.E. Schedule of Prices.[4]

For civil engineering works the I.C.E. Conditions of Contract[5] are in general use in private practice and by nationalised industries, such authorities as the National Coal Board or British Railways having a high proportion of civil engineering work.

The student should ensure that he has a copy of the standard form of contract, either the Standard form or GC/Works/1, according to his practice (preferably both), and study the text. Its application is largely a matter of experience which brings familiarity with the wording and knowledge of how in practice it is interpreted. In the case of the Standard form there is a useful commentary.[6]

In view of the 1980 edition of the Standard form, it must be remembered that the cases quoted in the chapters on law are based on the form of contract used in the particular case. Even when based on old Standard forms they are still useful where the conditions are unchanged.

STANDARD FORM.—The 1980 edition of the Standard form of contract is to be published in January of 1980. The new form is in five parts, the Articles of Agreement, Conditions: Part 1 General, Part 2 Nominated Sub-Contractors and Nominated Suppliers, Part 3 Fluctuations and the Appendix. Also published with the new form is the Nominated sub-contract prepared for the first time by the J.C.T. Accompanying these publications is a helpful guide[7] which includes a comparison with the 1963 edition, explanatory notes and worked examples. The following clauses in the Standard form are of particular interest to the quantity surveyor.

Clause

1   Includes the interpretation and definitions to be applied throughout.

[4] See footnote on page 2 and *P.S.A. Schedule of rates:* R.I.C.S. Journal, Q.S. Quarterly, December 1976, page 28.

[5] *General Conditions of Contract, etc.:* Institution of Civil Engineers.

[6] *The Standard Form of Building Contract* (Walker-Smith & Close): Knight. For some account of the development of this form see *The Evolution of the R.I.B.A. Form of Contract* (Close): N.F.B.T.E.

[7] *J.C.T.* Guide to the Standard Form of Building Contract 1980 edition and to the *J.C.T.* Nominated Sub-Contract documents.

2 Is the Contractor's obligations, deals with the preparation of the contract bill and sets out how errors therein are to be corrected.

5 Lists the contract documents.

13 Variations and provisional sums includes a revised definition of a variation together with the rules for pricing variations and the adjustment of provisional sums.

16 Includes the rules for payment for materials on and off site.

19 This clause is mainly about sub-letting to domestic sub-contractors but 19.3 is important to quantity surveyors as it sets out that a minimum list of three persons shall be named in the contract bills where it is specifically intended that the work shall be sub-let.

21 & 22 Are the insurance clauses with the various options available from which the quantity surveyor has to ascertain which are applicable. Clause 22 has slightly different coding in that the decimal numbering adopted throughout the rest of the contract is amplified by the letters A, B and C. 22A applies when the insurance for new construction work is the sole responsibility of the Contractor, 22B when it is the sole responsibility of the Employer and 22C, which applies to existing structures, when there is no option and the Employer is responsible for the insurance.

25 Extensions of time including the notices to be given and the grounds under which extensions of time can be granted. Important items upon which a quantity surveyor is often asked to advise.

26 Direct loss and/or expense. Here again the quantity surveyor is often asked to comment and sometimes to go even further in that the clause specifically gives the right for the quantity surveyor to ascertain the amount himself.

27 Determination by the Employer, important in the event of the bankruptcy of the main contractor.

30 Certificates and payments. This clause not only includes the rules for interim and final payments but explicitly sets out how the contract may be adjusted (30.6).

35 Nominated sub-contractors includes all the rules for nomination to be used in conjunction with the J.C.T. Form of sub-contract and includes the procedure for obtaining tenders, setting up the sub-contract and the form of Employer/Nominated Sub-Contractor Agreement.

36 Nominated suppliers include similar rules for nomination of suppliers.

37 Is the Fluctuations clause and refers to clauses 38, 39 and 40 which are published separately. 38 applies when only fluc-

tuations in Contribution, Levy and Tax matters are to apply. 39 when full Labour and Material and Tax fluctuations are intended and 40 when the Price Adjustment Formula is to be used.

Appen- The appendix to the contract is particularly important to a
dix   quantity surveyor. He is required (SMM. B.4.3) to set out in the bill of quantities how this appendix is to be completed as it very much affects the conditions under which the work is to be carried out and any change would have serious implications. The quantity surveyor will ask the architect what he wants in the way of such things as date for possession, amount of damages retentions and all the other points listed. He is prudent to get the answers in writing and may well use his query and answer sheet to record the architect's decision. These matters are too important for the quantity surveyor to say to himself "I think I know what he wants, I'll chance it".

The changes made in the 1980 edition of the Standard form are far reaching and a detailed study of the various contract documents together with the guide are recommended when instructions are first received to use the new form.

PRACTICE NOTES.—The Joint Contracts Tribunal from time to time issue "practice notes" on the Standard form, which express their view on some particular point in practice. Such view must, of course, be given due weight, but it must be emphasised that it does not affect the legal interpretation of the terms of a contract, any more than a discussion in Parliament affects the interpretation of an Act.

GC/Works/1.—There are not, as in the Standard form, separate forms for use with and without quantities. Clause 5A provides for a schedule of rates to be deposited by the contractor where no bill of quantities is supplied. There are no Articles of Agreement: the form of tender and acceptance constitute the contract. The clauses in the Conditions of particular interest to quantity surveyors are:—

Clause
1   The definitions should be understood.
4   Unlike the Standard form, this contract makes the Specification a contract document.
5   The bill of quantities. The effect of the subclauses on correction of errors is similar to that of the Standard form. It will be noted that the same Conditions of Contract are applied with Provisional or Approximate quantities or with a Schedule of

Prices.

7   S.O.'s Instructions and the conditions under which the relative work is chargeable.

8   Failure of Contractor to comply with Instructions.

9   Valuation of variations.

10   Valuation by measurement.

11   This clause (Price Variation) has been withdrawn from the printed document, but is added as a supplementary clause for contracts with price adjustment.

14   Statutory fees &c. There is no requirement for provisional sums: tenderers are expected to ascertain their liability.

20   The Contractor must not allow in his prices for being able to use such material as sand from the excavation. What he uses will be valued and he will be charged.

24   Rendering of daywork accounts.

25   There is no requirement for fire insurance &c. in the case of Crown property. The Government are their own insurers (see clauses 1 (2) (h) and 26 (2) (b) (ii).

26   Damage to Works or other things.

28   Delay.

29   Damages for Delay.

31   Sub-contractors.

37   Attendance of the Contractor for measuring.

38   Prime cost items. The cash discounts under the Conditions are the same (2½%) for both suppliers and sub-contractors. They are not guaranteed, being described as "obtainable."

39   Provisional lump sums and provisional quantities.

40   Advances on account. The percentages to be retained and maximum amounts are fixed and not left to be determined in each case, as in the Standard form.

41   Payments on completion.

42   Certificates.

43   Recovery of Sums due from the Contractor.

44   There is a unilaterial power to determine the contract and full instructions as to the procedure to be followed. The Contractor does not get compensation for loss of profit, but subclause D(5) makes provision for an *ex gratia* allowance in case of hardship (which is usually interpreted as losing money, not failing to make it).

45   Determination in case of default or failure of the Contractor.

46   A clause applicable to all cases of determination.

47   Injury to person and property. The Contractor's liability is defined. There is no reference to insurance: that is his affair.

48   The Contractor is not responsible for damage to highways &c.

61   Arbitration.

COMPARISON OF STANDARD AND GOVERNMENT FORMS.—The Standard form, being one negotiated between the building owner (represented by architects and quantity surveyors as well as officers of Local Authorities) and the contractor is one mutually agreed by or on behalf of the parties to a building contract. The Government form, unilaterally prepared, is a good deal longer, as, besides providing for the special circumstances of Crown property, is for use in both building and civil engineering works. Moreover, it seems to be elaborated in an attempt to cover as many unforeseen conditions as possible: the more that decisions which involve individual judgment, and perhaps prejudice, can be reduced, the less likely are inconsistencies between the rulings of different officers, possibly resulting in injustice. The tendency, accordingly, is for the Government contract to be more onerous on the contractor than the Standard form.

Neither form of contract defines "p.c. items" or "provisional sums". The implied meaning is that p.c. sums are sums to be expended either on materials to be supplied by merchants or on work to be done on the site by sub-contractors or statutory authorities, to be included in the tender and set against the relative account, with adjustment of any profit &c. added by the contractor. Provisional sums are lump sums to be included provisionally in the tender, usually for uncertain needs such as the contingency sum, against which may be set measured work, daywork and/or an outside account, with a profit for the contractor.[8]

FIXED FEE FORM OF PRIME COST CONTRACT, STANDARD FORM.[9]—The following clauses are of particular interest to the quantity surveyor under normal conditions:—

  1. Definitions.

  3. Architect's instructions.

  7. Labour, materials, goods and workmanship.

  8. Materials and Goods unfixed or off site.

 15.
    Insurances.
 16.

20. Loss &c. from disturbance.

23. Nominated sub-contractors.

24. Nominated suppliers.

 26.
    Payment.
 27.

First Schedule: Definition of Prime Cost.

It will be seen that the other schedules are blank forms to be filled in:—

---

[8] This meaning is confirmed by a definition in the *Standard Method of Measurement,* 6th Edition, clause A.8, which will apply to bills of quantities, unless otherwise provided.

[9] See footnote on page 3.

Amount of fixed fee.
Estimated cost of works.
Work to be done by nominated sub-contractors.
Goods to be supplied by nominated suppliers.
Work to be done under separate direct contracts.

FORM OF AGREEMENT FOR MINOR BUILDING WORKS.[10]—This
is a four-page document of thirteen clauses, being the standard edition in
a very abbreviated form, intended for work which is not technically
unusual or complex.

OTHER FORMS OF CONTRACT.—Certain other large Authorities,
besides the Government, have their own form of building contract, it
may be one based on the Standard form with modifications to suit the
particular Authority, or it may be one entirely different. The
representation of Local Authorities on the Joint Contracts Tribunal in
preparation of the 1963 form, which was not given them when the 1939
form was prepared, is tending to increase the use of the form by Local
Authorities. The former London County Council decided to change
over from their own form to the Standard form. If the surveyor meets a
form which is strange to him, he must study it, particularly to see what
differences have been made from what is in his experience normal
practice.

FIRM PRICE CONTRACTS.—With the greater stability in cost of
labour and materials which it was hoped had come, there was a tendency
for contracts to be placed on a firm price basis without any fluctuations
adjustment clause. In order that the contractor may reasonably tie
himself, it is more than ever essential for the project to be thoroughly
thought out and not extend too far into the future. The Joint
Consultative Committee of Architects, Quantity Surveyors and
Builders have published their recommendations.[11] Briefly they recommend

1. thorough preliminary planning.
2. acceptance of a tender within two months.
3. complete documentation.
4. notification to the architect by the contractor of his future
   requirements at the earliest stage.

When, after experiment, this procedure was decided on for Government
work, the Minister of Works stated in the House of Commons (April
30th, 1957) that it would be limited to cases where the estimated contract

[10] *Agreement for Minor Building Works:* J.C.T.
[11] R.I.C.S. Journal, April 1958, page 566.

period was not more than two years. In January 1974 the Government announced a relaxation in that the mandatory period for fixed price contracts was to be reduced from two years to one year, but this relaxation was linked to the introduction of the formula method of price fluctuations[12] as many more contracts would be let on this basis.

VALUE ADDED TAX ON BUILDING CONTRACTS.—Under Schedule 4 Group 8 of the Finance Act 1972 the construction, alteration or demolition of any building or of any civil engineering work is granted relief from V.A.T. by zero rating. All other types of building work, such as maintenance, repairs or improvements not amounting to alteration of the structure or appearance of the building, are liable to V.A.T. at the full rate.

The full text of Schedule 4 Group 8 of the Finance Act 1972 will be found in H.M. Customs & Excise Notice No. 701, Appendix A. Further details will be found in Notices No. 708 ("Construction Industry") and No. 715 ("Construction Industry—Alterations and Repairs & Maintenance"); all these Notices may be obtained on request from any V.A.T. Office of H.M. Customs & Excise.

All the main standard forms of contract for building or civil engineering works (i.e. the Standard Forms of Building Contract issued by the Joint Contracts Tribunal, the Government form of contract GC/Works/1 and the ICE Conditions of Contract Fifth Edition) exclude V.A.T. from the general operation of the contract but provide for any V.A.T. chargeable to be the matter of a separate transaction between Contractor and Employer with specific provisions for dealing with disputes over the amount of V.A.T. charged. The Joint Contracts Tribunal has issued a Supplemental Agreement which is to be signed by Contractor and Employer and attached to the main contract; the full text, together with explanatory material and other matter, may be found in Practice Note 17 issued by the Tribunal. Supplementary Condition No. 139A has been issued by the Property Services Agency of the Department of the Environment for use with the form of contract GC/Works/1. Provisions regarding V.A.T. have been incorporated into the text of the I.C.E. Conditions of Contract Fifth Edition as clause 70. The reader is referred to all these sources for further details.

[12] See pages 75-6.

6
RECEIPT OF TENDERS

DELIVERY AND OPENING.—In the case of public authorities tenders will probably be addressed to the Secretary or Principal Chief Officer, but with private clients they are usually addressed to the architect. When the time for delivery comes the envelopes received will be counted, as a check that all are in, before being opened. After opening, the official concerned or the architect, as the case may be, will prepare a list of the tendered amounts, have them arranged in order and typed for reporting. At one time it used to be the regular custom for builders tendering to be invited to a formal opening, so that they could see that all was fair and above board and could take down the figures. This custom has fallen into disuse and is not often followed, though it might with advantage be revived. Though this suggestion has been criticised by a reviewer as "outmoded," it nevertheless has the advantage of recommending a straightforward procedure, which makes it clear that from the employer's side there is nothing "under the counter." There seem to be no valid reasons against, though its recommendation in the *Code of Procedure for Selective Tendering* has been dropped since the 1965 edition.

The practice sometimes adopted of not giving builders the list of tenders, or giving the figures only without the names, is to be discouraged. Publication of the result is the least that can be done in return for the time and trouble taken by tenderers without charge. It is advisable that tenders delivered after the time fixed should be rejected, since after the published time of opening builders are apt to telephone each other as to figures, and an unscrupulous builder, if there were such a one, might take advantage of this. If the postmark showed the tender to have been despatched before the time for delivery, it might well be accepted. An alternative, if the lower tender is late, is to notify all tenders that the time for receipt of tenders has been extended by—say—7 days, and ask all to confirm their tenders.

REPORTING OF TENDERS.—In considering tenders other factors than the tendered price may be of importance. The time required to carry out the work, if stated on the form of tender, may be compared, as time may be very important financially to the client. Although there may be reasonable excuses for failing to keep to the time arranged, and even justification for avoiding the liquidated damages provided for by the contract, the time stated by a reputable contractor may be taken as a reasonable estimate, having regard to the circumstances as he knows them.

If the contract is subject to adjustment of the price of materials, the schedule of basic rates of materials must also be considered and the question asked: Has the tenderer assumed reasonable basic prices for materials? If he has based them too low he will be getting excessive "increased cost" on a rising market or allowing too little in "reduced cost" on a falling market. Where tenders are close the schedules of basic rates should be compared, as the lower tenderer may have less favourable rates. Only a preliminary examination will be made at this stage to ascertain which tender or tenders should be considered for acceptance, a fuller report, after supporting estimates are produced, being made later by the quantity surveyor.

The architect, having considered these matters in consultation with the quantity surveyor, or the Public Authority in consultation with both the technical advisers, will report the tenders to the client or committee concerned and set out clearly for their consideration the arguments in favour of acceptance of one tender or another, if there is any doubt. It should be mentioned that, when tenders are invited from a limited number of builders, the lowest, or potentially lowest, should be accepted. All go to a good deal of trouble and expense in preparing a tender, and the object of such tendering is to decide which amongst a number, all acceptable to the building owner, will do the work at the lowest price. Whether expressly disclaimed in the invitation or not, there is no legal obligation to accept the lowest or any tender, but there is in a limited invitation a moral one to accept the lowest, if any. When tenders are advertised and any Tom, Dick or Harry who can find the required deposit and surety may submit a tender, the circumstances are different. One can justly say "I didn't ask you and I don't want you," though even then, when the expenditure of public money is involved, there may sometimes be repercussions.

EXAMINATION OF PRICED BILL.—Before acceptance of a tender, the tenderer whose offer is under consideration will be asked to send a copy of his priced bill to the quantity surveyor for examination, if it has not been delivered with the tender, a blank copy being sent him for the purpose. Sometimes, to save time, he is asked to send his original bill, but a copy is sufficient. His own copy may be marked with estimator's notes which he may not wish to disclose. There is no justification for the certificate one has sometimes seen asked for that the copy of the bill has been compared and checked with the original. The tender is a lump sum tender and the sole purpose of obtaining the pricing is to provide a fair schedule for the adjustment of variations.

In the first place a check will be made of all mathematics, so that in the case of clerical errors it is quite clear what rate shall be used for adjustment. If, for instance, an item has been priced at £0.50 per m and extended at £0.05, it will not be fair that either additional quantity or omission of the item should be priced out at the incorrect rate in adjusting accounts. All clerical errors should be corrected in the contract copy of the bill, but, of course, the amount of the tender would not normally be altered.[1] The difference will be shown as a rebate or plusage in the Summary (see Appendix 1[2]) which will be applicable, in interim valuations and adjustment of variations, to all rates except provisional sums and p.c. prices.

Apart from the mathematical check a technical check should be made of the pricing by generally looking through the rates. A slip may be noticed of an item left unpriced, or one which is billed in sq. m being priced at what obviously is a lin. m rate, or vice versa. Or some obvious misunderstanding of a description may be noted. Here again corrections should be made so that a reasonable schedule of rates for pricing variations results.

A secondary reason for examination of the price bill is to ensure that the tenderer has not made such a serious mistake that he would prefer to withdraw the tender, as he may at any time before acceptance. If such a serious error is found out, it is advisable, subject to the architect's approval, to draw the tenderer's attention to it, otherwise, finding it out sooner or later, he will be constantly trying to recover his loss, possibly to the detriment of the building owner's interest.[3] If correction of the error does not bring the tender under consideration above the next highest, the architect may feel he can advise his client to allow amendment of the tender. Otherwise he will naturally pass on to the next tender. If the tender has been accepted, the tenderer strictly cannot withdraw, but it may not be policy to hold him to his tender for the above-mentioned reason.

If priced bills are delivered with the tender by all contractors, only the bills of tenders under consideration for acceptance should be opened, usually one, but sometimes, if tenders are close, two or three. All others should be returned unopened.

CORRECTION OF ERRORS.—Under Section 9 of the *Code of Procedure for Selective Tendering,* "Examination and Correction of the Priced Bills," two alternatives appear for dealing with genuine errors. Under alternative 1 the contractor either confirms or withdraws, the situation which previously existed and is dealt with in this book.[4]

[1] See page 54.
[2] Pages 201 and 202.
[3] Page 122.
[4] See pages 201 and 202.

The second alternative allows him to confirm or correct. The difficulty is to decide what is a genuine error, particularly as under 7.1 four days can elapse before he must produce his priced bill of quantities. This four-day period does not follow the recommendation of the Banwell Report,[5] with which this code otherwise generally agrees. Whichever alternative is to be adopted, it is important that a decision is made before tenders are invited and that such decision is communicated to the contractors tendering.

EXAMINATION OF SCHEDULE OF BASIC RATES.—Where a contract is to be subject to price adjustment, and the Formula Method is not being used,[6] when the copy of the priced bill of quantities is asked for from the contractor whose tender is being considered, he should at the same time be asked to submit estimates in support of his basic prices for materials on which he requires adjustment (if any). Any rates not the subject of specific quotation must be carefully checked. Certain materials, such as Portland cement, have standard prices, others, such as steel tubing or stoneware drain goods, are quoted at a percentage on or off a standard list. The current rates can be obtained from the trade association concerned. The bulk of the basic rates will probably be arrived at from *ad hoc* estimates from merchants. It should be noted that prices will often vary with the size of the "lot" quoted. A basic price for cement quoted "in 6 ton lots," or its metric equivalent, should be so marked, and if bought in smaller lots adjustment will be against the corresponding basic price of that size lot.

Quotations should be examined with a knowledge of prices in mind. It is not unknown for a merchant to make a mistake against himself in the price he quotes. It will probably be some months before the quotation is accepted, and then only after new tenders have been obtained by the contractor in an attempt to get a lower one. The mistake being discovered, the contractor may claim the correction as increased cost. Under the normal forms of contract he must prove fluctuation in market price, so cannot recover the amount of the error.

Again the introduction of the Price Adjustment Formula will negate this process and instead the quantity surveyor will be required to complete the Schedule of Allocation and the reduction of the work categories to the agreed number if required.[7]

REDUCTION BILLS.—If, as not infrequently happens, the lowest tender is for a higher sum than the client is prepared to spend, it may be possible to bring it within the financial limit by making some adjustments on the work required. This would be done by preparing an adjustment

[5] Clause 4.12.
[6] Pages 37 and 49.
[7] See page 38.

bill, incorporating the revisions and so revising the tender, in a similar way to the variation account referred to in Chapter 8. As this bill is prepared before the contract is signed, the contract sum would be the revised tender figure. The bill, in fact, modifies the original quantities and the quantities as so modified become part of the contract. The adjustments will probably be mostly omissions, but if balancing additions are required, for which there are no prices in the bill, the prices for these would have to be agreed with the contractor. Sometimes, if a variation is complicated but its value can be estimated fairly accurately, the adjustment could be made as a lump sum at this stage, either as a sum agreed by the contractor or as a provisional sum subject to adjustment in the variation account.

In the same way any afterthoughts or additional requirements could be made the subject of an adjustment or addenda bill, so that they are incorporated in the contract before signature.

PREPARATION OF CONTRACT BILL OF QUANTITIES.—A fair copy of the priced bill of quantities will be required for signature with the contract. If a blank copy has been sent to the contractor to be completed, this can be used as the surveyor's office copy after making any alterations necessitated by the check, but a corrected copy for the contract is probably best made in the surveyor's office either by hand or by photo-copying the original. If made by hand it should, of course, be in ink and contain the schedule of basic rates of materials or the allocation of the items so making them part of the contract. If the general copies are only stapled, the contract copy should be bound with strong linen or similar material to the back edge. It will then be sent to the architect, or Clerk in the case of a public authority, who will be getting together the contract documents.

The prices in the contractor's priced bill of quantities must be treated as confidential. They must be used solely for the purpose of the contract (see Standard form, 5.7). Though they naturally contribute to the surveyor's knowledge of current rates and he may refer to them for his own information, he must not, for example when discussing a price with a contractor, say ''Mr. X's price on such-and-such a job was so much.'' Where the contractors have been required to deliver their priced bills with the tender, those not considered for acceptance being returned unopened, their prices are not disclosed to anybody. (It is not unknown for a contractor to submit a tender out of courtesy, because he does not like to refuse, and in such a case the blankness of the ''priced'' bill will also be kept concealed by this procedure.)

THE SPECIFICATION.—This document now plays a less important part than used to be the case. Under the Standard form of contract with quantities it is not a contract document. It merely serves to indicate to

55

the builder's site representative matters which in themselves do not affect price and therefore are not mentioned in the bill of quantities. In other words, its principal function is to give the location in the building of the items measured in the bill. This can either be in a separate document or in the form of notes facing the relative items in the bill, which in that case would be printed on one side of the paper only. It need not appear in copies sent to tenderers, but sufficient copies of the bill can be kept unbound for printing it later. The GC/Works/1 form of contract (clause 1) retains the specification as part of the contract.

It is useful to have standard headings for consideration when preparing a specification. A large organisation may have its own system, but a suitable form is now published under the title of "Specification Notes" (see page 227.) This has spaces provided under a great variety of headings which serve as a reminder of what may be necessary. Naturally, with a form applicable to any type of building there will always be headings which do not apply to the particular case. It is easier to discard a heading than to rack one's brains trying to think what has been forgotten. This form is particularly useful for completion as the architect's instructions to the quantity surveyor. Or, if the architect's specification notes are found deficient, say, in one trade, the pages relating to that trade could be sent him as a guide to further information required.

The specification when required as a separate document is sometimes prepared by the architect, sometimes by the quantity surveyor. There is much to be said in favour of the architect supplying notes only, and the specification in its final form being drafted by the quantity surveyor, so ensuring that specification and bill agree in their wording. If the surveyor writes the specification he will have to do it at this stage, so that it is ready for signature with the contract, if a contract document, or for use by the foreman as soon as work starts, if it is not.

Payment for preparation of the specification when prepared by the quantity surveyor has always been a difficult point. Architects are tending more and more to regard the supply of brief specification notes, sometimes accompanied by schedules, as being the limit of what is required of them, and the specification becomes "nobody's baby." For their own satisfaction quantity surveyors have often prepared this without charge, but responsibility for payment is a problem still waiting to be clarified by the leading professional Institutions concerned. The R.I.B.A. scale of charges makes it part of the architect's duty to prepare a specification, but gives an alternative. It says:—

". . . preparing working drawings, specification or such particulars as may be necessary for the preparation of bills of quantities by an independent Quantity Surveyor, or for the purpose of obtaining tenders . . ."

Reference to a specification in the Contracts Documents clause of the

1980 Standard form (5.3) has been dropped and the architect's scale of fees will cover preparation of the documents referred to. The relevant clause reads as follows:—

". . . the Architect without charge to the Contractor shall provide him (unless he shall have been previously so provided) with two copies of any descriptive schedules or other like document necessary for use in carrying out the Works."

The Scale of the R.I.C.S. likewise makes no mention of a specification in such circumstances. In the case of Public Authorities it will be found that either they supply the full specification to the quantity surveyor, which serves both purposes, or they require the quantity surveyor to prepare one and recognise this as an additional service for which they make payment.

OFFICE DOCUMENTS.—The surveyor should have his own copy of the priced bill bound in the same way as the contract copy. In the "good old days" one had it bound in full cloth boards with gilt lettering on the back edge, but to do so now may be thought to make an unwarranted increase in overhead charges. If a dark linen is used for binding the back edge, lettering can be neatly written in white ink to be easily visible when on the shelf.

On a contract of any size, where dimensions and abstract will have a lot of handling, the surveyor may find it worth while to have these documents sewn and bound similarly to the bills. Otherwise the sheets will be secured by string tags, holing for which can be ordered at the time of purchase of the paper. It is much more convenient to refer to documents tagged or bound at the side, where pages can be turned over like those of a book, than to loose sheets tagged in one corner. A proper index to the dimensions should be drafted first and preferably typed on a sheet or sheets to be bound in at the head of the dimensions. If the dimensions make more than one volume it is advisable to have the index of the whole in each volume. Whichever volume is then picked up, any section of the dimensions can be looked up in the index.

The draft bill may be kept in order to trace how any mistakes in billing, which may be found later, came to be made, but otherwise it is of little further value, except, since it is usually written on one side only, as excellent scrap paper.

The documents being all in order and put away, the job can probably be more or less left out of mind until the time comes round when the contractor wants his first certificate.

When the "cut and shuffle" method of taking-off is used, rather different conditions govern the storage of dimensions. The loose dimension sheets will have been fastened together in batches with string tags and, instead of being bound, they, together with the photographed

57

copies of the uncut dimensions, would be stored in boxes of cardboard or similar material made to the required size and suitably labelled.

NEGOTIATED CONTRACTS.—This is perhaps the place to say something of negotiated contracts. They may be of two classes—original contracts or extension contracts.

There may be good reason in a particular case why a contract should not be let on competitive tender—perhaps the building owner has association with some firm and is prepared to give them the contract on a recommendation that the price is reasonable. If that is the case, a bill of quantities can be prepared in the normal way and sent to the builder to price. When priced, the bill will be returned to the quantity surveyor for examination and report. He will examine the rates and make notes of points on which he wants further information and then arrange an appointment with the builder to go through them. He will probably ask for production of estimates for the principal materials and for any work proposed to be sublet and for the build-up of any rates which he feels should be queried. The surveyor will get the adjustments agreed with the builder and then report that a tender of £x is in his opinion reasonable. This does not necessarily mean that it is as low as would be obtained in competitive tender, when profit may be cut below the normal, but that a fair price is being asked.

Another occasion for a negotiated contract is the addition of further substantial work on a site where a contract is already established. There are practical difficulties in employing two contractors concurrently on the same site, so it may be decided to negotiate a second contract with the same firm on the basis of the first. It may even be preferable to negotiate a price with the same contractor for a similar building on another site rather than invite new tenders, if the contractor has given satisfaction and his price is considered reasonable. In either of such cases the bill will be prepared as before and priced, so far as practicable on the basis of the rates in the existing contract, adjusted, if necessary, for fluctuation in labour and material costs which have arisen in the interval. The second building may be of quite a different type from the first, so that many items will appear in the bill of quantities which did not appear in the first bill. Rates of these items will be negotiated as before. Consideration will also have to be given to such economies as should arise by employing a contractor already established on the site and this with any other change of circumstances will probably be reflected in the pricing of the Preliminary Bill. Even with a contract which is to be subject to price adjustment, it may be advisable to bring the measured rates up to date and fix new basic rates for labour and materials, bearing in mind that the contractor has no profit on additions by way of increased cost brought into account.

7

VALUATIONS FOR INTERIM
CERTIFICATES

ACCURACY.—The valuation for certificates should be made as accurately as is reasonably possible. The contractor is entitled under his contract to the value of work done, less a specified retention sum. If the valuation is kept low the retention sum is in effect increased. To a contractor having a number of contracts in hand these excessive margins will mount up and demand additional capital. On the other hand, the building owner must be protected against the possible bankruptcy of the contractor, when an over-payment resulting from an excessive valuation cannot be recovered, and the building owner might have to meet extra expense in employing another contractor to complete the work.

DATES.—If, as is often the case, the contractor is entitled to certificates monthly, it will be found convenient to arrange the dates at the beginning of the contract—say, the last Thursday in every month. Sometimes the date must be fixed to suit the building owner's convenience, particularly when payment is passed at some board or committee meeting held at fixed intervals, as every effort should be made to reduce the interval between valuation and payment. It helps if the contractor himself submits a valuation statement, but the responsibility is, of course, with the surveyor. A meeting should in any case be arranged with the contractor's surveyor, as it is an advantage for the valuation to be mutually agreed.

Sub-contractors for whom provisional sums are included (nominated sub-contractors) should be notified by the general contractor of the dates of valuations and required to submit statements by those dates. If preferred, the surveyor himself can make the arrangements, but it should be part of the general contractor's responsibility to do so. Dealings with the contractor's private sub-contractors should only be through the general contractor with whose rates alone the surveyor is concerned.

EXTENT OF MEASUREMENT.—The extent to which measurement will be necessary in making valuations for certificates will depend on the nature of the job and the stage it has reached. It may very often be possible to take the price bill and pick out the items which have been done and to build up a figure in that way. Some items will, of course, be only partly done, and a proportion will have to be allocated in that case. At a first valuation, for instance, there may be little done beyond foundations, and to pick out the appropriate items in the bill should not be difficult. If it is decided that the foundations are two-thirds done, the relative figure is easily arrived at. When, however, it comes to the superstructure, it may be necessary to take approximate measurements of brickwork, floors, roofs, &c. In some cases to take measurements may involve excessive labour in proportion to the value of the work, if it is practicable to take a proportion of a section of the bill, e.g. half the Plumbing Bill or a quarter of the emulsion in the Painting Bill.

When dealing with Housing, where a large number of similar units is involved, it should be possible from the bill of quantities to arrive at an approximate value of one house at various stages, e.g.

Brickwork up to damp-proof course.
Do. to First Floor level, with joists on.
Do. to eaves.
Roof on.
Plastering and Glazing complete.
Doors hung.
Plumbing and Fittings complete.
Decoration complete.

The value for different types of the same size (e.g. 3-bedroom) house will not vary sufficiently to make difference for certificate purposes. The work done at any time can be valued by taking the number of houses which have reached each stage, and pricing out from the schedule, allowing in some cases, perhaps, for half and quarter stages.

When the end of the job is approaching it is a good thing to check what is left to complete the contract, as a safeguard against error made in a cumulative total. For the last two or three valuations the contract sum might be taken as a basis and deduction made of

(*a*) all p.c. or provisional sums and percentage additions,
(*b*) work not yet done,

the various accounts against (*a*) being added together with percentage additions *pro rata*, adjustment being also made for the approximate value of variations, price adjustments, &c.

In all cases throughout the contract the percentage addition or deduction on prices arising from insurances &c. and/or rebate in the Summary must be taken into account. It may be also found useful to have on the folder of valuation papers a note of the net amount of builders' work (excluding provisional sums), so that an eye can be kept on the proportion of this included in each valuation. The value of certificates at regular intervals could be graphically represented as an even curve. There may be reasons, such as site conditions or hold-up, or expensive specialist work which alter this, but any serious departure from regularity should be looked into, as it may reveal some slip in the valuation.

PRELIMINARY BILL.—Each valuation will take into account the pricing of the Preliminary Bill. This may have a number of items separately priced, or there may be one total for the whole. In the former case each priced item should be considered and a fair proportion of each included. The price for provision of offices, sheds, &c., could be split up into delivery cost, weekly rent and removal cost and valuation made accordingly. An item for cleaning up on completion would not be included at all till the end of the job. If the item of provision of foreman is priced in this bill, the sum shown could be divided by the period of the contract to give a suitable monthly sum. This principle could be followed for the whole bill, if preferred, particularly where the items are not priced individually. An even division of the total of the bill to give a figure per month would probably not be far out, early and late expenses more or less balancing each other. If there are signs that the contract time will be exceeded, suitable reductions should be made on the monthly figure to relate payments on account more accurately to the whole.[1]

SUB-CONTRACTORS.—It is advisable in building up a valuation from a priced bill to omit all provisional sums for nominated sub-contractors and to deal with them separately later (see specimen in Appendix 1[2]). The sub-contractor's claims will be taken one by one and examined and a suitable figure added for each. The surveyor should have received from the architect a copy of the sub-contractor's accepted estimate. This may or may not be the same as that used for arriving at a provisional sum when the bill was prepared. It may give some detail of measurements and rates or may just give a lump sum. If the latter and some sub-division is required, it can be asked for as a guide for valuations and a help at a later stage in measuring variations. To arrive at an interim valuation of the sub-contractor's work is sometimes very difficult. One may arrive on the site and find stacks of, say, metal windows and window walls in sections and pieces, with bags of bolts and fittings, and be presented with a statement "To materials delivered £5,000." There should be delivery notes indicating the portions of the sub-contract for which materials have been delivered, and, even though it is not practicable to make a complete detailed check, it should be possible to assess the portion of the relative accepted estimate. Deduction would, of course, be made for the cost of assembling and fixing still to be done.

[1] Adjustment of Preliminaries, R.I.C.S. Journal June & August 1970.
[2] Pages 204–5.

It is a good practice to notify each nominated sub-contractor of the amount included in the surveyor's recommendation, though the architect is himself required by Standard contract, 35.13, to notify him of the amount included in the certificate. The contract usually requires the surveyor to satisfy himself that payments included have been made, and this can be done either by asking the sub-contractor in such a letter for advice when payment has been made, or by requiring the contractor to produce the receipts at the next valuation. Any contra charges showing up on the receipts should be reported to the Architect.[3] A specimen letter to be sent to nominated sub-contractors is given in Appendix 1.[4]

UNFIXED MATERIALS ON SITE.—Besides the value of work done, most forms of contract allow payment to be made to the contractor for unfixed materials which he has brought to the site or, where the Standard contract is used, stored ready for the contract, though possibly subject to a higher rate of retention. The surveyor should ask for a list to be submitted by the valuation date, which he will check on his visit. On substantial contracts the list can be certified beforehand by the clerk of works, who has the necessary data easily available. It is important, unless there is a special condition otherwise, that only material actually on the site is included. The contract usually provides that unfixed materials so paid for shall become the property of the building owner, and if they are on the site they are under the control of the clerk of works on his behalf.

The Standard contract, clause 30.3 gives the Architect discretion to allow the value of materials destined for the job and ready in all respects, but stored off the site, to be included in interim certificates, on condition that the provisos listed are complied with. The amendment was introduced in 1966, following the guidance of the Joint Contracts Tribunal Practice Note No. 10. The Tribunal felt that the restriction in the then current contract to pay only for such "materials and goods delivered to or adjacent to the Works for use thereon" was inadequate under modern conditions of construction. A quantity surveyor faced with such an application should ask for the authority of the Architect who, when satisfied as to content, labelling and other provisions of this clause, would in all probability give his assent.

PRICE ADJUSTMENT.—When the traditional method of adjusting fluctuations is in operation, that is by the use of clause 39 of the Standard form, it will be found valuable to start checking the records of price adjustment at an early stage—at any rate the labour portion—when a running total can be kept month by month for inclusion in the certificate

[3] See page 123.
[4] Page 209.

valuation. Materials are rather more difficult to keep up to date than labour, owing to the time lag in rendering invoices. In either case increased cost, whether in respect of labour or materials, should not be included in interim certificates unless supporting details have been made available.

With the introduction of the Price Adjustment Formulae[5] reimbursement of increased cost is automatic in each interim certificate by the application of the formulae to the current indices relevant to the proportions of the work categories actually carried out. Because these payments for fluctuations are final payments, the final account being simply a summary of the monthly totals, valuations will need to be more accurate than has been necessary'in the past and one of the side effects of the introduction of these formulae is a significant increase in the time it takes to prepare an interim certificate valuation.

RETENTION.—The amount to be retained must be checked from the conditions of contract as agreed. A special note should be made of any maximum retention fixed. In the Standard contract 5% of the contract sum throughout is recommended, but this may be found varied. In the GC/Works/1 form (clause 40) there are limits set to the retention sum, varying according to the size of the contract.

When work is substantially complete part of the retention sum is released, the balance being held as security for making good of defects that may be found necessary within the defects liability period. In the Standard contract one-half is to be released, in the GC/Works/1 contract one-third, with an option to the Authority to release further amounts at their discretion.

One of the changes that has come about following the publication of the 1980 edition of the Standard form is that each and every nominated sub-contract is now treated as a small contract within the main contract with its own start and finish dates and its own certificate of practical completion. This means that nominated sub-contractors are entitled to release of part or all of the retention money held on their sub-contract at varying times and no longer have to rely on the goodwill of the architect to certify release of their money before release becomes due to the main contractor.

On the whole question of release the explanatory notes and the worked examples contained in the J.C.T. guide referred to earlier will be found to be very helpful and worthy of study.

In the case of the Private edition of the Standard form (clause 30.5.3) the retention money must be held by the employer as a fiduciary trustee in a separate bank account.

In some forms of contract (e.g. GC/Works/1, 40) the percentage retained of the value of unfixed materials is different from that retained

[5] See page 73.

from the value of work done, and the statement must be prepared accordingly.

Price adjustment is made without deduction of retention (Standard form clause 30.2.2.4) except when the Price Adjustment Formula (clause 40) is used. Such adjustments have in recent years been largely increases, and being regarded as an out of pocket expense of the contractor, on which he gets no profit, it would not be reasonable to make the same deduction from them as is made from a value which includes a profit.

PREVIOUS CERTIFICATES.—A careful check should be made to ensure that the figure shown as already certified is correct, as a slip here may make a serious error in the valuation. If the architect has not confirmed the amount of the previous certificate he should be asked, or the figure may be referred to as "previous valuations," the architect being asked to verify before certifying.

SPECIMEN VALUATION.—A specimen valuation is given in Appendix 1[6] set out on the standard R.I.C.S. certificate valuation form. These forms are similar in design to the corresponding R.I.B.A. certificate forms and give all the information necessary to enable the architect to complete his certificate. The lower half shows the gross payments included for nominated sub-contractors. The architect is required under the contract to notify sub-contractors of amounts included and to call for proof of payment[7]. Both of these duties he may delegate to the quantity surveyor, in which case it is his duty to issue the notification and satisfy himself as to proof of payment when he comes to agree the next certificate valuation. It should be noted that, in the event of failure to produce such proofs, the remedy is a direct payment by the employer to be deducted from the next certificate, rather than refusal to issue another certificate until such time as the sub-contractor is paid. Nominated *suppliers* are not included in the list. They are merchants in exactly the same relationship to the contractor as other merchants from whom he buys materials, except that they have been selected by the architect who has approved the price to be set against a p.c. sum. Care should be taken not to refer to the valuation as a "certificate" nor to the surveyor as "certifying." He only recommends and it is for the architect to certify, who may take into account other matters than those within the surveyor's sphere, e.g. defective work.

CERTIFICATE VALUATION PAPERS.—The Quantity Surveyor's copy of each statement should always be kept in a folder of certificate papers with possibly a carbon copy in the letter file. It is suggested that

[6] Pages 206–7.
[7] Clauses 35.13.1.2 and 35.13.3.

all the papers relating to one valuation should be fastened together with a strong fastener, the copy valuation being on top. The attached papers will include such things as sub-contractors' applications, lists of unfixed materials, interim statements of price adjustment, &c.

It may be found convenient to use a foolscap book for keeping the records of interim valuations of jobs of any size, a separate book being used for each. This ensures all the records being together, and provides a suitable place for entry of price adjustment details as they are checked from time to time.

VALUATION ON BANKRUPTCY.—In the event of bankruptcy of the contractor it is prudent to make a valuation of the work executed by taking the necessary measurements of the work up to the stage at which work ceases or is continued by another contractor. The valuation will include unfixed materials and plant, which the architect, or the clerk of works on his behalf, will be responsible for seeing are not removed from the site (see Standard form, 16 and 27, GC/Works/1, 45 and 46). The purpose of such a valuation is that all parties may be aware of the financial position and some idea of money outstanding to the bankrupt contractor can be known.

RELEASE OF RETENTION.—Under the Standard form, 17.1 the Architect is required to issue a certificate of practical completion of the works, on the issue of which the contractor is entitled under 30.4 to release of half of the amount retained. Under the GC/Works/1 form, 41(1), one third of the reserve is released on completion. The contractor will probably raise the question of release on one of the last interim certificate valuations and the surveyor can suggest to the architect that the necessary stage is being reached. It is, of course, for the architect to decide.

If, as is sometimes the case, the architect is prepared to release their final balances to nominated sub-contractors before that of the general contractor, a statement will be required giving the agreed totals of their accounts and showing the amounts of such final balances. If the variation account has not been forwarded to the architect, the sub-contractors' accounts might be sent for him to see, or, at any rate, any points which need his confirmation should be raised with him.

Application by the general contractor for release of the final balance of the retention on completion of maintenance work will probably be made direct to the architect, but it may be that, if the accounts are not completed, the need of this release will be applied as a spur to urge the surveyor to report the final figure.

COMPLETION OF CONTRACT BY STAGES.—Mention has been made in Chapter 4[8] of the erection of building by stages and in such cases the contract should provide for a maximum retention for each stage, and, for certificate purposes, each stage will in fact be treated as if it were a separate contract. In the case of housing estates where completion will be in small units of a few houses or flats, it may be that there will be no maximum retention less than the normal percentage, but provision will be made for prompt release of part retention as each unit is handed over and of the final balance in similar stages.

Although not altogether relevant to valuations it should be noted here that the Standard contract sets out how completion of a contract by stages shall be handled financially and provision is made in the sectional completion supplement for this to be a contract condition. This was highlighted by a case[9] where the phased handover required was described in detail in the bill of quantities but not referred to in the conditions of contract and the building owner failed in a claim for damages for late completion of a phase.

[8] Page 31, and see Standard contract, clause 18.

[9] M. J. Gleeson (Contractors) Ltd. v. London Borough of Hillingdon (*Estates Gazette* 18th July 1970).

8

VARIATION ACCOUNTS

ARCHITECT'S INSTRUCTIONS.—When making his visits for interim certificate valuations the surveyor should keep his eye on variations in the contract which have arisen. It is often valuable to have seen the work in course of construction. The responsibility for issuing instructions is with the architect, but as the surveyor requires these as his authority to measure he would do well to keep contractor and clerk of works up to the mark in getting them applied for. Something is said of the legal requirements in architect's instructions in Chapter 12. Provisional sums, p.c. prices and provisional quantities can be automatically adjusted without any instruction. The contract may also provide (Standard form, 2.2, GC/Works/1, 5) that errors in the bill of quantities shall be treated as a variation and adjusted. No specific instruction will then be required for doing this, but the architect who has to certify the final account should be told of any substantial items.

The surveyor will probably have received revised drawings from the architect from time to time. These should be dated on receipt, and it might be found an advantage to mark them with a large V (variation drawing) in a coloured pencil in the bottom right-hand corner. This will distinguish them clearly, when referred to later, from the drawings on which the bill of quantities was based.

A separate file for the formal architect's instructions should be kept with the variation papers. Besides these, the surveyor will often get copies of letters, &c., sent him, either from architect to contractor or contractor to architect, which affect variations. These may be kept in the same file, perhaps secured with a spring clip on the side facing the official orders. Such letters may be found to be explanatory of the orders and indicating their intentions, so helping when it comes to measurement.

COST CONTROL AFTER TENDER.—Important as cost control is considered at the design stage, it is equally important during the progress of a contract to prevent either architect or building owner ordering extra works without realising their effect on the final account. The extent to which the quantity surveyor will be expected to keep a check varies. With certain public authorities in particular, the surveyor may be required to price approximately all architect's instructions, so that a running account of variation in cost is kept. This is excellent in theory but depends on the instructions being issued promptly: if they are delayed till near the end of the contract, or if they are not issued and the contractor has to press for them at a late stage, their effect on cost will not be realised till too late.

The pricing of architect's instructions may need some time given to it. Some will be easily dealt with if there is an estimate, invoice or other definite guide. Daywork sheets (if they have been promptly rendered) may help with others and small items can often be quickly given a price which will not much affect the total. In some cases it may be necessary to take some approximate measurements. It is quite possible there will be some items in the instructions which the surveyor does not know about: he will have to see the clerk of works or foreman and find out the detail. Often it will be possible to defer such investigation till the next certificate valuation or other site visit.

The simplest way of pricing is to take the list of orders and superimpose + and − columns with figures in a coloured ink (to the nearest £). Where calculations are necessary, a sheet or sheets of dimension paper will be used, so that the working out is available for later reference. Probably the total net omission or addition will be all that is reported, but, if necessary, the list of items can be retyped with the figures against them. If the calculations are filed with the report they will be readily found when wanted.

Whether or not the surveyor is required to keep a running cost or to price architect's instructions, he should watch all important items and draw attention to anything seriously affecting cost which the architect may not realise.

SITE MEETINGS.—On most contracts the architect will probably arrange for meetings on the site at regular intervals of those concerned in carrying out the contract—consultants, clerk of works, contractor, sub-contractors, &c. Such meetings may be, perhaps, monthly or fortnightly. Quite often the quantity surveyor is invited to attend them, but as they are principally concerned with settling details and ensuring progress, he is apt to be superfluous. If estimates are required, there is little he can do on the spot, except in a very general way, and there is, therefore, usually no reason why he should not be asked in writing for anything required of him. On the other hand, as a means of keeping in touch with the circumstances under which variations arise, attendance at such meetings is useful, if the time is available.

PROPOSAL TO START MEASURING VARIATIONS.—At a certain stage, in order not to leave too much work to the end of the contract the surveyor will probably want to start the measurement of variations. He may not have formal architect's instructions, but he should have a fairly good idea from his knowledge of the bill of quantities and the work in progress as to what the variations are. He should before beginning measurement advise the contractor in writing that he proposes to do so (specifically required by Standard 13.6, GC/Works/1, 37) and ask for an appointment with the contractor's surveyor (see specimen letter in Appendix 1[1]). Most large firms of contractors will have their own staff of surveyors, but it is not uncommon, particularly on small contracts, for the builder to leave the preparation of the account entirely to the quantity surveyor, either because he knows his reputation, or because he believes that a professional man will give him his due. He is interested chiefly in the final total, and may not consider it worth the expense of having his own surveyor to go through all the detail. In large contracts, where a small difference in measurement or price may make a serious difference in the result, the builder is fairly certain to have his own representative, who by his acuteness and ability can make his employment worth while.

It is not advisable to start too soon on measurement of variations when future developments, which cannot be foreseen, might affect the surveyor's work. One might, for instance, measure a number of adjustments of foundations or drains, only to find later that the whole of one of these sections must be remeasured complete. On the other hand, when visiting a distant site for an interim valuation, which only occupies part of the day, it is useful to arrange with the contractor to spend any time available on work for the variation account. It is fatal to postpone the measurement of variations too long. The benefit of fresh memories is lost and the accumulation of such work may be a serious strain at a time when there is pressure in other directions. It must not be forgotten that the contractor is entitled to prompt payment for work done in such instalments as the contract provides, and both extra works and deductions should be assessed without delay to avoid penalising him. Contractors have told stories about accounts years late, which, if the delay was the surveyor's fault, are a serious blot on his copy book.

The legal position of the surveyor when appointed by both parties, as the case of the Standard contract, is referred to in Chapter 12.[2]

HIDDEN WORK.—Where there is a clerk of works the quantity surveyor should see him at an early stage and arrange for records of hidden work to be kept in the form that he requires. Clerks of works vary, of course, in their ability and experience, and it would be unwise to assume that the clerk of works knows exactly what is required without any guidance. The depths of foundations, position of steps in foundation bottoms, thickness of hardcore, special fittings in drainage, &c. are all items which the clerk of works may be asked to note and record. If these

[1] Page 212.
[2] Page 124.

records are carefully kept and agreed at the time with the foreman, the quantity surveyor and builder's surveyor should have no difficulties from lack of knowledge.

PROCEDURE.—When starting to measure, the surveyor should either have the architect's instructions or a list of items of variation compiled for which variation orders will be requested. Each should be taken in turn and the relative measurements made. As a general principle adjustment will be made by measuring the item as built and omitting the corresponding measurements from the original dimensions.

There will be occasions when it may be easier to adjust a contract item by either "Add" or "Omit" only. If all emulsion on walls is altered to paint, an "Add" item of the contract quantity as extra cost only would be suitable to soothe a client suspicious that the surveyor is out to pile up his fees and perhaps even quiet the surveyor's own conscience.

It is very important to keep omissions and additions distinct, and it is suggested that at the top of every page and at every change from omission to addition the words "Omit" or "Add" shall always be written. Each item of variation should be headed with a brief description and instruction number, if known. Particularly in the case of accounts for Public Authorities, the architect's instruction references may be required by the auditors.

It is not essential that the omissions shall be set down in the dimension book at the same time as the additions are measured. It is more usual whilst on the site to measure the "additions," leaving the "omissions" to be looked up and put down in the office. Sometimes complete items of "additions" can be measured from detail drawings in the office, particularly where the contractor has no surveyor taking down all the measurements. Where a surveyor is acting for the contractor, he can come to the quantity surveyor's office when such office measurements are taken. He may, on the other hand, be satisfied to let the quantity surveyor do this alone, raising any points on measurement after he has examined the account. The quantity surveyor must be prepared to produce his original dimensions to the contractor's surveyor to verify measurements taken from them. On the other hand, he cannot be expected to do his work twice, and a reasonable arrangement should be made with the builder's surveyor in such a case.

The surveyor should be supplied with a copy of specialists' estimates accepted by the architect, so that he has full particulars from which to check their accounts. These should be kept together in a folder marked "Specialists' Estimates" so that they can be easily turned up at a later stage. Many such estimates are subject to measurement as executed, and if no copy is supplied to the surveyor, he will have to borrow the architect's for reference when he measures.

GROUPING OF ITEMS.—Before any abstracting or billing of measurements is started the surveyor should, bearing in mind the explanation of the account which will have to be made later to the client, decide on the suitable sub-division into items which he will adopt in the account. Since items may or may not correspond with variation orders, they may be arranged in a different order: a variation order may be sub-divided or several grouped together, if their subject-matter suits.

Quite possibly the adjustment of foundations will be the first variation for which measurements are taken. At this stage it may not be known what other variations there will be, but the foundation adjustment can be regarded as an item with which other variations will not interfere. Supposing there is a minor change in plan for which a variation order is issued: that change will affect foundations, i.e. there may be a variation within a variation. Unless there is any special reason for distinguishing, the lesser variation will be absorbed in the greater. When it comes to adjusting for the change in plan, this will be done for the superstructure only. It might, however happen that the complete value of the change in plan is separately required, e.g. in the rebuilding of a fire-damaged building it might be that a change in plan was being made at the building owner's request and expense. In that case the foundation adjustment would have to be sub-divided to give the separate costs required. If the variation is a completely additional room, then it will be simple to keep the foundation measurements for that room separate from those for the foundations generally, and preferable as giving more accurate relative values.

As the list of variations develops the surveyor will be able to decide on how he is going to group them. For instance, there may be one order for increasing the size of storage tanks, another for omission of drinking water point and a third for addition of three lavatory basins. Each of these will be measured as a separate item, but the surveyor may for convenience decide to group these together as "Variations on Plumbing." On the other hand, the client having ordered the three lavatory basins and not knowing about the storage tanks or drinking water point (which are changes in the architect's ideas), it may be advisable to have the value of the extra for basins separately available for reporting. The form of report to the client is discussed below.

It will be convenient to group the very small items together under the heading of "Sundries," preferably in such a way that the value of each can be traced.

PROVISIONAL QUANTITIES.—It often happens that such work as cutting away and making good after engineers is covered by provisional quantities of holes through walls, floors, &c., making good of plaster, floor finishings, &c. The original bill may have been taken from a schedule supplied by the engineers, and the need for remeasurement on the site must not be overlooked. It does sometimes happen that the provisional quantities reasonably represent the work carried out and can therefore be left without adjustment, but this should not be done merely to avoid what is certainly a rather laborious job. Non-technical auditors are apt to frown on such procedure. One of the few things they can do to check a technical account is to go through the original bill and see that all provisional items have been dealt with. An appendix to the variation account, showing how this has been done, can be of help to an auditor.

DAYWORK.—Certain variations, which it may not be reasonable or possible to value at contract rates or rates analogous thereto, may be charged on a prime cost basis. Daywork sheets will be rendered for these by the contractor, which set out the hours of labour of each man and a list of materials used. If there is a clerk of works he will sign them as certifying that the time and material are correct. His signature is not in any way authority for a variation, nor that the item is to be valued on a daywork basis instead of by measurement. When there is no clerk of works the architect will generally sign the sheets. Neither architect nor surveyor, as they are not continuously on the site, can directly guarantee that the time and material are correct, but, if these appear unreasonable for the work involved, they can make enquiry to satisfy themselves.

The Standard contract (clause 13.5.4) provides for pricing daywork as a percentage addition on the prime cost as defined (clause 13.5.4.1).

The definition of prime cost is laid down in *Definition of Prime Cost of Daywork carried out under a Building Contract*[3] and the percentages are to be filled in in the space provided in the Appendix to the contract. Facility must be provided in the bill of quantities or the form of tender for the contractor to state the percentages he requires.

In the case of work within the province of some specialist trades, i.e. electrical and heating and ventilating there are different definitions of Prime Cost agreed and these must be taken into account in the preparation of sub-contracts. These have been agreed between the R.I.C.S. and the Electrical Contractors Associations, the Electrical Contractors Association of Scotland and between the R.I.C.S. and the Heating and Ventilating Contractors Association.

The provision made for daywork should be taken into account when considering the amount of any provisional sum for contingencies.

OVERTIME.—Though there is nothing to prevent a contractor's man working overtime (subject to trade union control), this is normally

[3] R.I.C.S.

entirely a matter for the contractor's organisation. No extra cost of overtime can be charged without a specific order. Where, therefore, overtime is charged on a daywork sheet, it will be entered at the standard time rates, unless there is some such special order.

It may be that, owing to the urgency of the job, a general order is given for overtime to be worked, the extra cost to be charged as an extra on the contract. Or the order may be a limited one with the object of expediting some particular piece of work. When a man paid, say, £2.00 per hour, works an hour a day extra at time-and-a-quarter rate, i.e. £2.50 the ¼ hour (50p) will be chargeable in such cases. As a matter of convenience on the pay-sheet, if the normal day is 8 hours, the entry, instead of being 8 hours @ £2.00 and 1 hour @ £2.50, will be 9¼ hours @ £2.00. The ¼ hour is not "working time" at all, and is therefore sometimes called "non-productive overtime," i.e. the extra cost of payment for overtime work over normal payment. Any charges which are to be based on working time, e.g. daywork (where overtime is not chargeable as extra), must exclude the ¼ hour. Where the extra cost of overtime is chargeable, the data will be collected from the contractor's pay sheets and verified if necessary from the individual workmen's time sheets.

PRICE ADJUSTMENT: LABOUR.—The traditional way of adjusting fluctuations in the cost of labour and materials is by way of a price adjustment clause (Standard form 39). Under such a clause any fluctuation in the officially agreed rates of wages or variation in the market price of materials is adjusted. The Standard contract (38.7 and 39.8) provides for a percentage to be inserted in the appendix to the contract at the discretion of the employer, such percentage addition to be applied to all fluctuations to allow for contractor's profit and overheads. Even with such a clause the contractor may still be faced with unexpected expenses, such as the increase of insurance contributions which arose on the establishment of the National Insurance Scheme (neither anticipated nor covered by the Standard contract of the time). This was neither payment of wages nor cost of materials and in most cases was therefore not recoverable, except as an *ex gratia* allowance made by the building owner. The current edition of the Standard contract makes provision for such sums to be recovered by clause 38 (in which case 39 is not used).

The checking of wages adjustment should be fairly straightforward on an examination of the contractor's pay-sheets. The rates of wages are officially published,[4] so there should be no doubt as to the proper amount of increases or decreases or the dates on which they came into effect. To these increases will be added allowances for increases arising from any incentive scheme and/or any productivity agreement and for

---

[4] By the N.J.C.B.I.

holiday payments as set out in Standard contract (clause 39.1.1). These increases will apply to work people (defined clause 38.6 and 39.7) both on and off the site and to persons employed on site other than work people (clause 39.1). This is a significant difference from the 1963 edition where increases were strictly limited to work people employed on the site, the foremen and the office being expressly excluded. For a few years while contracts are running, some using the 1963 edition and some the 1980 edition, quantity surveyors will have to be particularly careful.

Care must be taken that there is no overlapping with the rates charged for daywork when dealing with price variations. If daywork has been priced at actual rates (as required by Standard form 13.5—say with labour 1p hour above basic rates—the number of hours so charged in daywork must be deducted from the total on which price adjustment is being made. In this way the contractor gets, for the hours charged in daywork, a percentage on the difference in cost, whereas adjustments under the price variation clause are strictly net differences. If, of course, the contract provides for daywork to be valued at basic rates, the point does not arise.

GC/Works/1, 9 (3) (b) requires the rates for valuing dayworks to be provided for in the bill of quantities.

PRICE ADJUSTMENT: MATERIALS.—The adjustment of materials prices is more difficult. An attempt should be made to limit the schedule of basic prices to the principal materials involved (compulsory under GC/Works/1, 11 B (1)). The contractor will produce his invoices for those materials from which the quantities and costs can be abstracted and the value will be set against the value of corresponding quantities at the basic prices. Prices must be strictly comparable. If the basic rate for eaves gutters is for 2 m lengths, an invoice for 1 m lengths cannot be set against that rate. The 1 m length rate corresponding to the 2 m length basic rate must be ascertained. There is also the difficulty of materials bought in small quantities, perhaps by the foreman from the local ironmonger, when again the price paid is not comparable with the basic rate. The Standard form, 39, says "if the market price . . . increases or decreases" and these are material words. GC/Works/1, 11 B (3) says "the amount that the contractor necessarily spends in meeting increases properly payable in the basic prices." When in doubt the applicability of the contract wording must be considered.

As in the case of labour, reference must be made to the rates charged in daywork for materials, and adjustment made, if necessary, on the totals being dealt with for price adjustment.

Invoices should be called for in respect of *all* materials appearing in the basic list, as the surveyor is responsible for seeing that fluctuations in either direction are adjusted. This is another case where non-technical auditors are apt to worry if all items do not appear in the account.

The surveyor should also see that the quantities of the main materials on which price adjustment is made bear a reasonable relation to the corresponding items in the bill of quantities and variation account. An approximation, for instance, can be made of the amount of cement required for the concrete and brickwork, and any serious discrepancy should be investigated.

PRICE ADJUSTMENT: FORMULA METHOD.—A radical change in the method of price adjustment in building contracts has arisen following the introduction of formulae to calculate the adjustment.

The concept of these formulae is different from that of the present reimbursement provisions for price fluctuations. These latter are said to leave a considerable shortfall in overall recovery on the contract, and, what is worse, a shortfall which is unpredictable, particularly in unstable economic circumstances. Formulae methods, it is claimed, will greatly simplify the administration of price fluctuation provisions, facilitate prompt payment of fluctuations on interim valuations and reduce the scope for dispute. Contractors can quote competitively on current prices with the confidence that reimbursement will be in terms of current prices throughout the contract.

Two documents[5] have been published which explain the formulae and provide information and assistance to those using them. The formulae are of two kinds, the building formula and specialist engineering installations formulae.

The building formula uses standard composite indices (each covering labour, materials and plant) for similar or associated items of work which have been grouped into 48 work categories. The work categories are generally in accordance with the work sections of the S.M.M. The first eight categories are given by way of example.

(1) Demolitions.
(2) Site preparation, excavation and disposal.
(3) Hardcore and imported filling.
(4) General piling.
(5) Sheet steel piling.
(6) Concrete.
(7) Reinforcement.
(8) Structural, precast, and prestressed concrete units.

The formula is applied to each valuation which will need to be separated into the appropriate work categories. The formula method cannot be applied to any approximate valuations made between the usual monthly certificates.

There are alternative applications of the formula available. These are:

[5] *Price Adjustment Formulae for Building Contracts: a Guide to the Practical Application of the Formulae and Description of the Indices for Use with the N.E.D.O. Price Adjustment Formulae for Building Works.* H.M.S.O.

(a) The separate application of each of the 48 work category indices. This provides the most sensitive possible application of the formula.

(b) The 48 work categories may be grouped together to form 13 work groups. Although it is necessary to calculate weighted indices for each work group from the tender and for each valuation, there is less work entailed in separating the value of work carried out in every valuation. This application of the formula to the main building contract does not prevent the use of one or more of the 48 work categories to sub-contracted work should the parties so desire.

(c) The 48 work categories may be grouped into any other convenient number of work groups, more or less than 13 and even down to one. Clearly the fewer work groups used, the less sensitive will be the indices to changes. It must also be practicable to analyse the tender and the value of work carried out in each valuation period into the selected work groups.

These alternative uses are described in detail in the guide which also gives notes on the application of the formula at pre-contract, interim valuation and final account stages, with sample forms and worked examples.

As an example, the D.O.E. uses a 13 work group application for P.S.A. projects.

The specialist engineering installations formulae cover (a) electrical installations, (b) heating, ventilating and air-conditioning installations, (c) lift installations and (d) structural steelwork installations. They are applicable whether the work is performed by direct contract or by nominated sub-contract. These formulae use separate standard indices for labour and for materials, the respective weightings of which are to be given in the tender documents, except for lift installations where the weightings are standardised. In each case the formula is expressed in algebraic terms and has been devised in conjunction with the appropriate trade association. It is intended that these specialist formulae will normally be applied to valuations at monthly intervals.

NOMINATED SUB-CONTRACTORS.—The quantity surveyor is responsible for the checking of the accounts of nominated sub-contractors, and, when such accounts contain measurable items, he will need to take measurements, usually from the site, to check them. It is more satisfactory to meet and measure with the sub-contractor than to wait for his account to be rendered. If measurements are agreed and taken together, there should be nothing factually wrong with the account when it comes in. and much argument over measurements and correspondence over credit notes may be saved.

The quantity surveyor should have received from the architect copies of the accepted estimates of nominated sub-contractors (see page 36) and he must study these to see that the relative accounts are in accordance with them. They may include lists of basic prices of materials or merely state in general terms that the estimate is subject to adjustment in cost of labour and materials. If the latter, the sub-contractor will have to be asked to submit a statement with, in the case of materials, supporting vouchers. Labour rates will probably be governed by the working rules of the particular trade and can easily be substantiated.

If any extra items are chargeable on a daywork basis, the rates should be fixed in the same way as provided for the main contractor. Under the Standard form (clause 13.5.4) provision is made for the definition of prime cost of a particular trade association to be used, when works of a specialist nature fall within the province of such an association.

In checking price adjustment of materials, the discounts on invoices should be watched to ensure that basic rates and invoice rates are comparable from this angle.

BILL OF VARIATIONS.—When the items are billed they should be priced out. All contract rates which are binding should be written in ink and the survey's analogous or new rates in pencil. The contractor can then see at once which rates are subject to negotiation and which he is bound to accept. It is helpful if the item numbers in the bill from which the analogous rates are built up are marked against the rates to show the contractor their basis. It should be noted that contract rates are only binding if applied to work under similar conditions (see Standard form, 13.5.1). Any very serious difference in quantity, for instance, would justify a varied rate. A bill containing 500 m of 150 × 25 mm moulded wood skirting might be so varied that only 5 m are required. It is obvious that this length cannot be made to detail at the same rate per metre as 500 m, but, generally speaking, such departure from contract rates will only be made in extreme cases. A certain amount of "swings and roundabouts" must be expected.

It will probably be found that a number of invoices are required from the contractor for costs to be set against provisional sums and p.c. prices. It is best to make a list and send it to the contractor, who then knows exactly what he has to look out. These will be examined, compared with estimates and entered in their place in the account, profit being added *pro rata* with that in the contract bill, and any adjustment being made on the attendance item. If this latter is expressed as a percentage, it would also be adjusted *pro rata*.

When the account has been priced out, there will probably be some blanks which cannot be completed. It may be that further information on some point is required from the contractor. The summary will be made

77

as far as possible and approximate figures added for the blanks to give the surveyor some idea of how the account is coming out. He may at any time expect a question from architect or client on this subject, or an application for more money from the contractor, and he will then be able to give an approximate figure. In reporting to architect or client he should make some allowance for possible adjustment of prices after examination of the account by the contractor, and so be on the safe side.

Copies of the account may be typed or if neatly prepared, photographed: three copies should be sufficient, one copy for the client, one copy for the contractor and one for the surveyor's office copy. The pencil pricing should not be typed but left blank, and copied from the draft into the contractor's and surveyor's copies. It may be that the surveyor will not do his pricing until the account is in type, when he would do it direct in his copy. The contractor's copy will then be sent to him with a request for an appointment to go into any points he may have to raise, and accompanied by a list of vouchers or other matters required to complete the account. When the Standard form is used the requirement (clause 30(5) (a)) that the contractor shall be supplied with a copy of the bill of variations clearly intends that it shall be typed or photocopied, though in itself that clause cannot be authority for the surveyor to charge his client with the typing, as it is not a contract between them.

MEETING WITH CONTRACTOR.—The contractor, having examined the account sent to him, is fairly certain to have some criticism. If he writes agreeing the figure without comment, it might be wise for the surveyor to re-examine his figures and look for a big mistake! Unless the criticisms are of a minor nature which can be settled by correspondence, an appointment will be arranged for the contractor's surveyor to call at the quantity surveyor's office and go through his points.

There may be differences in the quantities between the surveyor's bill and the contractor's record as taken on the site with the quantity surveyor. Each will have to look up his original dimensions, and it may be found that something has been omitted or a mathematical or copying mistake made. A recollection of the item and the circumstances will probably put the matter right, and, if necessary, the surveyor will amend his bill.

Differences in the pricing are more difficult to straighten out. Each will produce his analysis of the disputed price and the value must be argued. The contractor may well produce information as to the circumstances in which an item was carried out, of which the surveyor was unaware or which he did not fully realise, and he may therefore feel justified in amending his price. If, however, the surveyor does not stick too closely to theory and the contractor does not open his mouth too

78

wide there should be no difficulty, with a little readiness to give and take on both sides, in getting through the account satisfactorily.

COMPLETING THE ACCOUNT.—Any necessary alterations to the quantities and rates having been made as a result of the meeting, the extensions and casts will be corrected and the total agreed with the contractor, who will have corrected his own copy in the same way. The top typed copy will then be completed in ink or type, and it will be found a useful practice to have all mathematics rechecked in this copy, to ensure that the actual document submitted is free from mathematical errors. If a clerical error is found the matter should be taken up again with the contractor and his agreement obtained to the revision.

The percentage adjustment for insurances, &c. in the Summary must not be forgotten. Preliminaries are not normally adjustable, but if the amount of the contract is very seriously increased, e.g. by the addition of another wing, the Preliminary Items should be adjusted *pro rata*, because the substantial extension of the contract time will involve increased expense of foreman, use of plant, huts, &c., telephone and other items which are priced in the Preliminary Bill.

A careful check is necessary to ensure that all p.c. and provisional sums have been adjusted. It is a useful practice to run through all such sums in the priced bill, marking them with a reference to the relative item in the variation account. Any that have not been dealt with will then show up clearly. When all provisional sums are together in an early bill, such a check is simplified. Special care is needed when some appear, say, in an External Works bill: it has been known for such an item to be missed and the error even pass a first technical audit. One of the things that a non-technical auditor will certainly do is to check that all such sums have been adjusted.

It is usual to ask the contractor to sign a copy of the final account as evidence of his agreement, or alternatively he can be asked to confirm the final figure in a letter. It may be advisable to see the architect with the account before final agreement with the contractor, in case he should raise something unexpected, or else to agree it "subject to the architect's confirmation."

In the case of public authorities the full variation account and summary will usually be required and examined by the appropriate officer who understands the technicalities involved. In the case, however, of a private client, whether an individual or a board of directors, a simplified statement showing the principal variations and their value will probably be more lucid. The full account would need a good deal of explanation of its form, the arrangement of omissions and additions, the meaning of provisional sums and p.c. items, &c. The simplified statement suggested, a specimen of which is included in

Appendix 1,[6] could convey all that the layman wants to know, and could be amplified with any further information asked for. This statement would be forwarded through the architect, with whom it may be advisable to discuss its form beforehand, and should be accompanied by the complete account for the architect's information, or for him to produce to his client if demanded. The surveyor's fees will usually be based on figures in the complete account, which must, therefore, be available to the architect, so that he can advise his client, if necessary, as to the accuracy of the surveyor's account. The client is, of course, entitled to have the complete account, if he asks for it.

AUDIT.—The variation account on a building contract will, in the case of public authorities, always be subject to audit. After examination by the technical officers of the authority, the account will be scrutinised by the Finance Division in the case of a Government Department or the District Auditor of the Board of Inland Revenue in the case of a local authority.

Though in the case of a private client the account may not receive any further financial check, the quantity surveyor must be prepared to have such a check made. A public Company will have an accountant on its staff responsible for finance, and the Company's auditors may raise questions. Even an individual client may feel dissatisfied and refer the account to an accountant.

Ultimately, questions might be asked in Parliament in the case of public authorities, at a shareholders' meeting in the case of a Company or in the seclusion of the study of a private client.

CONTRACTS WITHOUT QUANTITIES.—In the case of contracts without quantities a similar procedure will be followed. The bill of quantities will be replaced by a copy of the contractor's "schedule of rates" which he is required to furnish under the Conditions of the relative Standard contract (GC/Works/1, 5A). This schedule will often be found to be in a much abbreviated form, compared with a surveyor's bill of quantities, but must be used as a basis, so far as it goes. It must be remembered that it is solely a schedule of rates and that any quantities are not part of the contract. The quantity surveyor should see at his first opportunity after the contract is placed that he receives this schedule. The scantier the schedule is, the more will the surveyor have to fall back on the "fair valuation" referred to in clause 13.5.1 of the Standard conditions.

CLAIMS.—It sometimes happens that there are points outstanding on the account, on which surveyor and contractor cannot agree. Or it may

---

[6] Page 215.

be that the contractor asks for reimbursement of some alleged loss which he has suffered from some cause or other outside his control. The details of such claims should be investigated by the surveyor and a report made to the architect. The report should summarise the arguments, which can be elaborated verbally before the architect, and set out the financial effect of each claim.

Though the decision on claims rests with the architect, except in such matters of valuation as the parties to the contract have entrusted to the surveyor, the quantity surveyor in his preliminary consideration of them should remember the principles which must guide the architect in a decision. The following thoughts are suggested as a guide to a decision on claims:—

1. What did the parties contemplate on the point at the time of signing the contract? If there is specific reference to it, what does it mean?
2. Can any wording of the contract, though not specifically mentioning it, be *reasonably* applied to the point? In other words, if the parties had known of the point at the time of signing the contract, would they have reckoned that it was fairly covered by the wording?
3. If the parties did not contemplate the particular matter, what would they have agreed if they had?
4. If the claim is based on the contract, does it so alter it as to make its scope and nature different from what was contemplated by the parties signing it? Or is it such an extension of the contract as would be beyond the contemplation of the parties at the time of signing it? In either case the question arises whether the matter should not be treated as a separate contract, and a fair valuation made irrespective of any contract conditions.
5. The value of the claim in money should not affect a decision on the principle. If the claim is very small, however, whichever party is concerned might be persuaded to waive it, or it may be eliminated by a little "give and take."

In particular, any action of the building owner which may have been a contributory cause should be given due weight. If the claim is based on unanticipated misfortune, consideration of what the parties would have done, if they had anticipated the possibility, will often indicate whether it would be reasonable to ask the building owner to meet the claim to a greater or lesser extent.

If the architect is not able to give a decision himself, he will refer the matter to his client with his recommendation. If the contractor does not accept such offer as the building owner with the advice of his technical advisers is prepared to make, he must have recourse to the arbitration clause of the building contract.

Something is said of the public service angle on claims in Chapter 18.

9
OCCASIONAL SERVICES

SUPPLEMENTARY SERVICES.—So far the main duties of a quantity surveyor have alone been considered, viz. the preparation of bills of quantities and the appointment as quantity surveyor under a building contract. Even though one may try to limit oneself to this work, there are various supplementary services the quantity surveyor can render, if not to augment his own practice, it may be to help a friend or client.

REPRESENTATION OF BUILDER.—It sometimes happens that the builder wants to be represented by a quantity surveyor in private practice. It may be that he is short of staff or too busy, or he may feel that such representation will help him in a contract difficult through its specialised nature, or just that the surveyor appointed to deal with the account lacks his confidence. There are some surveyors who make a special feature of such work for builders and others who dislike it. In a country practice, where one is constantly dealing with local architects, it may put a surveyor in an awkward position through having to act as quantity surveyor under one contract and independently for the builder in another, both, perhaps with the same architect. In a practice in London or large provincial town, where surveyors generally go wider afield, there is not the same difficulty. If asked to act for a builder in a contract in which the architect is one with whom one might have to work at another time, it would be a courtesy to mention to him before accepting that it was proposed to act for the builder. If already working with that architect it is more a question of asking his permission, as the architect or client might feel that a strain would be put on the surveyor's impartiality. In the same way permission should be asked of a Public Authority by whom the surveyor is from time to time employed if he proposes to act for a builder on a contract of that authority.

DESIGN AND BUILD CONTRACTS.—When a prospective building owner decides to use an all in contract the duties of a quantity surveyor employed by him are described in Chapter 1. It sometimes happens, however, that for the same reason as stated above, a building contractor will involve an outside practitioner to assist him in putting his bid together. Such assistance will normally take the form of preparing a pricing document of some form or other, but can also include contract and planning advice. The terms of employment will be a matter to be settled between the surveyor and the contractor and is often a lump sum fee which the contractor can build into his tender. It may also sometimes happen that the surveyor is retained for the post contract side as well in which case the same difficulties referred to above can arise.

DISPUTES, LITIGATION AND ARBITRATION.—The building contract usually provides for disputes to be referred to arbitration. The duty of a surveyor engaged in a dispute will be to prepare, in consultation with the solicitor concerned, a proof of evidence, i.e. a summary of what he is prepared to say on oath in the witness box. This will be supplied to counsel, who will probably call a conference of solicitor, client and witnesses to discuss any points which he thinks need elucidation. This conference gives counsel an opportunity of seeing his witnesses and judging their evidence value.

The surveyor giving evidence is an "expert witness," i.e. he is giving his opinion as a technical expert and is not confined as is the ordinary witness, to stating his knowledge of facts. His professional position and reputation give support to the value of his opinion. Even though engaged by one part to a dispute it is fatal to show partisanship in giving evidence. He must not shirk an answer which may tell against his client, as by doing so he will shake the Court's or arbitrator's confidence in the honesty of all his opinions. He must answer the questions put to him without argument. He can rely on his own counsel to intervene if any of the questions are unfair, irrelevant or inadmissible. To try to get the better of opposing counsel will not pay, and, needless to say, to keep his temper is essential. It is over-anxiety to show support for his client that is probably responsible for the adage which circulates in legal circles "There are liars, damned liars and expert witnesses."

The subject of arbitrations is outside the scope of this work, but deserves the careful study of surveyors. The quantity surveyor is, on account of his expert knowledge of building accounts, quite often appointed as arbitrator in building disputes, and must be prepared and qualified to fill this position. The Institute of Arbitrators, whose members are drawn from many professions, does much on the educational side by holding practice arbitrations and in other ways.

PARTY WALL AWARDS (LONDON).—Under the London Building Acts (Amendment) Act 1939, sections 44-59, it is provided that if anything is to be done to a party wall as defined by the Act, notice is to be given in certain forms. If the two adjoining owners do not agree (and it is often unwise to agree in advance), each party must appoint a surveyor to whom certain powers are given by the Act to determine the difference and decide, subject to the provisions of the Act, what contribution each party is to make to the cost of the works. This statutory provision is limited to the Inner London Boroughs. This work is often undertaken by an architect, but as measurement and valuation are generally required, on the basis of which to apportion expenditure, a quantity surveyor may be appointed either in his own right or to assist the architect.

A study of the relative sections of the Act will make the procedure clear. It should be emphasised that both building and adjoining owners have statutory rights which they can exercise under the Act,[1] and those rights can never be overlooked nor set aside. Printed forms for the various notices are available,[2] and care must be taken to adhere to the periods of notice laid down. When acting for the building owner, the architect must, in view of the time required for notice, counter-notice and negotiation,[3] take early steps to set the machinery in motion, or he may find that the works are delayed awaiting settlement with the adjoining owners.

A notice setting out details of the proposed work will normally be accompanied by a drawing giving plans and sections of the party wall in question and as much of the proposed new building as may affect negotiation. The notice would be served on the adjoining owner, who would pass it either direct to a surveyor or to his solicitor to instruct a surveyor. If it is thought an advantage to give some explanation to the adjoining owner, it can be arranged to call and see him, when the proposal can be outlined, and the notice served personally. The Act[4] provides for the possibility of both parties agreeing on a single surveyor, but it is more usual for each party to appoint his own. It should be noted that silence does not give consent, but that in the absence of consent to a notice within fourteen days a difference is deemed to have arisen.[5] Where there are two surveyors appointed, the one acting for the adjoining owner will, on receipt of instructions, communicate with the building owner's surveyor.

The first duty of the two surveyors, before discussing the notice, is to appoint a third surveyor[6] in writing (the appointment must not be left until an actual difference between them arises), but the third surveyor will not be referred to except in the case of a dispute between the two surveyors. Having made this appointment, the two surveyors will then arrange to meet on the site and discuss the proposal, setting out their decisions in the form of an award, on signature of which the works can

---

[1] Sections 45, 46.

[2] *Notice Forms A to G for use under the London Building Act:* R.I.B.A.

[3] For instance, under section 47(2) of the Act two months' notice must be given of proposed work to a party structure (one month's in the case of a party fence wall). In case of difference, section 55 specifies periods of notice required if a party refuses to appoint a surveyor, if two surveyors appointed fail to appoint a third or if a surveyor appointed refuses to act.

[4] Section 55(*a*) (i).

[5] Section 49.

[6] Section 55(*a*) (ii)

proceed. It is advisable to register an award with the Land Registry by depositing a copy, though this is not compulsory.[7]

The adjoining owner's surveyor will watch his client's interests during the progress of the works, and further awards on matters arising and not settled by the first award can be made if necessary with reference, if need be, to the third surveyor. The amount of the adjoining owner's surveyor's fee is usually determined in the award, which will state that it is to be paid by the building owner (unless there is a special reason to the contrary).

ADJOINING OWNERS (OUTSIDE LONDON).—Outside Inner London there is no statutory control of relations between adjoining owners, but the normal common law rights of property owners must be respected. A surveyor may be called in by either party to advise, and, particularly if questions of measurement and valuation arise, a quantity surveyor may be employed in the negotiations.

SCHEDULES OF CONDITION.—In the case of new leases of substantial properties it is quite common to have a "Schedule of Condition" of the property prepared, setting out the condition of the premises at the beginning of the lease. This facilitates defence to a claim for dilapidations at the end of the lease, which would otherwise be based on recollected or imaginary conditions. It is naturally the lessee who initiates steps for its preparation, and, if possible, it should be agreed by the landlord. If his formal agreement is not obtained, a copy should be delivered to the landlord, when the onus to dispute it will be on him. The preparation of such a schedule may be regarded as the work of a building surveyor, no measurement or valuation being involved. It is, however, obviously an advantage for the same man to prepare the schedule and settle the dilapidations, of which there is a reasonable possibility in the case of shorter leases.

The Schedule of Condition should be arranged room by room, setting out the type of finishings and decoration, and noting particularly any defects which might later be alleged to be the lessee's responsibility.

DILAPIDATIONS.—The usual provision of a repairing lease that a lessee shall keep the structure in repair and redecorate at definite intervals is responsible for a good deal of argument and negotiation. Lessees at the end of their lease do not want to be bothered with doing repairs and decorating, with the possibility of the lessor having further complaints after the work is done, so are prepared to make a cash payment to settle their liability. The subject is usually opened by a notice from the landlord requiring that certain repairs set out in a

---

[7] See Land Registration Act 1925, Section 5a (1).

schedule should be done or payment of damages made for breach of covenant. The schedule will have been prepared by a surveyor acting for the landlord, who under the terms of the lease has made an inspection of the property. The lessee will appoint a surveyor, who will examine the schedule on the property, make his own valuation and meet the lessor's surveyor to negotiate a settlement. In most cases agreement is reached and reported, when a cash payment is made accordingly.

Instructions to deal with schedules of dilapidations usually come from solicitors, who serve the formal notice required by the lease, or whose advice is sought by a lessee receiving a notice. The subject needs some special study of the relative law and its detail is outside the scope of this book, but as measurement and pricing are a major part of the work involved, this service may be regarded as one for which the quantity surveyor can qualify himself.

FIRE LOSS ASSESSMENT.—In assessing fire damage to buildings the surveyor may be acting for the insurance company or for the claimant, and in either case will make a point of visiting the scene of the fire with as little delay as possible. If acting for the insurance company he will take notes of the condition of the premises and collect sufficient information to arrive at an approximate estimate of the value of damage, which the company are fairly certain to require immediately in anticipation of his report. His report to them should include his opinion as to the cause of the fire, which he will form as a result of questioning anybody available and after examining the débris. He will have been supplied with an extract from the policy, and he must, of course, identify the premises damaged with those referred to in the policy and see that their use was the same. If the building should have been separately insured, either because of its special construction or use he should refer to this in his report. He will also comment on any serious undervaluation in the sum insured. He will communicate with the insured advising him of his instructions to act as assessor and see that a form of claim is sent him.

If a surveyor is appointed to act for the insured, he will meet him and negotiate a settlement in much the same way as in the case of a schedule of dilapidations, and make recommendation to his clients accordingly. He must remember that it is not good policy for an insurance company to try to cut a claim to the bone. It is from their reputation for fair dealing in claims that they get their business. They will not want to lose a client for the sake of saving a few pounds. On the other hand the dishonest claimants exist, and there need be no hesitation in treating them as they deserve.

When acting for the claimant the surveyor is, of course, out to get as favourable a settlement as he can for his client. He must, however, remember that the basis of all insurance is good faith, and that the company is probably quite ready to meet honestly an honest claim, and to give the benefit of the doubt, when there really is doubt.

The assessment of fire damage naturally has a specialised side, as some knowledge of insurance business is necessary. It also, however, requires the special knowledge of the quantity surveyor in measuring and valuing building work, and in important cases may well involve the co-operation of the estate agent with the quantity surveyor.

VALUATION FOR FIRE INSURANCE.—As a building should be insured for the cost of re-erection in the event of a total loss, the same principles of approximate estimating as are set out in Chapter 3 will apply if the quantity surveyor is asked to advise on insurance value. An estimate will be prepared in just the same way as it would be for a new building, allowance being also made for removal of débris and credit given for salvage. In actual fact a very large proportion of fires do not involve a total loss, so it might be thought unnecessary to insure against entire rebuilding. However, even foundations which it might be thought could be reused, may quite probably be damaged, and in the case of buildings of some age they would almost certainly be insufficient to satisfy modern standards. The decision to take any risk must, of course, be with the client, but it should be pointed out to him that a total loss may be incurred, and that if he does not insure for full value he must be prepared to be his own insurer for the balance. If there are no drawings the surveyor will have to take measurements to enable him to estimate the cost of rebuilding. He must remember the usual requirements of insurance companies that separate values must be put on buildings in different uses, as the rate of premium depends on the use to which buildings are put. Buildings not of normal brick, concrete or stone construction with slate or tile-covered roofs must also be separately valued, as their premium too may be assessed at a different rate.

It is, of course, important to distinguish valuation for fire insurance, which depends on cost of rebuilding, from valuation for purchase or mortgage which depends on market value. This latter is outside the province of the quantity surveyor, and he would do well to pass any enquiries on to a valuation surveyor.

SPECIFICATION WRITING.—Specification writing by the quantity surveyor falls into two categories. The case where he has prepared a bill of quantities for the job has been touched on in Chapter 6.

But the quantity surveyor is sometimes required to write specifications on behalf of the architect for small work when there are no bills of quantities, because either he is short of time or prefers to entrust such detail to a surveyor. In this case, of course, the specification is part of the contract and must with the drawings fully convey the nature and extent of the work and the conditions under which it will have to be carried out. The surveyor must work through the building in his mind's eye as he would for preparing a bill, though by trades as far as possible, and must define carefully the work to be done. The preliminary bill and preambles to sections of a bill of quantities will appear in much the same wording, but as specification clauses.

REPORTS.—Although the surveyor may normally specialise in quantity surveying, in certain places it is inevitable that such work will be part of a general practice. In such cases the surveyor is fairly certain sometimes to have to report on buildings, if only for a friend proposing to buy a house. If however he carries a professional indemnity insurance policy he should examine the conditions carefully as often such policies particularly exclude structural surveys. The fact that he may carry out the survey without remuneration may not affect his liability. The essence of a successful report is that it shall cover the points on which the client wants information, and not contain a lot of unwanted or unnecessary matter. A prospective buyer's chief concern is the building's stability and state of repair, which will be reflected in his bills for maintenance during the coming years. He may contemplate certain alterations and want the report to cover that aspect. He may want a plan prepared to see how his furniture will fit in. He may be fussy about a drain test or he may not attach any importance to it. It is therefore important to get clear instructions as to the purpose of the report and the particular points on which the client wants information.

It must be remembered that, even if advice is given voluntarily, the surveyor may still be liable for negligence.[8]

PROJECT MANAGEMENT.—A new service that has emerged in the past few years is that of Project Manager, an all-embracing appointment of responsibility to the building owner to deliver the complete project. Such appointment can include amongst other things the responsibility for acquiring the site (and indeed sometimes the finance as well), the appointment of the consultants forming the building team, the letting of the contract and overall control of the building contract. Such an appointment is not restricted to any one profession and the discipline appointed can vary in accordance with the nature of the project. There have, however, in recent years been very successful projects completed where a Chartered Quantity Surveyor has been appointed and this service may well in the years to come be more and more common. One point to be borne in mind is that a Project Manager should be a personal appointment and if his firm is carrying out professional services as well it is better that they should be done independently of the Project Management.

[8] See page 112.

10
STRUCTURE OF THE BUILDING INDUSTRY

COMPOSITION OF THE INDUSTRY.—The Building Industry is a complex organisation centred on the building contractor. Besides the builder himself, ranging from a single individual to a large company who is responsible for carrying out the building work, the Industry comprises the builders' office and supervisory staff and workmen, the architect who designs the building and supervises the erection, the quantity surveyor who is the specialist on measurement and cost, merchants who supply the materials, sub-contractors who do specialised work and sometimes consultant structural or mechanical engineers who relieve the architect of certain specialised branches of the design.

THE PROFESSIONAL SIDE.—Something has been said of architects and consultants in Chapter 2. They, like quantity surveyors, have their professional Institutions organised for their respective assistance and advantage and the protection of their clients. These Institutions keep their members informed by current developments through their journals, have a library available for reference, hold meetings for discussion on topics of interest and exercise some disciplinary powers. They issue recommended scales of fees, and as negotiating bodies act for their members in dealings with public authorities. They also provide representatives where representation of their profession is required on advisory or executive committees.

It should be noted that the architectural profession is, by Act of Parliament, a registered profession. Nobody can call himself an architect unless he is on the register maintained by the Architects' Registration Council of the United Kingdom. Only those qualified in accordance with the regulations of the Council can be admitted to the register. Should a quantity surveyor feel any inclination to call himself an architect, he should see that he is suitably qualified and registered. But registration is of the term "architect" only, and does not prevent anybody unregistered from doing an architect's work: he can even apparently call himself an 'architectural engineer." In this respect registration of the architect differs from that of the doctor or dentist, who may not practise the profession at all unless registered.

THE BUILDER'S OFFICE.—The builder's office staff in the smallest type of firm undertaking contract work may consist of only one clerk looking after pay-sheets and invoices, whilst the principal does the outside management and ordering. The larger the firm the more will be the division of labour, so that a firm might have pay clerk, cost clerk, typist, estimator-surveyor and outside manager, all under a principal. Each of these will in the larger firms grow into a department with directors dealing with different aspects or sections of the business.

The organisation of a builder's office naturally varies with the individual builder and with the size of the firm, but briefly it may be summarised as follows:—

A. Workmen must be engaged and each individual's time, recorded in detail on his time sheet and then allocated to the various jobs, must be
> (a) converted into money payment due, after making allowance for insurance contributions, income tax, &c. and the money must be drawn and paid out.
> (b) charged to the cost account which is kept to record as accurately as possible the prime cost of each job.

B. Materials and plant required must be
> (a) ordered
> (b) paid for, either immediately or through a credit account.
> (c) charged to the cost accounts referred to above (or in the case of plants to "overheads").

C. Work must be tendered for either on quantities supplied or by taking particulars from drawings or site, the job in progress must be watched, interim payments applied for, variations adjusted and final accounts agreed.

D. A principal or manager must watch all the above, as well as deal with matters of policy arising in the general management of the business.

THE BUILDER'S YARD AND SHOPS.—Every builder, besides an office, generally has a "yard", where he can store his materials. Certain materials constantly in use he will keep a stock of, and they must be arranged and stacked to be easily accessible. Some, such as cement, must be kept under cover and the yard will have suitable sheds for these. Unless securely enclosed, such yards are apt to be a temptation to thieves, so there will probably be a lock-up shed or building for the more valuable and more easily portable goods.

Many materials have to be prepared before they can be put into a new building and the extent to which such preparatory work is done by the builder varies considerably. He must have his own joinery works, plumber's and painter's shops or he may sublet his plumbing and painting and the manufacture of his joinery.

The joiner's shop will have benches for hand work, also machines for sawing, planing and moulding, generally driven by electric power. In the larger businesses it will probably be dignified by the name of "joinery works" and have more complicated machinery. An open-sided shed fitted with racks will usually provide a store for stacking timber.

The plumber's shop, besides holding a stock of pipes, tubes and fittings, will have a bench with vice and pipe bending machines and be used for pre-fabricated work where suitable. Particulars will be taken from the job for such things as flush pipes, soil and waste branches, etc. which are more easily made up on a bench. On the larger contracts the equivalent of this plumber's shop will be established on the site.

The paint shop will be mainly used as a store for painting materials, augmented by the left-overs from each job. Now that paint is always used in standard tints direct from the maker's containers, the mixing and colour-matching that used to be done in the shop is not necessary.

The builder may undertake shop work in other trades. He may have his own smith's shop for ironwork or mason's yard for stonework, but such work is more usually done by specialist firms.

The above is descriptive rather of the small and medium sized builder. The large firms will be organised rather differently. They will probably have all materials ordered for and delivered to each particular job and have no yard as such holding a stock. They will have somewhere to house their lorries and plant (though that may be largely hired). Surplus material at the end of a contract might be sold off locally, or if worth while, transferred to another job.

Such large firms may have a "Small Works Department" which would probably be organised very much as if it were a separate business, but carrying the reputation and power of the controlling firm's name.

THE BUILDER'S SITE STAFF.—On larger contracts the agent or foreman[1] may have several sub-foremen looking after different trades or sections of the work. There will be a timekeeper responsible for recording the time worked by each man and generally assisting the foreman in administration. Where the size of the contract justifies it, the staff may be augmented by a pay clerk to whom is specially allocated the keeping of the pay sheets, insurance and holiday credit cards, and a store-keeper. There may be a bonus clerk dealing with incentive payments or this work may be undertaken by the contractor's surveyor

---

[1] See page 14.

93

or an assistant of his. Where there is danger of theft from a site deserted at night the contractor may employ a nightwatchman or more likely today, a security firm. According to the size of the site staff the builder will have to provide office accommodation, which varies from a small wooden shed for a lone foreman to substantially built and centrally heated temporary buildings on a long-term contract.

On very large contracts, particularly in remote country districts, there may be a camp for workpeople with sleeping and feeding accommodation with supervising, catering and maintenance staff.

It might even be that the whole office organisation of the job is transferred to the site office, so that the contract is run almost as an independent unit.

BUILDERS' FEDERATIONS.—The principal building firms of the country are organised into Regional Federations affiliated to the National Federation of Building Trades Employers with headquarters in London. These Federations do for the builders what the professional Institutions do for surveyors. They provide a representative negotiating body which can look after the members' interests, keep their members informed of developments in the Industry and help them with advice when necessary.

Most of the specialist firms which are normally sub-contractors on building contracts have their own federations.

OPERATIVES' TRADE UNIONS.—The main representative bodies of the operative's side of the building trade are the Union of Construction and Allied Trades and Technicians (UCATT), the Transport and General Workers' Union, the Furniture and Timber Trades Union and with the rise of Direct Labour Organisations, the General and Municipal Workers' Union. To these organisations are affiliated the various trade unions of bricklayers, plasterers, plumbers, &c. The various individual unions, through their representations on the National Joint Council of the Building Industry, maintain contact with the Employers. The duty of the trade unions is to watch the interests of their members in such matters as wages, working conditions, &c. On large contracts a "shop steward" will be appointed by each trade union, through whom complaints are made and negotiations take place. Smaller contracts will be visited when necessary by full-time union officers. Regular contributions are paid by workmen to their union, but this is, of course, done direct and not through the medium of the employer's pay-sheet. As in the case of the Employers, the Operatives have regional organisations, which hold regular meetings and maintain closer contact with the men than would be possible from a central organisation.

MANUFACTURERS' TRADE ASSOCIATIONS.—There are a number of associations representing manufacturers from whom useful information and advice can be obtained as to the use of the material which their members manufacture or use. They include associations for the development of some particular material, such as aluminium, copper, lead or timber as well as those concerned with manufactured goods, such as concrete, joinery or clayware. In fact, nearly all manufacturers have some sort of publicity organisation for their particular Trade.[2]

THE BUILDING CENTRE LTD.[3]—Mention should be made of this organisation which is backed by the manufacturers of building materials and maintains an exhibition in London where samples of many materials can be seen. It is an agency from which names and addresses and often leaflets of manufacturers can be obtained, particularly useful sometimes when one only knows the branded name of the material. Enquiries can be made by telephone, or, for those some distance from London, post-paid enquiry cards can be obtained from the Director.

There are other similar Centres in Belfast, Birmingham, Bristol, Cambridge, Coventry, Dublin, Glasgow, Liverpool, Manchester, Nottingham, Stoke-on-Trent, and Southampton.

THE NATIONAL JOINT COUNCIL FOR THE BUILDING INDUSTRY.[4]—However true it may be that "unity is strength," if there are two "unities" there will be two "strengths," and unless there is some machinery for bringing opposing or diverging parties together there is little hope of efficiency. The National Joint Council is composed of equal numbers of representatives from the employers and operatives, appointed by the Employer and Operative organisations adherent to the Council, and covering some of the specialist or individual trades, as well as the general Industry. There are Regional Joint Committees and Area Joint Committees as connecting links between the Council and individual members. The Council has done much to stabilise and improve working conditions in the Industry. Mention is made below of the principal matters dealt with by the Council, as the quantity surveyor will meet them in checking prime cost accounts or in making adjustments under the price variation clause of lump sum contracts.

WORKING RULES.—The Council is responsible for the framing and revision of the National Working Rules[5] which cover the following sub-heads:—

[2] See *Trade Associations and Professional Bodies of the United Kingdom* (Millard): Pergamon Press.
[3] 26 Store Street, London WC1A 7BT.
[4] *Constitution, Rules and Regulations,* published by the N.J.C.B.I.
[5] *National Working Rules for the Building Industry*: N.J.C.B.I.

Rule   1   Wages.
,,   2   Working Hours.
,,   2A   Guaranteed Weekly Wages.
,,   2B   Conditions of Service and Termination of Employment.
,,   3   Extra Payments.
,,   4   Overtime and Holidays.
,,   5   Shift work and Night Work.
,,   6   Travelling and Lodging.
,,   7   Recognition of Trade Union Officers.
,,   8   Payment for absence due to Sickness or Injury.
,,   9   Grievances, Disputes or Differences.
,,   10   Register of Employers.
,,   11   Death Benefit Cover.

Regional Conciliation Panels are set up to hear complaints of breaches of the Working Rules and the Council has established a National Conciliation Panel to hear appeals from the Regions.

SUPPLEMENTARY RULES AND MEMORANDA.—The following are included as supplements with the published National Working Rules:—
Tool Allowances—List of Tools
Supplementary Rules of Woodworking Factories and Shops
Operation of Paint Spraying Machines
Industrialisation of Building Processes
General Principles Concerning Incentive Schemes and Productivity
    Agreements
Use of Safety Helmets and Safety Equipment
Safe Use of Electricity on Building Sites
Racial Discrimination in Employment.
Code of Health and Welfare Conditions.

DETERMINATION OF WAGES.[6]—One of the principal functions of the National Joint Council for the Building Industry is the determination of rates of wages in the Industry. The rates of wages vary with the district and the whole country has been graded by districts into two categories. The basic category is Grade A, but London and Liverpool have rates ½p per hour above those in Grade A localities. Labourers' rates are fixed below the standard skilled operative's rate.

Watchmen are paid by the week and the rate per week is also subject to annual review at the statutory meeting of the N.J.C.B.I. and adjusted according to the retail price index.

The rates for apprentices are fixed at a percentage of the skilled operative's rate, varying according to the age from 50% at 16 to 85% at

[6] See National Working Rule 1.

19. Young male labourers similarly get a percentage of the labourer's rate, from 50% at 16 to 100% at 18.

A national scheme is being introduced for the training and qualification of scaffolders who will be graded in three categories:

Trainee Scaffolders, Basic Scaffolders and Advanced Scaffolders, the first category being equated with labourers and the other two with skilled operatives. There are also national "differential rates" for other skills set at levels below the standard rate for skilled operatives and known as "national differential margins".

Workmen are entitled to the various extra payments under headings which are classified as being for

Discomfort, Inconvenience or Risk (e.g. work at heights, in water or in foul conditions),

Continuous Extra Skill or Responsibility (e.g. timbermen, drivers and operators of mechanical plant),

Intermittent Responsibility (e.g. scaffolders working as such part time),

Large Scale Demolition.

Full particulars will be found in Working Rules 3A-C.

Certain tradesmen are entitled to receive a weekly tool allowance (National Working Rule 3 D), provided they equip themselves with tools, in some cases in accordance with an approved list appended to the Working Rules.

APPRENTICESHIP.—The National Joint Council has instituted a scheme for encouraging and promoting apprenticeship in industry.

Very briefly the apprentice on leaving school at the age of 16 signs a Training Services Agreement which lasts for three years. The agreement covers all aspects of the apprentice's training both on site and at the appropriate College of Technology. The scheme is under the supervision of the Local Joint Training Committee who is a party to the agreement. General supervision is exercised by the National Joint Training Commission.

HOLIDAYS WITH PAY SCHEME.—There is a scheme covering general or "annual holidays," based on an agreement between the employers' and operatives' organisations in the Building Industry and the corresponding bodies in the Civil Engineering Industry. The scheme is administered by a non-profit-making company limited by guarantee[7] and is covered by National Working Rule.[8]

The principle of the general holiday scheme is that the operative is entitled to two weeks summer holiday in the year, and a further week

[7] The Building and Civil Engineering Holidays Scheme Management Ltd., Manor Royal, Crawley, Sussex.

[8] Rule 1 (i).

covering Christmas Day and the statutory winter bank holiday. From 1980 a similar arrangement is being made to cover the Easter Holiday. The employers pay for this holiday by buying special stamps from the above-mentioned company and stamping a card for each person. The employer in whose employ the operative is at the date of the annual holidays pays out the total value of the stamps on the card to the operative and by forwarding the card to the company is reimbursed.

POST 19 TRAINEE SCHEME.—In an attempt to bring more labour into the building industry a scheme has been introduced whereby older persons can train as skilled operatives. This is usually done through the Government Skill Centres operated by the Manpower Services Commission, a training which is combined with related site experience.

WELFARE.—A building contractor is responsible for the welfare facilities on all sites and must, of course, comply with the requirements of the Health and Safety at Work Act 1974, which will gradually supersede all previous statutory regulations. Regulations are also in force governing the use of woodworking machinery,[9] lead paints[10] and electricity,[11] also on such special subjects as work in compressed air and diving operations.

THE CONSTRUCTION INDUSTRY TRAINING BOARD.—The C.I.T.B., as it is usually known, was set up in July 1964 following the enactment of the Industrial Training Act. This act is intended to secure an improvement in the quality and efficiency of industrial training and to make sure that an adequate supply of men is properly trained for all levels in the industry. The C.I.T.B. raises a levy on contracting firms based on the number of employees and by so doing is able to make grants to employers who provide approved training and is able to co-operate with Colleges of Technology in proving the courses necessary for such training.

CO-OPERATION OF CONTRACTORS AND THE PROFESSIONAL SIDE.—The various professional Institutions and trade Federations have their liaison committees for co-operation, who by the personal contacts established at their meetings do much to remove difficulties and misunderstandings. Apart from these, there are several joint bodies which do valuable work in a particular sphere. Five of the more important to quantity surveyors are:—

(a) Joint Consultative Committees.—There is a National Joint

<hr>

[9] S.R. & Os. 1922 No. 1196 and 1945 No. 1227.
[10] S.R. & Os. 1927 No. 847.
[11] S.R. & Os. 1908 No. 1312 and 1944 No. 739.

Consultative Committee of Architects, Quantity Surveyors and Builders for Liaison between these branches of the Industry and study of subjects of mutual interest. They have produced the Code of Procedure for Selective Tendering[12] and have issued various notes. Besides this National Committee there are similar Regional Committees.

(b) *Joint Contracts Tribunal.*—This body, composed of representatives of the R.I.B.A., R.I.C.S. and N.F.B.T.E., as well as several associations representing Local Authorities, is responsible for the Standard form of contract referred to above and its periodic revision. Their work includes considering questions raised by and through the constituent bodies on the forms of contract and the issue of periodic practice notes.

(c) *The Standing Joint Committee for the Standard Method of Measurement of Building Works.*—This Committee is composed of equal numbers of quantity surveyors and builders nominated respectively by the Royal Institution of Chartered Surveyors and the National Federation of Building Trades Employers. The original Committee produced in 1922 the first Standard Method of Measurement and this has been succeeded by revised editions to meet new suggestions and changed conditions. This Committee is responsible to the two parent bodies for publication of the document as well as for the Code of Measurement for Small Dwelling Houses. The Committee occupies itself in the interim between revisions in watching developments, noting suggestions for improvement of the Standard Method and dealing with practice queries raised on interpretation of the document. A development unit is currently studying the problems concerned with future editions of the S.M.M. relative to the recommendations made in the *Report of the Working Party on Measurement Conventions* (R.I.C.S.).

(d) *The British Standards Institution.*—This Institution has a scope much wider than that of the Building Industry. A study of the list of Standards will reveal such differing subjects as women's dresses, rubber rings for preserving jars, and castor oil. However, there are a large number of Standards established for building materials, as mentioned in Chapter 16[13] and the Committees responsible for framing these have representatives of builders, architects and surveyors as well as experts in the

[12] Page 39.
[13] Page 158.

manufacture of the material concerned. The B.S.I. also publishes the Codes of Practice referred to.[14]

(e) *The National Consultative Council of the Building and Civil Engineering Industries*.—This Council is an advisory body appointed by the Secretary for the Department of the Environment to advise him on matters concerning the Industry. They are able to convey to him the views of the Industry as a whole as distinct from the advice which he can obtain from his own technical staff.

CIVIL ENGINEERING WORK.—The main professional organisations associated with civil engineering work are the Institution of Civil Engineers and the Association of Consulting Engineers. The national employers' organisation is the Federation of Civil Engineering Contractors. The various specialised branches of the industry, e.g. plant hirers, demolition contractors, road surfacing contractors, &c., have their own trade associations. The wage negotiating body is the Civil Engineering Construction Conciliation Board for Great Britain, which issues working rules and procedure for the settlement of disputes. The Federation of Civil Engineering Contractors constitutes the Employers' side, and the Operatives' side consists of representatives of the Labour Unions of Transport and General Workers and General and Municipal Workers, and also representatives of Craft Unions, notably those of the Bricklayers and Carpenters.

A distinction between the Civil Engineering and the Building Industry is that the former, being often concerned with large scale works, comprises a comparatively small number of large firms with one central federation, whereas the latter includes a very large number of small firms with the federation organisation largely decentralised.

STRUCTURAL ENGINEERING WORK.—The professional institutions mentioned under "Civil Engineering Work" are also concerned with this branch of engineering, as also is the Institution of Structural Engineers. The employers are organised into the Engineering and Allied Employers' National Federation who publish the working rules. The British Constructional Steelwork Association deals with the Employers' side on such matters as prices, methods of measurement, &c.

THE BUILDING RESEARCH ESTABLISHMENT.—This establishment at Garston near Watford, a branch of the Department of the Environment, carries out research on building materials and is prepared to advise on difficulties within its sphere. It has a number of

[14] Page 159.

publications, a list of which is obtainable from H.M.S.O. The B.R.E. now incorporates the Forest Products Research Station at Princes Risborough. This research station is not confined to building matters, but has a wider outlook. It is engaged in research into such things as the seasoning of timber, the causes of and the remedies for dry rot and similar troubles, and has several publications on these subjects, issued by H.M.S.O.

11

LAW—THE QUANTITY SURVEYOR
AND HIS CLIENT

INTRODUCTORY.—It is proposed here to deal with law purely from the personal angle of the quantity surveyor, considering first his legal relation to his client, and then certain legal problems he may meet in carrying out his share of the administration of the building contract or in other branches of his work. It is not for him to give legal advice to others, but it is important that he should understand, so far as possible, something of his own legal position, his rights and his duties.

The decision which will be given by the courts is often uncertain until put to the test of an action. If it were not so and experts in law agreed, there would be little reason for recourse to the Courts. Only salient points of common occurrence are therefore dealt with in these chapters, and they must be considered as generalisations, subject always to the particular circumstances of an individual case. They are only a warning in the hope of keeping the surveyor out of legal trouble; if he finds himself in such trouble he cannot hope to solve his problems by the study of text-books, but must turn to those who have a very much wider field of legal knowledge and experience.

Some of the matter on the subject of contracts will have been covered by the reader in his study of the general law of contract, but the particular application of the principles to the case of the quantity surveyor himself justifies their repetition and emphasis.

CASE LAW.—A number of leading cases are quoted below, as being the authority for various points settled in the Courts. The technical interpretation of law reports is outside the surveyor's province, but it is as well that he should have some knowledge of the principal cases bearing on the work of his profession. The illustration presented by a report puts a legal rule in its proper perspective and should help in memorising it.

The surveyor must bear in mind when comparing cases that the basic circumstances which gave rise to the decision must be the same if the ruling is to hold, and he must remember to study the provisions of any written contract in his particular case, as its terms may entirely reverse the decision, so far as that contract is concerned. Many of the cases quoted are 50 to 100 years old and even more. The position of the quantity surveyor and his relation to the parties to a building contract were different then, and there were no accepted forms of building contract, such as the Standard form or the Government form GC/Works/1, already referred to, by one of which many building works are now governed. Moreover, the bill of quantities was in earlier days not made part of the contract, as it now almost invariably is, and, further, there may be customs which can now be established as so general and well-known as to have legal significance, which could not be so established at the time of the case quoted. All these varying conditions affect the interpretation and application of reported cases.

A very short précis is given of the leading cases referred to, limited to the point under consideration, and references are given to the Law Reports which will enable the surveyor to look up the case more fully in the Library of his professional Institution or any Law Library.

AGREEMENT FOR APPOINTMENT.—The relationship between the quantity surveyor and his client is contractual; that is, it depends on the terms of agreement made between the parties. Such an agreement must exist, otherwise the surveyor will have no grounds on which to sue for his fees, if his client fails to pay them. Apart from the case of Public Authorities, with which he usually has a formal written contract, the quantity surveyor quite often has nothing to show in the nature of a written agreement. The architect, perhaps, has handed him drawings and specifications, which the surveyor has accepted without any mention of terms. What passed at that meeting may be the only semblance of an agreement, and, as will be seen later, certain terms may be implied by the action of the parties at the meeting. In short, if any dispute arises between quantity surveyor and client the test always is: what was the intention of the parties at the time of the agreement? The parties can, of course, at any time mutually agree to vary or add to the terms already settled. If the agreement makes no reference to the point at issue, the Court will try to ascertain what the parties' intentions were and to give effect to them.

There is no reason in law why the agreement should not be made by word of mouth, but, as human recollection is fallible, it is obviously advisable that the terms should be put in writing. It is therefore a good general rule that, where an appointment has been made verbally, the quantity surveyor should confirm in writing at the earliest opportunity both the appointment and the terms of the agreement. Similarly, if he receives any letter from his client containing anything inconsistent with his own recollection of what their agreement was, he should at once write to place on record his own understanding of the matter. This should prevent any misunderstanding arising later, or, if any dispute does arise, should provide good evidence of what the agreement in fact was.

Certain formalities governing contracts with Corporations were abolished by the Corporate Bodies Contracts Act, 1960. Accordingly the surveyor need not trouble himself about taking any special precautions when dealing with a Corporation in order to ensure the validity of his contract with it.

STAMPING OF AGREEMENTS.—A written agreement made after 1st August 1970 does not require to be stamped unless made under seal. A written agreement under seal requires a 50p stamp impressed by the Inland Revenue within 30 days of execution. Failure to stamp an agreement is never fatal. Though the Court may refuse to accept a document in evidence before it is stamped, the normal procedure is to accept it on an undertaking being given that it will be stamped. The Commissioners of Inland Revenue have power to impose a penalty up to £10 in the case of late stamping, but this may be remitted or reduced.

RESPONSIBILITY FOR APPOINTMENT.—The most satisfactory procedure is for the building owner to appoint the quantity surveyor himself, generally on the recommendation of the architect, if he has no particular choice. If appointment is so made and confirmed in writing, there should be no doubt as to the building owner being liable for the quantity surveyor's charges. If, however, the architect appoints the quantity surveyor, the building owner will not be liable for the quantity surveyor's fees unless the architect had authority to make the appointment. If the architect had no express authority the question will be whether there was implied authority. Authority will usually be implied if the architect was instructed to obtain tenders on a bill of quantities basis, or if tenders could not be obtained without quantities.

MOON v. WITNEY UNION (1837): 3 Bing. N.C.814; 6 L.J.C.P.305; 43 R.R.802.

The architect to the Guardians prepared drawings and instructed the plaintiff to prepare quantities. Builders were notified that quantities could be obtained on payment of a deposit and that the successful competitor would have to defray the expenses of taking out the quantities, the charge for which was stated at the foot of the bill of quantities. A dispute arose between the architect and the Guardians and the architect sent in his account together with that of the plaintiff. The Guardians said they had never heard of Moon. Evidence was given to prove the custom of employment of a quantity surveyor and a verdict for the plaintiff was given by the jury.

Application was made to set aside the verdict on the ground that there was no privity of contract and that the usage had not been sufficiently proved. Tindal L.C.J., rejecting the application, said that the defendants themselves had had notification of the usage when they incorporated the architect's statement of it in their notice to builders tendering. So far as privity of contract was concerned this was a conditional contract, one under which it was arranged that the expenses of making out the quantities should be paid by the successful competitor, if any, but if by the act of the defendants there should be no competitor, then that the work which was done by their authority should be paid for by them.

Each case will turn on its own facts. If, for example, the building owner was a private individual unaware of the usual professional practice, implied authority would be more difficult to establish. However, provision is made in the R.I.B.A. Conditions of Engagement (1971 edition) for the appointment of a quantity surveyor by the architect at the expense of the building owner. The building owner may say to his architect "Yes, you may obtain tenders, so long as it costs me nothing." Then the architect would not have authority to appoint a quantity surveyor.

> RICHARDSON & WAGHORN v. BEALES (1867): "The Times," June 29th, 1867.
>
> Beales and others formed a committee to establish a Club. Their architect instructed the plaintiffs to prepare quantities. Tenders were too high and the scheme was abandoned. The architect in evidence admitted that in informing him that his design was accepted the committee had desired him to get tenders, provided he did not pledge the committee in doing so.
>
> Held that this letter put the plaintiffs out of court, and that action should be against the architect. The plaintiffs were thereupon non-suited.

If with such limitation of his authority the architect did appoint a quantity surveyor, he would be liable himself for the quantity surveyor's charges either on the basis, if nothing was said about the architect's authority to engage the quantity surveyor, that the architect had contracted personally with the quantity surveyor, or, if the architect purported to engage the quantity surveyor on behalf of the building owner, on the basis that he was in breach of warranty of his authority.

RESPONSIBILITY FOR PAYMENT OF FEES.—The question of who is responsible for payment of fees depends on the intention of the parties at the time of appointment. If the surveyor was appointed by the building owner, it is clear that the parties intended that the building owner should pay the fee. This is also the case where the appointment is made by an architect acting on behalf of a building owner, disclosing that he is so acting and giving the name of his principal. Indeed, even if the architect does not disclose the name of the building owner, he will not be personally liable for the surveyor's fee, if it is clear that he is only entering into an agreement as an agent for another party. If the architect by his words or conduct implied that he was entering into the agreement on his own behalf, then he would be personally liable. If it turned out later that he was, in fact, acting on behalf of another person, he would not be absolved from liability and the surveyor could choose whether to sue architect or building owner. If, however, the architect asked the surveyor to render some service which was normally part of the architect's work, as, for instance, taking the levels of a building site, it could not be implied that he gave such instruction on behalf of his client, and the architect would be personally liable for the charges.

METHOD OF PAYMENT.—The method and time of payment of quantity surveyor's fees will depend on the terms of the agreement. Whatever method or time is stipulated by the surveyor and is agreed can be enforced.

There was an old custom, now falling into disuse with the closer contact between building owner and quantity surveyor and better understanding of his work, by which the quantity surveyor's fees were added at the end of the bill of quantities, included in the builder's tender and paid by him out of his first interim payment on the contract. This is a survival from the early days when the quantity surveyor was appointed by the builders tendering, who in order to save each of them the expense of preparing a separate bill of quantities agreed that one man should do the work and that the successful builder should pay him. The custom was approved in the following case:—

NORTH *v.* BASSETT (1892): 1. Q.B.333; 61 L.J.Q.B.177; 66 L.T.189; 40 W.R.223.

This was an appeal from a judgment of non-suit in the Mayor's Court. The plaintiff was employed by an architect to take out quantities under a specification which contained the words "To provide for copies of quantities and plans, twenty-five guineas to be paid to the surveyor D. H. North, out of the first certificate." The defendant tendered and his tender was accepted. In due course he was paid a cheque for his first instalment, but refused to pay the plaintiff, who thereupon brought this action. At the trial the plaintiff failed on the grounds that there was no contract between the parties.

On appeal the decision was reversed and the Court held that there was a contract between the parties.

This is a cumbersome procedure and, if the architect has not approached his client on the matter, may even conceal the existence of the quantity surveyor from the building owner, making it difficult to obtain payment if the scheme is abandoned and no building contract executed. However, the custom is well established, and it is possible that, if nothing is said, the Court might recognise the custom and imply into the agreement a term that the payment was to be made in this way.

Further, supposing a contract was signed and the builder went bankrupt before the fees were paid—what then? It has been held that where provision is made in this way for paying the quantity surveyor by the builder a conditional contract exists. In other words, the building owner has agreed "if I place a contract with you and include the surveyor's fees in the contract amount, then you will pay him; if I don't sign the contract, I will pay him myself": *Moon v. Witney Union* (1837).[1] If, however, the builder becomes bankrupt between signature of the contract and payment, the quantity surveyor has no redress, as the liability has been transferred to the builder.

See YOUNG *v.* SMITH (1880): Hudson on Building Contracts, 10th ed., p. 196.

It will be seen from the above that the complicated relationship which arises in such cases is a strong reason against the practice of including quantity surveyor's fees in the bill of quantities and in favour of direct appointment and payment by the building owner, specific provision for which should be made in the terms agreed.

FINANCIAL STABILITY OF BUILDING OWNER.—It sometimes happens that the surveyor thinks it necessary to enquire into the financial position of a prospective client. Building is often the subject of speculation and may be embarked on with a reliance on mortgages and insufficient capital and the intention to sell out when the building is completed (or even before then). The architect, of course, probably has first contact with the building owner, and if he has prepared drawings one may think that he is satisfied that they will be paid for. However, he may not have been sufficiently cautious, and, particularly if the scheme is a substantial one, the surveyor may want to make enquiries. His bank will usually be able to obtain a reference from the building owner's bank, though this may be found to be couched in rather vague terms. The surveyor must form his own judgment and decide whether to refuse or accept the work and whether to make any special terms as to payment either in advance or by instalments. When payment is due and the building owner is found to hedge, the prompt service of a writ is the only thing to bring him to his senses and possibly save the surveyor before his client's bankruptcy.

A director of a limited company is not personally liable for the debts of his firm, even though the firm may consist of little else but himself, unless he holds himself out as being personally liable. The only remedy on obtaining judgment for a debt is to distrain on the company's assets, which may be found to be no more than a little notepaper. On the other hand a principal in partnership is liable for his firm's debts to the full extent of his personal wealth.

AMOUNT OF CHARGES.—Again the agreement must be the criterion of what the amount of the charges are to be. Failing any mention of the

[1] See page 105.

amount of fees, the Court will imply a term that the surveyor shall be paid a reasonable remuneration for his services. It has been a custom in the profession for many years for the charge for preparation of bills of quantities to be a percentage on the amount of the lowest bona fide tender. Though the percentage may not bear a direct relation to the work done, it is the most satisfactory way of determining the fee, so that the building owner can budget for his expense and the fee can be precisely fixed without argument.

Scales of fees setting out rates for these and other services are issued by the various Professional Institutions. It should be noted, however, that the Monopolies and Mergers Commission has published a Report on the Supply of Surveyors' Services with Reference to Scale Fees. The principal recommendations of this Report in relation to quantity surveyors are as follows:—

(i) the rules of the relevant professional bodies should be amended so as to permit their members freely to quote fees to clients in competition with other quantity surveyors and so as not to prevent competition for business on the basis of fees;
(ii) the publication of scales of fees should be permitted provided that the scales are recommended and not mandatory;
(iii) the actual scales should be determined by an independent committee appointed by the Government on a personal basis and not as representatives of quantity surveyors or their clients;
(iv) all documents in which recommended scales are published should state prominently:
  (a) by whom the scales have been determined;
  (b) that the scales are not binding in relation to any particular transaction;
  (c) that quantity surveyors and their clients are free to settle fees without reference to the scales; and
  (d) that quantity surveyors may quote fees in competition with other quantity surveyors.

If these recommendations are implemented it may be that prospective clients will increasingly seek specific agreement on fees with quantity surveyors at the time of their contemplated appointment so as to secure for themselves the benefits of competition between quantity surveyors in the matter of fees. Nonetheless, in cases where no fees are specifically agreed, the recommended scales may provide some indication of what remuneration would be fair and reasonable. It is most unlikely, however, that if the question of what remuneration would be fair and reasonable came to Court it would be held that the matter could be concluded simply and solely by reference to the recommended scales. The most satisfactory course, therefore, is always to agree the amount of remuneration or the basis upon which it is to be calculated when the quantity surveyor's appointment is agreed.

It is sometimes argued, if a scheme is abandoned after the surveyor has completed his bill of quantities, that he should not receive the full fee agreed. But, in fact, if the surveyor has completed his draft bill he has completed his part of his contract and is entitled to the full agreed remuneration. It does not affect the extent of his work whether the building contract proceeds, and there is no implication that the quantity surveyor must wait for such a possibility.

INMAN v. LUBLINER (1942): Estates Gazette Digest, 138.

The plaintiff prepared quantities for two buildings for the defendant, one of which was erected and for which his fees included in the tender were paid by the builder in the normal course. Erection of the second building was abandoned and the defendant refused to pay the plaintiff's charges for preparation of quantities. The defence was that the builder would pay when the building work proceeded.

Held that the person responsible for paying the quantity surveyor was the building owner, and it could not be held that the plaintiff had agreed that if the building work did not proceed he would wait till such time (possibly years later) as it did.

A small amount of clerical work is certainly involved in reading a proof and on receipt of tenders in checking the mathematics of the builder's priced bill and reporting. These are considered as services which the surveyor gives without charge, and are in no way part of his contract for preparation of the bill of quantities. Further services given during the progress of a building contract are the subject of separate fees under the usual scales. The only excuse that can be found to justify a reduced fee if work is abandoned is the fact that the surveyor is relieved of a responsibility which he would have had. The proportion of the fee covering such responsibility, i.e. indemnity insurance premiums, is very small.

If, of course, the surveyor is prevented by the action of the building owner or his architect from completing his draft bill, e.g. when the scheme is abandoned whilst the bill of quantities is being prepared, there is a breach of contract by the building owner, who will be liable for payment of damages to the surveyor. Assessment would be made based on the time the surveyor and his staff expended, with allowance for overhead charges and profit. Loss of profit owing to abandonment of the scheme can also be brought into the claim, including the time of staff left idle through loss of the work. Whether it is policy to claim one's full pound of flesh is another matter, and a frank discussion of the position between surveyor and client should provide a reasonable settlement.

Where the quantity surveyor arranges and pays for the duplicating of bills of quantities the question arises whether he may retain any discount offered by the lithographer. The answer is that the benefit of any trade discount must be passed on to the client, but the quantity surveyor is entitled to retain for himself any cash discount.

LONDON SCHOOL BOARD *v.* NORTHCROFT (1889): Hudson on Building Contracts, 10th ed., p.174.

The plaintiffs employed the defendant as quantity surveyor and brought an action against him with three separate claims:—

    (*a*) for the surrender of certain papers containing calculations and memoranda used in the measurement.

    (*b*) for negligence in respect of two clerical errors of £118 and £15.

    (*c*) for payment to the Board of a discount of 15% allowed him by the lithographer.

Held—

    (*a*) that the Board had no right to the memoranda.

    (*b*) that as he had employed a competent skilled clerk who had carried out hundreds of intricate calculations, the defendant was not liable for negligence in respect of the errors in question.

    (*c*) that as it was agreed that the defendant should employ his own lithographer he was entitled to retain the discount which was in the nature of a cash discount. He was not acting as the Board's agent when instructing the lithographer, in which case an undisclosed commission would have been illegal and improper.

Whilst the surveyor is entitled to make a charge for reading and correcting proofs, if this service is not included in those covered by his fee, such a charge should, if made, be separately shown. It is, however, unusual in private practice to make such a charge, and it is now customary for all recoverable disbursements to be charged net, which removes any possibility of an accusation of receiving a hidden commission. The scales of some public authorities specifically allow the surveyor a percentage on the lithographer's bill for his services in checking proofs.

NEGLIGENCE.—A professional man holds himself out as being qualified to do the work entrusted to him. If he fails to possess that amount of skill or experience which is usual in the profession or if he neglects to use the skill which he in fact possesses, he will be guilty of negligence. To succeed in an action for negligence the plaintiff must establish

    (*a*) that the defendant owed a duty to him.

    (*b*) that the defendant's error was carelessly made, e.g. that he omitted to check what by the general practice of the profession he should have checked, or that, making a check, he did so carelessly.

    (*c*) that the plaintiff suffered damage.

The duty in (*a*) above may be contractual, but it may also be imposed by the general law of tort.

111

DONOGHUE v. STEVENSON (1932) AC 562

This appeal to the House of Lords, though not a building case, established an important principle that an action for damages for negligence may lie in tort, even though there was no contractual relation between the parties and no fraud. The particular case was one in which the plaintiff had consumed part of a bottle of ginger beer containing the decomposing remnants of a snail. She claimed against the manufacturers, who pleaded that they had sold to the distributor and therefore had no liability to her. The distributor could have no reason to suspect that the contents of an opaque bottle were other than indicated, and therefore had no liability for negligence. It was decided that the manufacturers were liable.

The facts of this case are plainly of no direct relevance to surveyors. However, the principle that a person owes a duty, regardless of contract, to take care not to cause damage to persons whom he could foresee might be harmed by his actions, is of very great importance. It is upon this foundation that other decisions of the courts, of more significance to surveyors, have been based. It is clear that if a surveyor should by his negligence cause physical injury to person or property he will be liable. In 1963 the House of Lords decided that a negligent though honest statement, or negligent advice might give rise to an action for damages for financial loss.

HEDLEY BYRNE & CO. LTD. v. HELLER & PARTNERS LTD. (1964) AC 465

Heller & Partners as bankers gave a favourable reference to the plaintiffs in respect of one of their customers who subsequently went into liquidation. The plaintiffs claimed damages for negligent misrepresentation.

In fact, the plaintiffs failed on appeal because the reference was specifically given "without responsibility on the part of the bank or its officials". Apart from this qualification, all five Lords of Appeal agreed on the defendant's liability in tort.

Lord Reid in his judgment said:—

"Where it was plain that the party seeking information or advice trusted the party supplying it to exercise such a degree of care as circumstances required, and it was reasonable so to trust the person supplying information, and the latter knew or ought to have known that the enquirer was relying on him, the law imposed a duty of care on the party making the statement or giving advice."

Lord Morris added:

"If a professional man such as a doctor or banker voluntarily undertook a service by giving deliberate advice he was under a duty to exercise reasonable care."

Lord Devlin put it this way:—

"A promise given without consideration could not be enforced as a contract, but if the service promised was performed and performed negligently the promisee could recover in tort."

The case is of great importance to professional men for, taken in conjunction with *Donoghue v. Stevenson* referred to above, it means that when advice is given even voluntarily, or to a third party with whom the professional man has no contract, the professional man may be liable for any resulting damage either through personal injury or financial loss, if his advice was negligent, or if he made a negligent misstatement. However, the exact scope of the rule in Hedley Byrne's case is at present in doubt. In an Australian case reaching the Privy Council in 1970 two conflicting views were expressed.

MUTUAL LIFE LTD. *v.* EVATT (1971) AC 793
  The defendant life insurance company allegedly advised the plaintiff carelessly in respect of certain investments made by the plaintiff in an associated company. The majority of the Privy Council (Lords Diplock, Guest and Hodson) held that liability for gratuitous advice is limited to cases where the advisor carries on the profession of giving advice of the kind sought. Since the defendant's business did not include the giving of advice on investments they were not liable. The minority dissented (Lords Reid and Morris). They thought that the appropriate question was whether the advice was given on a business occasion or in the course of the defendant's business activities. They held the defendants liable.

The decisions of the Privy Council are not stricty binding upon the English courts, but they are of great persuasive authority. In fact it appears that the English courts, while accepting the principle upon which all their Lordships in the Privy Council agreed, namely that there is no liability for gratuitous advice given on a casual or informal occasion, are not inclined to follow the reasoning of the majority in Evatt's case in preference to the reasoning of the minority—see Esso Petroleum Co. Ltd. v. Mardon (1976) 1 QB 801; Arenson v. Casson Beckman Rutley & Co. (1977) AC 405; Midland Bank Trust Co. Ltd. v. Hett, Stubbs & Kemp (1979 Ch 384). Thus, the surveyor should always take the greatest care in expressing views on professional matters during the course of his practice, whether he is to be paid for his opinion or not. To the extent that he may be asked for his views on professional matters on a social occasion, for example at a cocktail party, he need not be too fearful concerning his position in law if he expresses views carelessly, but it is plainly undesirable for any professional man ever to give an opinion which is not based upon proper consideration of all material matters. It would be best, therefore, simply to avoid expressing views on professional matters on casual or social occasions.
  A particular area in which it is clear that the surveyor must take care is in making valuations. Until comparatively recently it was believed that where a person such as an architect or quantity surveyor was in the position of having to value property or work done for the purpose of a payment to be made by X to Y, the person making the valuation was in

the position of a quasi-arbitrator and not liable if his valuation was made negligently. Two decisions of the House of Lords establish that that is not so and that the valuer owes a duty of care both to X and to Y to make the valuation properly although the valuer may be paid only by X, or only by Y.

SUTCLIFFE *v*. THACKRAH (1974) AC 727

The defendants were a firm of architects engaged by the plaintiff in the first instance to design a house for him. Subsequently the plaintiff entered into a building contract in the usual standard form with a firm of builders under which the builders were to build the house as designed by the architects. The defendants were appointed architects and quantity surveyors under the contract. During the period the builders were at work the defendants from time to time issued interim certificates under the contract. Before the builders had completed the works the plaintiff terminated their employment and required them to leave the site. Another firm of builders completed the house. The original builders went into liquidation. The plaintiff alleged that the defendants had been guilty of negligence and breach of duty in certifying for payment work not done or improperly done by the original builder, so that the plaintiffs had paid the original builders too much for the work done before they left the site. The House of Lords held that the defendants were liable in negligence for over-certifying.

ARENSON *v*. CASSON BECKMAN RUTLEY & CO. AC (1977) 405

The defendants were chartered accountants and the auditors of a private company. Under an agreement between the plaintiff and a third party, the controlling shareholder of the private company, the plaintiff was, in the events which happened, under an obligation to transfer a parcel of shares in the private company to the third party at a price to be fixed by the defendants as a fair value. There was no contract between the plaintiff and the defendants in relation to the valuation. The defendants placed a value upon the parcel of shares and the plaintiff transferred the shares to the third party at the price fixed. Subsequently the plaintiff formed the view, as a result of information coming into his possession, that the defendants had been negligent in discharging their function as valuers. The House of Lords held that an action would lie in these circumstances against the defendants at the suit of the plaintiff.

The quantity surveyor is obviously under a duty to prepare the bills of quantities skilfully. However, he will not be liable if he makes a few arithmetical errors in the course of carrying out a large number of intricate calculations—see London School Board v. Northcroft, p. 111 above. This does not mean that the quantity surveyor should not take all possible care to ensure that the bills of quantities are completely accurate. Not only would errors affect the surveyor's reputation but also it is not possible to say how many errors are allowed before the surveyor would be held liable in negligence. The only safe course is to try to ensure that there are none. Substantial errors could have serious consequences. For instance, by carelessly omitting to multiply by 2 for the two slopes of a roof, or making other such substantial error, he might cause a tender to be so low that a client would accept it, whereas, had the error been corrected, the tender would have been too high for acceptance. The quantities being part of the contract, the error would have to be corrected in the final account, and the building owner would have to pay the builder the difference. He might well claim very substantial damages, i.e. more than either the actual value of the omitted work or the surveyor's fee. The measure of damages is the damage which flows from the negligence. Thus in *Saunders & Collard v. Broadstairs Local Board* (1890) (Hudson on Building Contracts, 4th ed., ii. 164) damages of more than £4,600 were awarded against engineers who had been negligent. Their own fees for professional services in the matter had amounted to only £521.

A surveyor's estimate must be reasonably accurate, or he would be liable for negligence.

MONEYPENNY *v.* HARTLAND (1826): 2 C. & P. 378.

Best C. J. in his judgment said, "If a surveyor delivers an estimate greatly below the sum at which a work can be done, and thereby induces a private person to undertake what he would not otherwise do, then I think he is not entitled to recover."

If the normal contract procedure is followed and the quantities are part of the contract, errors in the quantities will not affect the builder. He will have them corrected under the terms of his contract. If the quantities are not part of the contract the builder will have no remedy against the building owner but he will have a remedy against the quantity surveyor in the form of an action for damages for negligence.

Two more cases are worth noting on the subject of negligence in a report on property to a prospective purchaser (though not the specialised work of quantity surveyors, still a service sometimes undertaken by them as part of the general practice of a surveyor):—

HARDY *v.* WALMSLEY LEWIS (1967): Estates Gazette Digest 614.

The defendant surveyed a house for the plaintiff who, on the strength of the survey, bought it for £4,600. It was left entirely in the hands of the defendant to survey the property and advise the plaintiff. The defendant noticed dormant dry rot but did not mention it in his reports and he did not inspect the loft. Later he asked the plaintiff if he would like a further report with the carpets removed and with an examination of the loft. Again no mention was made of dormant dry rot. The plaintiff replied that he was satisfied with the defendant's report. Paull J. held that the defendant should have warned the plaintiff about dormant dry rot, so as to put him on his guard, and held that the defendant was also negligent in not discovering extensive dry rot and damp. The plaintiff had to sell the house at a loss. The measure of damages was held to be the difference between the market value at the time of purchase (£4,300) and the market value on resale (£3,500), plus the solicitors' costs on resale, the agreed costs of the case and cost of levelling the floor.

KER *v.* ALLAN & SONS (R.I.C.S. Journal, July 1949, page 64).

In the Scottish Court of Session Lord Birman, in giving judgment in favour of the defendants, said he accepted it that the possibility of dry rot was a thing that ought to be in the mind of the surveyor and he should always be on the look-out for any evidence that might to his skilled mind be suggestive of dry rot. He was unable, however, to accept the view that in the absence of any suspicious circumstances the surveyor's duty required him to cause carpets and linoleums to be lifted and to go underneath floors.

The difference between the two cases is that in the first the Court found that there were in fact indications that should have been noticed by a competent surveyor, but in the second case there were not.

There are two things which the lay client, who asks for a report on property in contemplation of purchase, usually seems to live in fear of, viz. dry rot and bad drains. These cases emphasise the need of making it clear in a report if conditions are such as to encourage dry rot, even if none is actually visible and, if so, of including a recommendation for closer inspection. In the same way specific enquiry should be made of the client as to whether he requires a test of drains, and, if not, it should be stated in the report that drains were not tested. Even if instructed that no test is required, care is necessary that any visible defects, such as broken manhole covers, blocked gullies &c. are noted.

Another case (*Sincock v. Bangs* (1952): C.P.L.562; 160 Estates Gazette, 389) emphasises that, even if the client says he only wants a general survey, the surveyor has a responsibility to discover important defects. In that case the plaintiff, an architect, was instructed to inspect a farm. He was told not to make a detailed survey, but to give a general opinion. After the purchase had been completed, dry rot, woodworm and settlement were discovered. Barry J. held that, although the plaintiff had only been asked to give a general opinion, nevertheless he had been negligent in not discovering these defects.

The purchaser of a property is so often in a hurry to secure the property by paying the deposit, that a surveyor must be particularly careful not to be so hurried that he cannot meet his client's requirements. If, as has been known to happen, the client takes him to the house one afternoon, walks round with him quickly and then expects an answer, he should confirm in writing that he has not had an opportunity to examine the premises in sufficient detail to ensure that there are no structural defects of importance.

The surveyor is responsible for his staff and cannot avoid a charge of negligence by saying that the mistake was one made by his assistant, even though he may prove that he has taken every precaution to employ qualified and efficient staff.

It should be noted, however, that when the surveyor is giving advice based on judgment, where two opinions are possible, he will not be liable for an error of judgment.

The Defective Premises Act 1972, in force since January 1st, 1974, imposes an additional duty to those owed under the law of contract and tort upon all persons working in connection with the provision of a dwelling-house (including provisions for conversion). The duty is one to see that his work is done in a workmanlike or professional manner so that the dwelling will be fit for habitation when completed. The duty is owed not only to the employer but to every person who acquires an interest in the dwelling.

RESPONSIBILITY OF PARTNERS.—Partnership is dealt with in Chapter 17 and some mention is there made of the relationship of the partners to each other and to their client.

DEATH OF THE SURVEYOR.—Whether the liability to carry out a contract passes to the representatives of a deceased person depends on whether the contract is a personal one, i.e. one in which the other party relied on the "individual skill, competency or other personal qualification" of the deceased. This is a matter to be decided in each particular case. In the case of a surveyor with no partner the appointment must be regarded as personal, and the executors could not nominate an assistant to carry on the business, except in so far as the respective clients agreed. With a firm of two or more partners the appointment may be that of the firm, in which case the death of one partner would not affect existing contracts. But the appointment may be of one individual partner, e.g. as an arbitrator, where another partner in the firm could not take over, even though he may be entitled to a share of the profits earned by his partner in the arbitration.

The fact that a contract between a quantity surveyor and his client is a personal contract, if such be the case, does not mean that the quantity surveyor must personally carry out all the work under the contract, unless it is obvious from the nature of the contract, for example a contract to act as arbitrator, that the quantity surveyor must act personally in all matters. In other cases, such as the drawing of a bill of quantities, the quantity surveyor may make use of the skill and labour of others, but he takes ultimate responsibility for the accuracy of the work.

DEATH OF THE BUILDING OWNER.—The rule referred to in the previous paragraph as to a contract being personal applies equally in the case of the death of the building owner. Here the contract is unlikely to be a personal one, and the executors of the building owner must discharge his liabilities under the building contract and for the fees of the professional men employed. The fact that the appointment of the surveyor was a personal one will not be material in the case of the death of the building owner.

BANKRUPTCY.—Again the question arises as to whether any particular contract is a personal one with the bankrupt. The trustee in bankruptcy would be responsible for the debts of the bankrupt, but, if the contract was a personal one with the bankrupt, could not continue the work in hand on his behalf. In other words, the trustee of a bankrupt builder might carry on the building contract to completion (apart, of course, from a specific clause in the contract terminating it in the event of bankruptcy) whereas the trustees of a bankrupt surveyor whose contract was a personal one could not continue the work.

COPYRIGHT IN THE BILLS OF QUANTITIES.—A word should be said on the subject of copyright. Copyright is established by Section 2 of the Copyright Act 1956 in every "original literary, dramatic, or musical work." It is not clearly established whether there is copyright in a bill of quantities. The Royal Institution of Chartered Surveyors took the opinion of Counsel,[2] and were advised that in his opinion copyright existed, on the ground that the bill was an original literary work within the meaning of the Act of 1911 which used the same wording. But this is only an opinion, and, as has already been pointed out, opinions differ, and by so differing produce defended actions at law. There are inevitably many clauses in a bill of quantities which are more or less standard and used in very similar form by many surveyors, but the quantities are undoubtedly original, and there will be in all bills a number of items which are original and peculiar to that particular bill.

> WATSON & CARTER *v.* COOPER (R.I.C.S. Journal, February 1932, page 381).
> The plaintiffs had prepared quantities for a school, one of a number which were required of identical plan. The defendant was engaged to prepare quantities for another of these, and copied exactly the quantities and descriptions of a number of items in the plaintiffs' bills. The defendant admitted infringement of the plaintiffs' copyright, and agreed to give a perpetual undertaking in the terms of the writ and pay damages. Judgment was given in the terms agreed with costs.

As the judgment in this case was by consent, it was not strictly a judicial decision, and another Court may decide not to follow the case. There sometimes are good reasons for submitting to an adverse judgment, and such cases cannot, therefore, be taken as certain precedents.

---

[2] Counsel's opinion reported in full: R.I.C.S. Journal, April 1928 (page 617).

As there might be those who would take advantage of an opportunity to re-use a surveyor's bill, the best protection would appear to be specific reservation by the surveyor in his agreement with the building owner of the rights of reprinting and re-using the bill. If, of course, the surveyor is advised, when he is instructed, that it is proposed to use the bill again as and when required, and he accepts that condition, he cannot complain. The difficulty is sometimes got over by agreeing a small royalty for every house for which the bill is re-used. If it is made clear in correspondence that employment is in accordance with the "Scale of Professional Charges for Quantity Surveying Services" of the R.I.C.S., there will be no doubt, as copyright in the bills of quantities is reserved to the quantity surveyor in clause 2 of that scale.

The Court of Appeal has recently decided that an architect whose employment has been determined impliedly licenses his employer to use his plans for doing the very work for which the plans were prepared.

BLAIR v. OSBORNE & TOMKIN; (1971) 2 QB 78
    The plaintiff architect prepared plans for a building owner and was paid for his work. The building owner ceased to employ the plaintiff and handed over the plans to the defendant surveyors and builders for them to use in the actual construction of the buildings to which the plans related. The plaintiff sought an injunction and damages for breach of copyright. It was held that in return for his fee the architect impliedly licenses the owner to use the plans but only for the work for which they were prepared. The licence extends to enable copies to be made for that purpose by the builder or another architect, and also to avail a purchase of the site from the building owner.

A quantity surveyor would be in an analogous position in respect of the bill of quantities.

The dimensions, abstract and other memoranda from which the bill of quantities is prepared are in a different category. These are the surveyor's own means to attain an end—the bill of quantities which he has contracted to provide. It has been held (*London School Board v. Northcroft*[3]) that the surveyor is entitled to retain these documents (unless, of course, as is sometimes the case, his contract with his client provides otherwise).

Blair v. Osbourne & Tomkin should be contrasted with *Stovin-Bradford V. Volpoint Ltd.* [1971] Ch. 1007: there an architect prepared improvements to existing plans for the purpose of a planning application for the modification of certain buildings. He charged an agreed nominal fee of 100 guineas which was well below the scale fee. The Court of Appeal held that there was no licence to be implied to use the plans beyond the point of obtaining planning permission since the fee was truly nominal when measured against the scale fees.

[3] See page 111.

12

LAW *(continued)*—THE QUANTITY SURVEYOR AND THE BUILDING CONTRACT

TENDERS.—An invitation to tender sent out to builders is not an offer which can in any way directly result in a binding contract. It is only an invitation to submit offers. A tender submitted is, however, an offer, the *unqualified* acceptance of which forms a binding contract. If the tenderer adds some condition to the form of tender sent him, that condition, in the event of unqualified acceptance, becomes part of the contract. If in accepting the architect objects to the additional condition there is no binding contract. It is a rule of law that the parties must be *ad idem*—of one mind—before the existence of a contract can be established.

The specification or bill of quantities will usually have stated that the contractor will be required to enter into a particular form of contract, and a tender referring to those documents therefore expresses agreement to do so. The completion of the contract referred to follows as a matter of form, to which the contractor cannot object. It is, of course, essential that he should be advised before tendering how the blanks in a standard form will be filled in, e.g. in the case of the Standard form, percentage of value to be retained in interim payments, period of maintenance, amount of liquidated damages, &c. If any of these have not been settled before tendering they must be mutually agreed. It obviously will save possible disagreement if such matters are clear to the contractor before tendering.

The following case draws attention to the need for careful consideration of insurance requirements:—

GOLD v. PATMAN & FOTHERINGHAM (1958) 2 All E. R. 497.
The plaintiff was the owner of a site in London. The defendants were building contractors. By an agreement in the RIBA standard form (1939 edition) the plaintiff employed the defendants to erect an office block on the site. Piling operations were commenced. These led to damage to property adjoining the site. The owners of the property adjoining the site transmitted a substantial claim to the plaintiff.

By clause 14 (b) of the contract the defendants were liable, subject to immaterial exceptions, to indemnify the plaintiff againt any loss, liability, claim or proceedings in respect of any injury or damage whatsoever to any property real or personal in so far as such injury or damage arose out of or in the course of or by reason of the execution of the works, and provided always that the same was due to any negligence, omission or default of the defendants, their servants or agents or of any sub-contractor. The bill of quantities provided inter alia that the defendants should insure properties adjoining the site against subsidence or collapse. The plaintiff brought an action against the defendants for failing to insure him against the risk of properties adjoining the site being liable to subsidence or collapse and for an indemnity against his liability to the adjoining property owners. The Court of Appeal held that the obligation imposed by the bill of quantities upon the defendants was to insure themselves, not the plaintiff. There being no negligence by the defendants, the plaintiff's action failed.

It will be seen, therefore, that it is important that insurance clauses in the bill of quantities should clearly cover the responsibility of the employer.[1] A requirement that such insurances shall be in joint names of contractor and employer is the best.

ERRORS IN TENDERS.—The importance of drawing the contractor's attention to errors in his tender, which was mentioned on page 53 above, is emphasised by a case[2] in which a contractor claimed damages for fraudulent representation against an architect and his principal, Louth Corporation. The contractor alleged that the architect had noticed an error of £10,000 in the bill of quantities and had not drawn his attention to it, as the result of which he was misled into signing the contract with the Corporation. The trial Judge gave judgment for the contractor against the architect and the Corporation. This decision was reversed by the Court of Appeal on the ground that the architect had informed the contractor in general terms that there were serious errors in his bill of quantities (though he had not specified the particular error) and was entitled to assume that the contractor would check his tender before signing the contract. Although the architect was successful in the end, the dispute might have been avoided altogether if the contractor's attention had been specifically drawn to the particular error.

CONFLICT BETWEEN BILLS AND CONTRACT CONDITIONS.— Although not primarily the surveyor's responsibility, it is important to ensure that nothing in the contract conflicts with matters set out in the contract bills. Under clause 2.2.1 of the Standard form the contract prevails in cases of conflict.

---

[1] The Standard Form (1980) requires such insurance to be in joint names and the premium to be covered by a provisional sum (clause 21.2).

[2] DUTTON v. LOUTH CORPORATION AND ANOTHER. "The Builder," February 25th, 1955, page 344. On Appeal, "The Builder," August 18th, 1955.

VARIATIONS.—A building contract is, unless otherwise provided, an "entire contract," i.e. an indivisible contract in which the contractor undertakes to complete the whole of the work specified for the sum agreed. Such sum is not due until he has completed, and if he does not complete there is a breach of contract, which lays him open to an action for damages. He cannot claim *pro rata* for a proportion of the work done. But such terms are nearly always over-ridden by the written contract, which makes provision for interim payments and for variations either of omission or addition without vitiating the contract (Standard form, 30.6 and 13.2; GC/Works/1,40 & 9(1)).

INTERIM CERTIFICATES.—The responsibility for issuing certificates for interim payments is normally with the architect, but, either officially or unofficially, he often certifies on the advice of the quantity surveyor. Many public authorities make it part of their agreement with the quantity surveyor that he shall make valuations for interim certificates and a specific fee is then provided for this service, and with private clients in contracts of any size similar valuations are made by the surveyor. Whether the architect has authority to employ a surveyor for this purpose without reference to his client is very doubtful, particularly if, as is usual, the contract provides for the architect to certify and makes no reference to a valuation of the surveyor. It often happens that on smaller contracts, the amount involved being small, the architect does not ask for formal valuations for which a charge can be made, but nevertheless asks advice. The fact that no fee is charged does not relieve the professional man of his responsibility or save him from liability for damages—see under the heading negligence.[3] The surveyor who undertakes or assists in the valuation of works for the purpose of interim or final certificates owes a duty to both the building owner and the contractor to use due care in making his valuation and he will be liable in damages at the suit of the building owner or the contractor, as the case may be, if the building owner or the contractor suffers damage as a result of negligent over- or under-valuation.

THE EFFECT OF INTERIM CERTIFICATES.—A line of cases has been relied upon as establishing that upon the issue of a certificate the contractor is entitled to payment in full subject only to the deduction of certain specific and ascertained sums and without any allowance made for unliquidated cross-claims or contra-charges. In *Dawnays Ltd. v. F. G. Minter Ltd.*[4] the Court of Appeal held that an interim certificate issued under the standard sub-contract was like a bill of exchange and payment in full, subject only to the deductions permitted by clause 11(*b*) of the sub-contract and 27(*b*) of the Standard form (1963), must be made

[3] Page 111.
[4] (1971)1 W.L.R. 1205.

to maintain the sub-contractor's cash-flow; the main contractors would have to wait till later to pursue their counter-claim for damages for delay.

The principle was extended to payment under a final certificate by *G. K. N. Foundations v. Wandsworth L. B. C.*[5] It was extended still further by *J. Thompson Horsley Bridge Ltd. v. Wellingborough Steel and Construction Ltd. (The Times,* February 23rd, 1972) where there had been no architect's certificate, on the grounds that the sub-contractors had received the very sums claimed to be due to the plaintiff sub-sub-contractors. The so-called "rule in Dawnays' Case" caused considerable hardship. It was finally considered in detail in *Modern Engineering v. Gilbert Ash*[6] by the House of Lords. The House was unanimous that the sub-contract in question did not prevent the main contractor setting up his unliquidated counter-claim against the sub-contractor's claim upon a certificate. The majority of the House also held that Dawnays' case and those which followed it were wrongly decided. Although therefore it is arguable that the Court of Appeal decision in Dawnays' case has not been overruled, it is most unlikely that any claim founded upon it would now succeed.

UNFIXED MATERIALS.—The property in unfixed materials on the building site is with the contractor, but both the Standard Contract, 16 & GC/Works/1, 40(2) make provision for including their value in interim certificates (subject to a reserve retained), on payment of which the property in the materials so included is to pass to the building owner. In the event of the bankruptcy of the contractor, after transfer of the property in such materials, they would not be subject to the control of the trustee, but would be at the absolute disposal of the building owner.

On the other hand, the contractor has no lien on the building he has erected as security for payment of his account. What has once been attached to the land belongs to and must pass with the land.

APPOINTMENT TO ADJUST VARIATIONS.—The Standard form of contract makes provision in the Articles of Agreement for insertion of the name of a surveyor. The surveyor so named is to measure and value variations (clause 13), and, it should be noted, is appointed by both parties for this purpose. Where quantities have been prepared, the surveyor who has prepared them will usually be named to adjust variations. When there are no quantities, the architect's name is sometimes entered in the space for the surveyor's, when the settlement of the account will be in his hands, but even in small contracts without quantities an independent surveyor may be named. The naming of the surveyor in the building contract is not a contract with him, on which he

[5] (1970)70 L.G.R. 276.
[6] (1974) AC 689.

could sue, it is merely an agreement between the two parties appointing him. If the architect is named to carry out the duties of the surveyor, then the terms of the surveyor's employment, if engaged, will be a matter between architect and surveyor.

The surveyor under the GC/Works/1 form of contract is in rather a different position. He is not mentioned by name, but is merely the representative of the Superintending Officer (clause 37), in fact usually an employee of the Department concerned. This may in practice be a "distinction without a difference", but the distinction is that the surveyor under the Government form cannot legally say "No" to the instructions of the S.O.; the surveyor under the Standard contract can say so to the Architect on those matters for which he is named by the contract to give a decision. It may, of course, be most impolitic for him to do so, and his conscience may be every bit as much troubled as that of his official colleague.

It will be seen that the GC/Works/1 form, 41(2) puts the obligation on the contractor to prepare the account, though in practice it is generally prepared by the surveyor.

ARCHITECT'S INSTRUCTIONS.—The contract usually provides that only variations for which the contractor has written orders shall be adjusted (Standard contract, 13.4; GC/Works/1, 9(1)). It therefore falls on the surveyor to see that the written orders are produced when he is measuring. Some architects issue formal orders in a standard form, others give the orders by letter. A drawing unless signed by the architect is not a sufficient instruction: *Myers v. Sarl* (1860),[7] and where authority in writing is required for variations this means previous authority, unless otherwise specially provided: *Lamprell v. Billericay Union* (1849).[8] In fact, the Standard form of contract makes provision for confirmation of the orders by the architect at any later stage, if previous written authority is not given (clause 13). Some contractors have their own variation order form, filled in by their foreman and submitted to the architect for signature. A system of this sort safeguards the contractor against the possible overlooking by the architect of the routine work required of him by the contract.

There might be a loop-hole by which a contractor could recover for extras without a written variation order, even though the contract makes this a condition precedent to payment for extras. If the building owner or architect orders work, knowing or being told that it involves an extra, it might be argued that there was an implied promise to pay for the extra work, or even that it was fraud to accept the benefit of such work and not pay, just because a formal order had not been issued.

[7] 3 E & E 306; 30 L.J.Q.B.9; 9 W.R.96; 122 R.R.710.
[8] 3 Ex.283; 18 L.J.Ex.282.

HILL *v.* SOUTH STAFFORDSHIRE RAILWAY (1865): 11 Jur. 192; 12 L.T.63.
Turner L.J. said—"I think it would be a fraud on the part of the company to
have desired by their engineer these alterations, additions and omissions to
be made, to have stood by and seen the expenditure going on upon them, to
have taken the benefit of that expenditure, and to refuse payment on the
ground that the expenditure was incurred without proper orders having being
given for the purpose."

ERRORS IN THE BILL OF QUANTITIES.—Bills of quantities are now
usually part of the contract, i.e. the contractor undertakes to do no more
and no less than the quantity and quality of work set out in the bill of
quantities. Provision is made for the correction of any errors (Standard
form, 2.2.2; GC/Works/1, 5) and no variation order is consequently
required to make such corrections. The quantity surveyor is not liable
financially for errors, unless they are so extensive that they justify the
charge of negligence referred to in the last chapter.

COMPLETE REMEASUREMENT.—It sometimes happens that variations are so extensive that the only practical way of adjusting them is
by complete remeasurement of the work. The surveyor cannot decide to
do this of his own accord, and should obtain the agreement of both
parties before doing so, as the procedure provided by the contract is
being altered. It is difficult to say at what stage adjustment by omission
and addition becomes impracticable, and caution is therefore necessary
when starting measurement at an early stage, before there is opportunity
of seeing the nature of variations as a whole.

It may be that the entire foundations or drains are so varied that entire
remeasurement of these is evidently necessary. But this is not a
complete remeasurement of the contract work, each is an item for which
omission and addition can be made on a variation order from the
architect to adjust foundations or drains.

POSITION OF SUB-CONTRACTORS.—Sub-contractors' work is
work delegated by the contractor to another firm, who are responsible to
him for carrying out that portion of his contract. Contractor and
sub-contractor make their own terms, with which the building owner is
not generally concerned, as he looks to the main contractor to be
responsible to him. The building owner may, however, retain some
control over the nomination and terms of employment (Standard form
35; GC/Works/1, 30 & 31). Where this is so, the contractual relations
between the contractor and sub-contractor are unchanged, but the
building owner may have a duty as regards nomination.

T. A. BICKERTON & SONS *v.* NORTH WEST METROPOLITAN HOSPITAL
BOARD (1970) 1 AII ER 1039
Under the Standard form, clause 27, the employer's architect nominated a

sub-contractor who, after he had done some of the sub-contract work, went into liquidation and repudiated the sub-contract. The architect did not appoint another sub-contractor and the main contractors completed the sub-contract work. They sued to recover their fair charge which exceeded the prime cost under the sub-contract. The House of Lords held

(1) the contractors were under no obligation to carry out the sub-contract work
(2) the architect was under a duty to nominate another sub-contractor and that, as he had not done so, the contractors were entitled to recover their fair charge.

The sub-contractor cannot sue the building owner, as there is no privity of contract between them, nor, of course, can the building owner withhold money from the main contractor and pay it direct to the sub-contractor, unless special provision is made by the contract for this (e.g. Standard form, 35.13). If such provision is made, it continues in force even after the bankruptcy of the main contractor: *Re Wilkinson, ex p. Fowler* (1905).[9]

SUB-CONTRACTORS' WORK OMITTED AND PAID DIRECT.—A problem occasionally arises when work for which a provisional sum appears in the bill of quantities is dealt with as a separate contract paid for direct by the employer and the provisional sum is, therefore, omitted from the contract. If the work is carried out, it is regarded as reasonable that the contractor should not be deprived of the profit which he has added in pricing the bill of quantities. Further, there may be a separate item for attendance on the sub-contractor. How far this may be omitted must depend on the extent of the services the contractor is required to provide. He may have to render just the same services as if the specialist had been the sub-contractor anticipated by the contract. What has in practice been contentious is the cash discount which the contract provides shall be allowed on the sub-contractor's account. The intention of the contract is that this discount shall pay for the financing that may be required (the contractor having to pay within 14 days, whether he has received payment or not) and the risk which the contractor takes in being responsible for the sub-contractor's work. As, however, the usual discount is more than enough to cover this, contractors treat it as part of their profit; sometimes adding no profit to the provisional sum at all and relying on the discount. If the work is paid for direct by the employer, the discount does not come their way and they feel aggrieved. The answer is, however hard it may seem, that it is a *cash* discount and, no cash, no discount. Similar circumstances arise with nominated suppliers and, *mutatis mutandis*, the answer is the same.

[9] 2 K.B.713; 54 W.R.157; 74 L.J.K.B.969.

127

The circumstance where the employer decides to pay direct for sub-contractor's work carried out pursuant to an agreement between the sub-contractor and the main contractor, and the contract between the employer and the main contractor permits this, should be distinguished from the case where the employer wishes to omit *work* which it was contemplated would be executed by a sub-contractor from the main contract and either do the work himself or enter into a direct contract with a third party for the execution of the work. Once a contract for the execution of specified works has been entered into by the employer and the main contractor, the employer cannot, under a power to order variations, order the omission of any works from the contract works unless it is genuinely intended that those works should not be done at all. If the employer orders the omission of works so that he or a third party can undertake them, the employer will be liable to compensate the main contractor for any loss of profit or loss of discount suffered in consequence.

BANKRUPTCY OF THE CONTRACTOR.—On the bankruptcy of a contractor the work will fairly certainly stop temporarily. The liability to carry out the contract, as it is not a personal one, falls on the trustee in bankruptcy, and if he does not proceed within a reasonable time the contract can be terminated. The particular contract must be studied. Under the Standard form 27.2 the employment of the contractor is automatically terminated in the event of bankruptcy, and the rights and duties of the parties thereupon are set out in clause 27.4.

It will be necessary to have a valuation of the work completed as at the date on which the contractor stops work, so that the necessary adjustment of moneys due can be made.

The power of the architect to certify for direct payment the balance of accounts of nominated sub-contractors depends in the case of the Standard form on clause 35.13. He can call for receipts to show the amounts paid, and if the contractor has defaulted on any payments already certified, he can certify direct payment. What the contractor has already received in respect of such payments and has not passed on will then count as a general payment to him. That, under the Standard contract, this direct payment can be made after bankruptcy or liquidation of the contractor has been confirmed in a High Court case.[10] This case also confirms that the contractor's interest in retention moneys of the sub-contractor is fiduciary, i.e. the liquidator holds them for the benefit of the sub-contractor not of the creditors. The Standard form has since clarified this by referring to both the employer's and general contractor's interests in retention moneys they hold as being "fiduciary as trustee" (30.5).

[10] RE TOUT & FINCH LTD. (1954): 1 W.L.R.178; 1 AII E.R.127; "The Builder," December 18th, 1953, page 976.

It should be noted that there is no power given to the architect to certify direct payment in the case of nominated suppliers (clause 36). They are in exactly the same position as other merchants and must rank with the ordinary creditors.

The position in regard to unfixed materials paid for in interim certificates has already been referred to.[11] The employer under clause 27.4 retains the use of temporary buildings, plant, &c., on the site, but when no longer required they must be returned to the trustee in bankruptcy.

In the case of the GC/Works/1 form, apart from the special powers of determination under clause 44, there is provision for the case of the contractor's default or failure under clause 45, and clause 46 governs both cases.

ARBITRATION.—The law of arbitrations is an important subject to be studied in detail by the surveyor. It has its own textbooks and forms a separate subject in the examinations of the Royal Institution of Chartered Surveyors, so it is passed over here with no more than this mention.

[11] Page 62.

13

POLICY

SOURCE OF WORK.—A surveyor starting practice may do so knowing that certain work will come to him, or he may do so merely in hope, filling in his time by giving temporary assistance to others on an hourly rate basis, so always being ready for anything that might turn up for him to do on his own account. As a professional man he must not advertise and he must be careful not to make attempts to take away somebody else's work. As a general rule he should not ask for work, though a notice in the personal column of the technical press that he is starting practice or moving office, giving address and telephone number, is permissible, and he may well tell or send such notice to personal friends. Certain public authorities have a panel of quantity surveyors, and where the surveyor has some connection with such authority, e.g. as a ratepayer, he may expect an opportunity of being put on the panel of surveyors. However, such bodies obviously cannot accept every quantity surveyor who applies, and are therefore very unlikely to accept a surveyor just starting practice, some considerable experience as a principal usually being one of their requirements. The R.I.C.S. permits its members to make any such application on a presented form, a copy of which must be lodged with the Institution.[1] This does not preclude a surveyor, already a member of a panel or regularly employed by an Authority, from asking when he is slack, if there is anything available just as he may sometimes have to refuse when he is too fully committed to be able to undertake something further.

The professional Institutions have their own standard designs for boards for exhibition of their members' names, addresses and telephone numbers on building sites. These can either be exhibited separately or incorporated in the general contractor's display board.

The normal channel through which work comes is the architect, who is in a position to advise his client as to the appointment of the quantity surveyor. One's acquaintanceship with architects begins at an early stage from contacts with architects' assistants. They in their turn become practitioners and naturally turn to those, probably of similar age, with whom they have co-operated whilst assistants.

However, the architect is only an agent, and it may be that the

[1] *Directions to Members on Advertisements and Announcements* (Q.S. Edition): R.I.C.S.

surveyor is himself acquainted with the building owner. Difficulty sometimes arises because the architect presses his own recommendation, preferring to deal with somebody he knows than with a stranger recommended by the building owner, who may know little or nothing of the technical ability of the man he recommends. However, the man who pays should have the last say, and it is up to the architect to enquire into the technical qualifications of the nominee, give his advice and leave the building owner to decide.

EXPANSION OF THE BUSINESS.—Once the surveyor has enough work to keep himself going in his own office he will probably find that *sooner or later* more comes, but it may take time. Everybody he meets is a potential source of work; even the builder's foreman may one day remember him, when he is in a position to influence the placing of work. It is not standing people lunches or drinks that will bring the work, but doing one's job carefully without fear or favour, but nevertheless as a human being without self-conceit, and ready to learn.

There is also the inevitable influence of that undefinable thing, personality. Nobody can either judge or alter his own personality, but it is undoubtedly an important factor in forming an impression, favourable or otherwise, on those with whom the surveyor comes in contact. It is from such an influence, of which one is quite unconscious, that a new practice gradually grows, rather than from any deliberate seeking out of work. There are always, of course, exceptions; for example, the surveyor who has family or other connection with architects or "big business," who will so spoon-feed him that he can hardly help swallowing!

Another element in the building-up of a practice is opportunity: it may come before the surveyor is ready for it, it may be hard to recognise or be accompanied by difficulties and risks—it may even never come at all. When it comes the surveyor must weigh all the circumstances, personal, financial and otherwise, and make his decision, for an opportunity missed has a habit of not coming a second time.

The surveyor will later have a further decision on policy to make, viz. is he to allow his office to go on growing, or is he to put on the brake? The brake is very difficult to apply, because one cannot refuse old clients, even if they come with obviously unprofitable jobs when a new client comes with something much more attractive.

BRANCH OFFICES.—One method of expansion may be by the formation of one or more branch offices, if a suitable foundation of work is available. One does not simply say "let's have an office at X town." If one did, there might not be enough work to pay for the name plate on the door. There will usually be some local connection which determines the locality of the office. Such an office should be under the control of a principal regularly in attendance, not merely making visits at infrequent intervals.

There is, of course, one type of branch office, the site office, which is set up for the specific purpose of dealing with a single or series of contracts, where the work is so extensive as to need constant attendance on the site. This arises particularly in measurement for contracts based on a schedule of prices or approximate bill of quantities, where the surveyor and contractor have to measure up extensive works as they proceed. An office of this nature does not usually look for other work, and when the contract in question is concluded will be closed down.

THE TIME FACTOR.—One of the quantity surveyor's problems has always been how to meet and resist excessive pressure in the matter of time. The building owner sees the drawings complete, and if he is not technical finds it difficult to understand a comparatively long waiting period. Public bodies usually have a technical representative concerned with arranging time, but there is, perhaps, a tendency to rely too much on nice calculations as to the number of man-hours required for the job, overlooking in the anxiety for speed such things as the surveyor's other work, availability of staff, delay in delivery of drawings, holidays, illness and many other hitches which may arise. There is a practical limit in the number of takers-off who can work on a job; except in a large office not more than three can be expected and often two only may be available. The more sub-division there is of the work the bigger the risk of error or overlapping. It is in the surveyor's own interest to get his bill out in as short a time as possible, but he should not be so pressed as to find shortage of time a cause of mistakes. The word "urgent" has lost most of its cogency through constant misuse, and the surveyor will be well advised to think first of doing his job properly in such time as is reasonably necessary, leaving "programmes," "progress schedules," &c. as a secondary consideration. There are, of course, cases when time is really important, e.g. in the national interest in war-time or in the peace-time race in armaments or scientific development. Special efforts can be made when necessary by working longer hours or putting aside other work, but the surveyor and his staff cannot be expected to work at abnormal pressure *all* the time. The quantity surveyor's work being the last stage in the obtaining of tenders (except the pricing by the contractor) is apt to suffer in the allotment of time from the cumulative effect of deficiencies in others.

In the case of approximate estimates the degree of accuracy required should be ascertained. Much time can be spent on detail which may be unnecessary for the particular purpose.

STAFF.—The surveyor when setting up his practice will have to make early decision as to what staff, if any, he requires. One of the greatest difficulties facing a surveyor in practice is to spread his work so that he and his staff are always fully occupied and yet there is no large accumulation of arrears. He may start with a trainee technician, who can also do a little taking-off, and a junior. This is the smallest balanced staff that can be used. With younger members of the staff it is not so important to keep them fully employed, as they probably are studying for examinations and can have their own work at hand to do during slack periods. Senior members of a staff must, however, be kept fully employed, if for no other reason, because they are expensive. With a small office it is not possible to keep watertight compartments. Each member of the staff must be prepared, if necessary, to square dimensions or do other routine work. There is no room for either a secretary or an office boy, so the junior must be prepared to type letters, do the filing, stick on stamps and take messages. This is not so uninteresting as it may sound. Access to all the correspondence should give a good insight into the working of the office, and even the taking of messages broadens the knowledge of local topography. If the work of the office develops, a year may see the technician doing more taking-off, the junior doing some working-up and a new junior providing No. 2 with welcome relief from the chores. The normal growth of the office will probably be in this way by bringing in new blood at the bottom, but some particular turn of events, e.g. a series of larger jobs, may necessitate importing a taker-off at the top. The stage will be reached, too, where the clerical work is excessive for the junior members of the staff, so that they do not get sufficient technical work. Then enters the secretary, who can take charge of all non-technical administration and can from his (or more probably her) confidential position also look after such things as salaries book, P.A.Y.E. cards, &c., which would previously have been handled by the principal.

SALARIES.—Salaries will normally be paid monthly by cheque, more often than not by direct debit to the employee's personal account. A careful record must be kept of all salaries paid, together with the various adjustments made for overtime, insurances, income tax, &c. A specimen page of a suggested form of salaries book is shown in Appendix 1.[2]

One thing which must be expected to a greater or lesser extent is the payment of unproductive salaries during illness of members of permanent staff. The employer should have a personal interest in his staff, both for their own sake and to maintain the organisation of the office. The time for which the employer will continue to pay a salary during illness will probably vary according to the rank and length of service of the individual. He obviously cannot continue indefinitely, but in the case of long illness may be able to make payment for a while at

---

[2] Page 221.

half-pay rate before finally severing the connection.

Since the coming of National Insurance, a benefit has been payable during periods of illness. This was, of course, designed to help those who, as in the case of most manual workers, are paid by the hour and would very soon be without any income. When the employer continues to pay a sick member of his staff, it is only reasonable that the amount of benefit received should be deducted from salary. This is allowed by the Inland Revenue authorities and saves the employee income tax, since the benefit is not taxable nor even declared as part of income.

Consideration may have to be given to the question of subsidies (in the literal sense of the word—grants-in-aid) for the staff. In large towns luncheon vouchers can be provided, either bought by the employees or given as supplementary salary, the advantage of these being that they are free of income tax. Then there is the question of time off for juniors for study: a day a week off means a four-day working week generally, which is a serious matter. Expenses incurred when out of the office which are chargeable to the firm may need some definition. Whilst luncheon vouchers bought by the employees are a legitimate economy on their part and involve only a small commission charge to the employer, the other cases must necessarily be reflected in salaries.

PENSION SCHEMES.—Introduction of the Government Pension Scheme has meant that fewer employees now rely on a pension scheme arranged by their employers. However, facilities exist whereby an employee, if he is contracted out of the Government Scheme, can make his contributions to a scheme arranged by the employer and more often than not these days it will be 'index linked' to cover inflation. Alternatively; an employee may wish to 'top up' his pension provision either by contributing to a specially set up scheme or by arranging it personally. Self employed persons have no option, being excluded from the Government Scheme they must make their own arrangements.

TRAINING OF STAFF.—The surveyor will probably find that assistants whom he has trained himself are more valuable than staff trained elsewhere, who may be slow and even reluctant to accustom themselves to his ways and requirements. The methods of entry to the profession are well set out in the leaflets published by the R.I.C.S., the I.Q.S. and the S.S.T.

When taking the beginner into his office without any previous training, the principal must decide whether he prefers an indentured pupil or an assistant. Whilst the system of taking articled pupils at a high premium has disappeared, the junior must not in his years of training expect to receive in salary the full value of his services. He must expect to pay for his opportunity for tuition and the time of the principal and his staff who have to teach and guide him. Though his starting salary may be very moderate, increase according to progress made is recommended rather than a fixed salary decided in advance, as providing both an incentive to work at an age when there may be distractions and a method of rewarding efficiency. The days when the pupil was tied for three, four or five years with "part of the premium returnable as salary" are best forgotten both from the employer's and the pupil's point of view. Whether formal articles are signed or not the relation of employer and pupil should be much the same.

Whether the alternative of full time school or university training referred to in the above-mentioned leaflet is an advantage or not is a contentious point. Such training obviously gives more scope for study of what might be called "outside subjects," i.e. those subjects necessary for examination, but not often met with in the office. It also gives opportunity for a certain amount of research and a more academic approach. On the other hand, the study of the office subjects must be much more theoretical. It is difficult to learn the cut and shuffle process without continuous practical experience. There is a great advantage in working on a "living" job, in feeling that you are achieving practical results whilst learning, not merely solving a theoretical problem to be given so many marks. If the student in the office supplements his work by day release at a Technical School (or if such is not accessible by a correspondence course) he will get in more training time and can make use of the advantages of school tuition whilst still benefiting by the office experience.

The problem arises, if one has staff constantly in training, of what to do with them when they have finished their examination course and can call themselves "qualified". They become too expensive to do junior work, new blood is constantly being introduced at the bottom, and the senior section of the staff may get overweighted. The gradual increase of a small practice may quite probably absorb them, but there will come a saturation point when some must find their place elsewhere. As conditions are at present it seems likely that they will have no difficulty in doing this for some time to come.

MECHANISATION.—In recent years steps have been taken by almost all quantity surveyors in mechanising their work to a greater or lesser degree. The introduction of the metric system of measurement has meant that squaring dimensions manually will no longer be an economic proposition, even if the labour is available to do it and every office is likely to have at least one calculating machine. Such machines are also invaluable for pricing out bills of quantities, invoices, &c., particularly as they will make a running cast providing a total when the bottom of the page is reached. Now that decimal currency is introduced it is no longer necessary to convert figures into decimals for feeding into the machine and to convert the answer back into duodecimals.

Some surveyors make use of a tape recorder for dictating letters, &c. or a miniature machine of this type which they can take with them to a site for dictating spot items. Theoretically these can then be typed direct in their final form, but it is not easy on the site either to choose the best wording or to get the most satisfactory sequence, for which the draft needs consideration as a whole.

The introduction of metrication and the "cut and shuffle" systems has not only made calculating machines essential but has necessitated the use of photocopying machines. The adoption of the system makes it essential that there should be two copies of the dimensions, one retained in the order of taking off, the other sorted into bill order. It is possible to use carbon paper for making the second copy, but this is not very satisfactory. There is a variety of types and makes of machine which needs consideration before purchase. Such a machine will also be found a time saver in making copies of letters and other documents.

A more radical form of mechanisation is the use of an electronic computer.[3] With this machine one, practically speaking, hands in the dimensions and receives back the finished bill. It is used for many other purposes, and before use for bills of quantities it has to be instructed (in code) as to the job it has to do. A computer relies on the use of standard descriptions (of which a very large number is available in each trade), which for feeding into the machine are coded and punched on to a tape. The machine sorts and collects the material and produces a result on a tape which can be fed into a teleprinter machine. The use of this process is obviously expensive: only a very large concern such as a Government Department could make full time use of it, but, as will be seen from the articles referred to in the footnote, the computer can be hired, the dimensions being sent to the firm that works it to deal with.

The use of such a machine is advocated for two reasons: first, that it is quicker than traditional practice, and, secondly, because there has been in recent years a dearth of workers-up. Time—well, we all know about that, and how often we really need not have hurried, but workers-up are an admitted difficulty. The man who in years gone by was content to remain a worker-up all his life (and consequently become an expert) is rarely found now, and his substitute today is often a youngster still struggling to pass his educational qualification and thinking hopefully that he will become a surveyor. Against all this, it should be remembered that a taker-off can do the working-up, perhaps, three times as fast as the available worker-up of poor standard, and so much better that editing is either eliminated or reduced to a minimum.

[3] *Report on the Use of Computers for Working-Up:* R.I.C.S. Journal, April 1961, page 561 and November 1961, page 248. *Computers and their Application to the Production of Bills of Quantities:* Ibid., November 1961, page 258. *Is Automation Here for Quantity Surveyors?* The Builder, March 16th 1962, page 564. *The Quantity Surveyor and the Computer:* I.Q.S. Journal, May/June 1966, page 133.

Moreover, it stands to reason that to make alterations and corrections during the taking-off is much more difficult with this mechanised procedure. By the use of a machine one loses the brain work of a good worker-up, who can spot mistakes in the taking-off in a way no machine can. As for standard clauses for the bill, when one sees what an obscure, illiterate and botched mess *can* be made by adapting a standard specification, one is really horrified at the idea. Has any standard specification ever been adapted without a good many special clauses? Special items in this process, though not impossible, are apparently very difficult to cope with.

One must not forget that the accuracy of a machine is entirely dependent on the human brain that works it.[4]

STATUS OF THE QUANTITY SURVEYOR.—This urge to save time and money brings one to consideration of the status of the quantity surveyor. Is he a merchant selling goods costing him as little as possible, for which he is trying to get as much as possible, or at any rate a "ring" price? Or is his main purpose to do a job and do it well, making his fee, important though it is, a secondary matter?

FEES.—A difficulty facing the young surveyor, particularly when newly established in practice, is his obligation to work for a fixed scale of fees, and his inability to offer to quote a lower fee than that generally recognised. He rightly says "I am a beginner, I have low overhead charges, I do much of the work myself and can afford, in fact should be glad, to accept a lower fee. Why," he adds, "must I let the work go to so-and-so who has a good practice and does not need it, whereas I do?" It seems hard, but if he had practised 50 years ago he would have seen regularly in the weekly technical papers advertisements of the proposed appointment of a quantity surveyor, applicants being asked to examine the drawings and quote their terms. Surveyors quoted ridiculous terms in order to get the job. The general insistence since those days on scale fees and the refusal to quote in competition has ensured a reasonable fee for everybody receiving an appointment. In the end, therefore the newly established practitioner benefits, who might otherwise be told "look here, you are a young fellow only just started practice, I expect you to do this at a reduced fee."

Whilst on the subject of reduced fees, there is another case in which the suggestion may be met. It has been known for an architect introducing work to expect a share of the fee. The answer is: yes, certainly, provided your name, not mine, appears on the bill. The surveyor is then working as an assistant and has only an assistant's

---

[4] The failure of a rocket (only worth about £7 million) aimed at the planet Venus is ascribed to "somebody's mistake in working out the 'programme' fed into an electronic computer": *The Daily Telegraph*, July 28th 1962.

responsibility, but the proviso will quite possibly be enough to cause withdrawal of the suggestion. This is not a question of sharing a fee. The architect accepts full legal responsibility, but pays his assistant on a percentage basis instead of a weekly or monthly salary.

There is, of course, no objection to a mutual arrangement between quantity surveyors; it is with other professions, e.g. architects, solicitors, &c. that fees must not be shared. Greater co-operation between quantity surveyors who have too much work and those who have too little is to be encouraged.

The application of a scale of fees has been referred to above (page 106). Where there are alternatives, as in the R.I.C.S. scale for post-contract work, the alternative to be applied should be settled on the surveyor's appointment, not left to the option of either party which may cause dissatisfaction. The whole subject of scales of fees is now under scrutiny following the report of the Monopolies and Mergers Commission.[5]

RENDERING OF ACCOUNTS.—The surveyor's fee for preparing a bill of quantities is considered to be due on completion of the draft bill. It is usual to await the signature of the building contract, if this is within a reasonable time, before rendering an account. If proceeding with the building is unduly delayed the account would be sent in two or three months after delivery of tenders. If issue of the bills for tender is postponed, so that there are no figures on which to base a definite account, request for a suitable payment on account can be made. On advice of definite abandonment of the scheme the account will be rendered, based on any approximate estimate that may have been given or other agreed basis.

The account for adjusting variations and any other services since preparation of the bill of quantities can be forwarded when the variation account is reported. In protracted contracts payments for such work as advising on interim certificates may be asked for at, say, quarterly or yearly intervals during progress of the building contract.

Small accounts for reports &c. are probably best sent out at the end of each quarter.

RECORDS OF OFFICE COSTS.—A question of policy to be decided is how far costing of the work in the office is to be carried. There are some who like to see the financial result of every job, others may feel that there is little satisfaction in this, as the fees are in most cases fixed according to scale and what is spent is spent. It may be thought that such checking of costs will give warning for the future, but a similar job may not recur, and a quantity surveyor cannot refuse future work from a

[5] See page 109.

client just because it does not pay well. A professional practice differs from a trade in that it is not the principal's concern to make as big a profit as he can: his first aim must be to do his job properly. Moreover, he cannot, like the manufacturer, adjust his prices to his factory costs, since he normally charges according to scale.

Whether the surveyor decides to establish a full costing system or not, it is essential that careful record should be kept of the time worked by each member of staff, so that a cost can at any time be built up for a particular job. This may be required for calculation of a fee which must be based on cost, to estimate a fee to be quoted for similar future work which is not covered by a scale fee, or, perhaps, to try to establish the reasonableness or otherwise of the scale fee in a particular case. The keeping of staff time records is referred to in Chapter 15.[6]

Whether full or only occasional costing is required, the calculation should be as accurate as possible. Time records will give the numbers of hours worked, and a system must be adopted to arrive at the accurate hourly rate of each individual. If a man is paid £100 per week and works 40 hours (8 hours a day for 5 days), his hourly rate is not, as might appear at first sight, £2.50 per hour. Holidays must be taken into account, both the annual holiday and public holidays, to ascertain what the actual cost per hour of the man's time is. Assuming three weeks' summer holidays and six public holidays (two at Christmas, two at Easter, one in Spring and one in Summer) the man would be working 1912 hours in the year (49 weeks at 40 = 1960, less 6 days at 8). The actual hourly cost would be obtained by dividing 1912 into the annual salary of £5,200, giving, say, £2.72. Overtime would normally be costed at the actual rate paid, though, in fact, extra time worked reduces the principal's overheads as a percentage of staff cost. If overtime were substantial, this might be taken into account.

There are other considerations which might yield greater accuracy. In the case of an assistant paid a monthly or an annual salary, the hourly cost would be different in a leap year, when he gives an extra day's work. If the financial year is from April to March, one year may have two Easter holidays in it. Owing to the day of the week on which Christmas falls, there might be an additional holiday, perhaps the Monday before a Tuesday Christmas. However, it is probably best to ignore these unusual circumstances. There is one commoner case that might be reckoned. Under present conditions it is often arranged for a trainee to have one day a week at a technical school, or time off each week for private study. This substantially increases his hourly cost.

There is another factor which affects the cost of an assistant's time, viz. time off for illness. This is obviously very variable and, therefore, is best treated as an overhead charge with which the principal may be lucky or otherwise.

[6] Page 163.

The method to be followed in costing and the form of the record books are referred to in Chapter 16.[7]

PROFIT SHARING.—The sharing of profits by all who helped to make them is in theory excellent, but rather difficult to put into practice. Apart from the selection of salaried partners or associates referred to in Chapter 17,[8] there seem to be only two ways of distributing a share of profits. One is to divide part of the profits in settled and known proportions between members of the staff, the other is for principals to distribute bonuses at their own discretion, probably at the end of each financial year.

In the first of these cases it must be decided whether the profits and full accounts will be disclosed, making the whole business, so to speak, a co-operative society, or whether principals will just say "we are distributing £1000 in the proportions agreed." In the second the principals may follow a similar course, without disclosing how much is distributed or in what proportions, or the bonuses may depend on a particularly profitable job, or be awarded to individuals whose work deserves it, either for past services or as an encouragement for the future.

The disadvantage of the co-operative principle seems to be that the partners in making decisions will feel (or ought to feel) a responsibility to those who are rather like shareholders, and that their actions are accordingly restricted when decisions on policy will directly affect the pockets of their staff. In management, though two heads may be better than one, since they can be a check on each other, the spread of responsibility too far can be a drag. Moreover, those who have worked up a business and put the capital into it may, quite naturally, feel that they want to retain full control.

The fully co-operative method should not present much difficulty in the working, but the giving of bonuses at the discretion of principals has this disadvantage. An assistant receives a fixed salary, and, perhaps, at the end of the year is given a bonus of £100. There is a natural tendency to regard that as part of the salary and to budget in the next year accordingly. The next year may not be such a profitable one, but the principals may feel that the bonus has been relied on and that they must give it. The same difficulty does not arise in the co-operative business, where the bonus is a definite dividend plain for all to see, and the onus is on the recipient to judge what return he is likely to get.

On the whole, the best solution seems to be to see that the fixed salaries of the staff are not skimped, even if this means profits lower than they might be, so that all feel that their work is appreciated and satisfied

[7] Page 170.
[8] Page 179.

141

that they are being fairly treated. After all, even a fixed salary can include a share of profits. The part which senior assistants take in management should be recompensed by a salary higher than would be economic for one who is solely a taker-off, and the amount of such additional salary can be looked on, at any rate in part, as a share of profits. But even so, there may be occasions when a bonus might well be given. It happens sometimes that one job is particularly profitable (a percentage scale fee inevitably leads to this occasionally, just as it leads to jobs that are a dead loss), but it should be made clear that any such bonus is due to the particular exceptional case. Appreciation can also be shown by increase of salaries, but it must be remembered that it is much easier to increase salaries than to lower them.

The answer to the co-operative-minded is this. Do you tell the butcher or baker, whom you employ, what your income is? You choose your joint and pay according to quality, and, if your income is high enough (and you are lucky enough to get the service), you give the butcher's boy £1.00 at Christmas, as a share of your income for services that you appreciate.

WORK FOR BUILDERS.—Whether the surveyor shall undertake work for builders or not is a matter of policy to be decided, and something has been said of this subject in Chapter 9.[9]

The work required is usually in one of two categories, either measurement or pricing, sometimes perhaps both. Measurement may be required where no quantities are supplied for tender, for the adjustment of variations on a contract or, in the case of schedule contracts, the complete measurement of works as executed. Any of these are within the province of the quantity surveyor.

Pricing of estimates is rather a different story. The quantity surveyor has, of course, the theoretical knowledge of price analysis which he can apply in practice, but success in tendering in competition depends very largely on a detailed knowledge of current prices, what firms to go to for the best terms and the best service, and above all a decision on the risks to be taken. In the first two of these the builder, constantly dealing with merchants and handling invoices, is obviously more expert, and the last, after all, is his affair. If A is entrusted with taking risks with B's money he is apt to be more cautious than B might be himself, as he will be blamed for any loss. Measurement is a question of fact, but pricing is opinion based on judgment and that knowledge which the constant handling of labour and purchase of materials alone can give. To price estimates merely by taking rates from price books or other bills may, when carefully done, be suitable for approximate estimates: it does not give the accuracy necessary for pricing tenders, where quite a small

[9] Page 83.

margin one way may lose the job or the other may seriously reduce or even eliminate the profit.

GIFTS.—One of the suggestions for subjects to be dealt with on one revision of this book was the acceptance of gifts from contractors. The authors do not regard themselves as Lord Keeper of the Professional Conscience and it is, perhaps, rash to say much. That the promise or receipt of a gift in consideration for giving some specific favour in the future, whether that gift is in cash or kind, is bribery and a criminal offence should be obvious. Where a problem may present itself is in the matter of Christmas presents, which are often offered in a genuine spirit of goodwill without any ulterior motive. These are undoubtedly gifts, which by saving expense are the equivalent of a cash payment, whether the expense is that of a wall calendar, office diary, turkey or half a dozen bottles of wine. The surveyor examining a variation account with a contractor is not likely to feel "Ah! he gave me a turkey last Christmas, I must try to make up for it." Any contractor who thought so would do better to reduce this branch of his overhead charges. On the other hand, there are in this world those who are naturally suspicious, even clients who think that everybody is trying to take advantage of them, so it is best to be, like Caesar's wife, above suspicion. A wall calendar or a desk diary could hardly be regarded by the most suspicious as given with evil intent, but when it comes to larger gifts the answer is not only "What does your conscience say?" but "What might the suspicious-minded client, however unjustly, think?" The recent spate of cases concerning corruption in the building industry will no doubt make prospective givers and indeed receivers even more aware of the pitfalls.

14

OFFICE ORGANISATION—PROVISION
AND EQUIPMENT OF THE OFFICE

It is proposed to attempt to say something of office organisation, though this is very difficult, owing to the great variety in size and type of offices. What may apply to an individual, with perhaps one or two young assistants, will probably be quite inapplicable to the large office with several partners and a staff of 100. However, it is the beginner in practice who principally needs consideration here, and if suggestions are made to meet his needs, he can can develop them as his office expands.

ACCOMMODATION.—One of the first problems facing the prospective practitioner will be the finding of an office. He will presumably have decided on the town or locality in which he wants to practise, but will have to find the floor space to use. Whilst a position with good access to buses, trams and trains is valuable in a large town, the practitioner in the smaller country towns will probably do most of his travelling by car, and so be independent of the public services. His staff, however, may not be so independent, so good access to communications is usually important.

The quantity surveyor is not visited often by his clients: he more usually visits them, whether architect or building owner, so he need not consider them much in settling on his office. There are those who think they impress by having a palatial approach to their offices, but the good quantity surveyor does not need that form of advertisement, and is probably better without the type of client it might attract. A lift to offices on upper floors is convenient (except when it is out of order), but if he is not higher than second or third floor climbing the stairs will do no harm, in fact they will provide some exercise in what is often a day of sedentary work.

Enquiry as to offices available may be made of the local estate agents, may be looked for in local papers or the surveyor himself may advertise. It sometimes happens that somebody offers to let a share in offices, though if he contemplates expansion this may be only a short-term proposal. It may suit a beginner well, as the offer may include a share in telephone or even clerical assistance.

It is advisable to over-estimate rather than under-estimate the space required. A small office successfully established will expand, and it may later be difficult or impossible to get further space near. The beginner may as a temporary expedient, until he can see how the practice will develop, take a single room or share in a room, but if there is confidence in the establishment of the business there should be not less than two rooms. When he employs staff he will then still have a room to himself, where he can see his clients and have his discussions with builders and others without disturbing the rest of the office.

Redecoration of ceilings and walls, unless they are already in good condition, will do a lot to brighten up the office, even if paintwork is not renewed.

An agreement for tenancy of offices should be in writing and specify any outside service provided, such as use of lavatories, arrangements for cleaning, payment of rates, fire insurance, &c. It should make the landlord responsible for structural repairs. Decoration is a matter of arrangement, sometimes being the responsibility of landlord and sometimes of tenant. Provision should be made for cesser of rent in the event of destruction by fire. An agreement for more than three years is a lease, and must be prepared by a solicitor.

If circumstances allow and suitable property is available, the surveyor may buy and become his own landlord, sub-letting some of the rooms as necessary. This, however, makes a heavy demand on capital and belongs to the sphere of property investment rather than quantity surveying.

OFFICES, SHOPS & RAILWAY PREMISES ACT 1963.—This Act makes provision for the safety, health and welfare of people employed in such premises which must now be registered by the employer with the authority responsible for enforcing the Act's provisions. These are the councils of county boroughs, London boroughs, county districts and the City Corporation of London. For offices of local authorities, government departments, certain factory and railway premises the Factory Inspectorate is the enforcement authority. Within their areas the authorities of the Middle and Inner Temple act.

Responsibility for complying with the provisions of the Act is laid generally on the occupier of premises to which it applies, although the actual employer of persons working in the premises has certain specific responsibilities. In certain buildings some of the occupiers' responsibilities are transferred to the owner of the building, who is also responsible for complying with provisions relating to "common parts," e.g. entrances, passages, stairways and lifts.

The Minister has power to exempt by order a class of premises from certain requirements where in his opinion it would be unreasonable to require compliance because of special circumstances. If the enforcing authority are satisfied that compliance is not reasonably practicable, they may exempt individual premises from certain requirements. Application for an individual exemption must be made to the enforcing authority on Form OSR.5. If it is refused, there is a right of appeal against the refusal to a magistrates' court within 21 days.

The provisions securing health and welfare lay down minimum space standards to prevent overcrowding, having regard to space occupied by furniture, fittings, machinery, &c., as well as to the number of persons. They lay down reasonable environmental standards in terms of temperature, lighting and ventilation which must be provided.

Sanitary conveniences, washing facilities and drinking water must also be provided in accordance with the requirements of this Act.

The safety provisions are based upon those set out in the Factories Act, 1961, as to construction of floors, stairs and passageways and freedom from obstructions. Handrails must be provided to all stairways and fencing and fixed guards provided for dangerous machinery.

The Act lays down detailed fire precautions in relation to means of escape, alarm bells, etc., and for certain classes of premises a Fire Certificate must be obtained before it is lawful to employ anyone in them. The local Fire Authority is responsible for enforcing the fire provisions and application for a Fire Certificate should be made on form OSR.3 together with copies of plans showing the proposed means of escape. The authority may refuse to issue a certificate unless certain alterations are made within a specified time (which may be extended if necessary). There is a right of appeal against the decision to a magistrates' court within 21 days. Any order which the court may make will be binding on the authority, but the applicant may further appeal against the order to a court of quarter sessions.

FURNISHING.—A taker-off should have a table preferably large enough for double elephant size drawings. When working on large contracts even more space is advisable, and a side table on which to keep drawings not in use is helpful. Whether tables should be of drawing-table height for use with a stool or of ordinary desk-height with a chair is a matter of taste. With large drawings the drawing-table with stool (or standing) is probably preferable. For a worker-up a desk-height table with chair is usually sufficient.

The principal will require a desk with drawers in which to keep his papers, a substantial chair, as well as one or two chairs for callers, and some floor covering according to taste and pocket. A standing cabinet of suitable drawers will be found useful for keeping the various kinds of paper in the office and for additional space to supplement the drawers of the desk.

A door-height steel cabinet with folding doors would provide about a dozen pigeon-holes in which to keep separate all the papers relating to each job and a letter filing cabinet will be required as time goes on. More will be said as to letter filing later. A safe is useful for keeping documents of which there are no copies in existence and which quite a small fire might destroy. A little shelving should be provided, and if possible a bookcase and small cupboard. Text-books, catalogues, &c. need a home, as do note-paper, stationery sundries and the omnipresent tea crockery.

A little something spent on pictures for wall decoration will add to the appearance of the office, unless the surveyor's taste is limited to the advertising art of manufacturers and the stereotyped calendars of lithographers.

SMALL EQUIPMENT.—A variety of small equipment will be necessary:—
2 m Measuring rod (2 fold or 6 fold).
30 m Linen or fibreglass tape.
Set of scales: 1:5, 1:50, 1:10, 1:100, 1:20, 1:200, 1:1250, 1:2500.
Dividers, pencil and ink compasses and spring-bows.
Protractor.
60° and 45° set squares.
Ruler for ruling ink lines (for which scales should *not* be used).
Perforator (for filing).
Letter balance.
Drawing board and T-square.
Cash box.
Typewriter.

There are other things not essential, which can be omitted in the first instance, and acquired as the surveyor feels the need for them. Amongst such items may be listed:—
Plan chest.
Stapling machine.
Numbering machine.
Rotary pencil sharpener.
Drawing edge binder.
Set of stencils.

Stationery and items which can be classed as "consumable stores" will be dealt with in the next chapter.

The quantity surveyor is not likely to have much use for dumpy level and staff, chain and ranging poles, &c. If he should have occasion to use them, they can be hired.

HEATING AND LIGHTING.—A good light on a dark winter's day and a reasonable temperature on a cold one are both necessary to maintain production, as well as for the comfort of the occupants of the office. The system of heating will depend on what is available. Electric light points should be moved as necessary to provide a pendant for each person. Ceiling lighting if used instead of individual pendants, must be ample to assist in close examination of drawings, and fluorescent lighting will be found effective.

OFFICE CLEANING.—Here the surveyor's labour troubles may begin. In some cases cleaning service is provided by the landlord, but, if not, the surveyor must find some means of getting his floors and tables kept clean and waste paper baskets emptied.

TELEPHONE.—A telephone or share in one is essential. If allowed the use of somebody else's telephone, an extra entry of the user's name can be made in the telephone directory on payment of the appropriate fee. An intercommunicating extension line from the general office to the private office will be useful for speaking to the staff, as well as to enable a member of the staff to take incoming calls in the first instance. In the larger offices an independent inter-communicating system may be used with either telephone or loudspeaker instruments, so that the principal can by pressing a button speak to any room and be answered. This saves an assistant's time coming in and reduces disturbance of his work.

FIRE INSURANCE, &c.—Insurance of the building will usually be the landlord's responsibility, but the surveyor will need to cover the contents of his office against damage by fire and burglary. The general furniture, stationery, &c. will present no difficulty, and he should be able to fix a suitable replacement value for them. A serious consideration, however, in the event of fire is the replacement of documents in the office, particularly those referring to bills of quantities in course of preparation. The dimensions of a job and even abstract may be complete and billing be in hand. If everything is destroyed there is nothing to be done but begin again. The client will not, of course, pay a double fee. It is, therefore, advisable to insure the documents in the office under a special item. It will be very difficult to assess a figure, but it should be substantial, the premium being a comparatively small matter when the contingent liability is considered. The cost of replacement, i.e. salaries and proportion of overheads, will alone be covered, unless a "Loss of Profit" policy is also taken out.

EMPLOYERS' LIABILITY INSURANCE.—An employer is liable to pay compensation for injury caused to his employees "arising out of and in the course of their employment." Such compensation might be very heavy in the case of serious injury, and insurance against the risk is essential. Premiums are based on the class of employee and salary paid,

149

and are normally adjusted following a return of wages and salaries made each year by the employer to the insurance company.

INDEMNITY POLICY.—A surveyor is prudent to protect himself against claims by his clients for negligence, for which he might be sued as a result, not necessarily of his own mistake, but of that of an assistant. The risk may be small, but it is there. It would have to be a serious mistake to lay him open to the charge of negligence, and he may feel that the risk is sufficiently small to let him be his own insurer. He must, however, realise that a claim, if made, might be large enough to put him out of business.

OFFICE ORGANISATION
(continued)—MANAGEMENT

NOTE-PAPER.—Headed note-paper will be a first requirement. A neat design for the heading and a good quality paper are important. It should look like a surveyor's notepaper—that of a practical man who gets down to facts—with a heading neither florid nor insignificant. The surveyor will have discovered from his reading of architects' drawings how much more legible Roman capital letters are than the small, often italic, letters so much in favour today. Name, address and telephone number must all be easily legible. A letter from a stranger on poor note-paper badly printed is like a badly written examination paper, it prejudices from the start. It is convenient if the heading is so arranged that it can be stamped equally well on foolscap, A4, A5 or half-foolscap, the last a convenient size which was popularised by the need for paper economy in war time, and which (or A5) can be made to serve for the very large proportion of letters which are brief.

GENERAL STATIONERY.—General stationery which will be required includes:—
Plain paper to match note-paper.
Plain foolscap or A4 paper.
Thin paper for carbon copies, note-paper size and foolscap.
Dimension paper, single or double sheets according to choice, or "cut and shuffle" paper.
Abstract paper.
Single cash column bill paper.
Double cash column bill paper.
Dimension books.
Foolscap and letter size carbon paper.
Envelopes to suit letter paper sizes.
    ,,   for foolscap or A4 paper, used flat, halved or folded.
Foolscap or A4 folders.
Foolscap and quarto sizes of paper have now largely given way to International Standard sizes.[1] These have been determined for economical cutting from a standard manufacturers' size for large sheets.

---

[1] B.S. 4000: Sizes of paper and boards.

The equivalent of the usual quarto note-paper is the A4 size, 297 × 210 mm (11¾" × 8¼"). This would have to serve as a substitute for foolscap as well, there being no other suitable size in the series. For smaller note-paper the A5 size would be used. The next size, A6, would be suitable for a variety of memorandum forms and the like. Envelopes are, of course, made to suit each size. It may be noted that each size in the series is half that of the next largest, and that the sides have a fixed relation to each other, a fixed proportion of $1:\sqrt{2}$. Change will possibly be a slow process, but there are signs of its beginning. It has recently been announced that, to facilitate mechanical sorting, postage will be higher for square than for oblong envelopes!

There is a British Standard for size and rulings of quantity surveyors' paper[2] which covers dimension and single and double bill paper (both "left hand" and "right hand" billing). Both the usual foolscap and the A4 size are included. The Standard also specifies the punched hole for filing sheets. Whilst paper may be more easily available from stock to these rulings the surveyor may have his own ideas for improvement. No binding margin is provided for bill paper. Variation accounts in draft or type are sometimes bound. Though papers intended for printing and lithography are specifically excluded, they must necessarily have a binding margin, and one would have thought the standard could have been simplified by including this for all paper instead of necessitating two separate rulings. Abstract paper is not covered by the Standard, though there is a promise to include it "should conditions warrant it". If the surveyor prefers a special ruling, this will not involve much extra expense, if he orders in quantity, say 6 reams at least.

Dimension and abstract papers must be strong quality, as they have a lot of handling. Bill paper does not need the same strength as it usually serves as a draft only, so ordinary strong typing paper can be used. A thin paper with similar ruling will be found useful where several copies of an account on bill paper have to be typed. It should be noted that when bill paper is specially ruled, it is important that the ruling of every order should be exactly the same, otherwise the typist may get apparently similar rulings mixed and the column ruling in carbon copies will be wrong.

It is useful to have a memorandum form with or without a printed heading, on which telephone messages can be recorded. If a paper of a bright distinctive colour is used it will catch the eye lying on a desk, even if mixed with other papers. It should be large enough to be easily seen and to be filed with correspondence. Messages should not be written on small scraps of paper, which are likely to be mislaid, and messages about different jobs should not be written on the same piece of paper.

Two printed items are useful in addition to note-paper. One is a half or

---

[2] B.S. 3327: *Stationery for Quantity Surveying.*

quarter sheet of note-paper printed with a heading. "From Mr. X. Y. Z.——" and with the address at the bottom. This can be used when sending documents that do not need a covering letter and would have space for small memos. The second is a slip of similar size printed "With the compliments and thanks of Mr. X. Y. Z.——," also with the address. This serves for sending with receipts for payment of fees &c.; it is more polite than sending the receipt by itself and saves the writing of a letter. In both these cases the printing should be well done and the paper good.

BUSINESS CARDS.—The surveyor in practice should have business cards, so that he can quickly and easily give his name and address to a stranger who wants it. He may need to do this on introduction to a possible client or when on visiting some building he has to identify himself. The centre of the card should bear the individual's name and designatory letters with immediately underneath "(Chartered) Quantity Surveyor"; below should appear the address in one corner and telephone number in the other. If the surveyor is a partner in a firm, the name of his firm could appear in one of the top corners.

STATIONERY SUNDRIES.—A variety of small sundries are necessary in an office—paper clips, paper fasteners of varying sizes, elastic bands, string tags, pencils—black-lead and coloured, inks—blue and coloured, india rubbers, &c. A useful collection can be made by going round a large stationers' shop, or they can be left to be bought as they are found to be required.

LETTER-WRITING.—The office being now all ready, something must be said of its use. There will be correspondence about every job, from the first letter of instruction to a final letter sending in an account for fees. The science and art of letter-writing constitute a subject well worthy of study, but only a few points can be mentioned here, which are suggested by letters and reports seen in practice.

The object of writing is to convey the ideas of one person to the mind of another, who is not present to be addressed verbally, and at the same time to make a permanent record of the communication. Owing to the lack of expression of the face and inflection of the voice the writer must convey by his words alone both the emphasis he requires and the tone in which he is writing. Words and phrases must, therefore, be more carefully chosen.

Without going into the subject, a few suggestions may be made:—

1. Be quite sure that the points you make are clear.
2. Be as brief and simple as possible. Do not use two words where one will do. Avoid long words and periphrasis (the long word

153

here is balanced against the less expressive alternative of several).

3. Start a new paragraph with each new point, and do not split up the point into more than one paragraph.

4. If a long letter develops, consider whether it is not better to put the matter in the form of a schedule or report, with a short covering letter only.

5. Be sure to write with your reader in mind. Do not use technical terms in writing to a non-technical client, which a little thought would show you he could not understand.

6. Avoid commercial *clichés*, journalese, Americanisms and slang.

7. Avoid spelling mistakes and bad grammar. They give a poor opinion of you to an educated reader.

8. Avoid the impersonal. "It is regretted" means nothing. Regret is a personal sentiment, and, if you feel regret, say "I regret" or "We regret." You may or may not feel you can say "the Minister, the Board or the Directors regret."

9. Be definite. If the decision is with you, do not say "this *appears* to be correct." If you are satisfied that it is correct, say it is.

10. Have reference books by you, from which to settle any doubts on language which arise when you write.[3]

11. When you know that an enclosure must be detached, use a slip-on clip. It is irritating to have to open a staple to separate, for instance, a cheque from its covering letter.

DESPATCH AND FILING OF CORRESPONDENCE.—There are four points in connection with despatch of correspondence which need emphasis:—

1. Letters received should be answered promptly. If an answer is likely to be delayed more than a few days, the letter should be acknowledged with notification of the delay and explanation, if necessary.

2. A check to see that the proper enclosures are put in. Various reminders are used, such as a marginal mark against the reference to the enclosure in the text, a footnote "3 Encs.," or a coloured adhesive label stuck on the letter to catch the eye before inserting in an envelope.

3. A check to see that the right letter is in the right envelope (a mistake might put one in an awkward position—to say nothing of the possibility of a libel action!).

4. Care to see that overweight letters are weighed and correctly stamped with instructions as to whether they are to be sent by first or second class mail.

[3] Books suggested are:— *The Concise Oxford Dictionary; Modern English Usage* (Fowler); *Complete Plain Words* (Gowers).

The main classification of letters will be into the jobs to which they belong, but in the case of larger jobs they can be sub-divided into several files, e.g. architect, contractor, sub-contractors and merchants, &c. If all letters are kept in order of date in the file belonging to the job any letter can be turned up at once. In practice it is not uncommon either for it to have got into the wrong file, or by mistake classified under the wrong month or even year, or it may be that somebody has kept it out to refer to and never put it back. Careful filing is most important as much time can be lost searching for a letter in such circumstances, and cases have been known where one has just had to give it up! There are various systems of filing. The simplest is to keep letters in a foolscap pocket folder, but it will be found more satisfactory to have them securely fastened to their container by one of the methods on the market. The files can be kept horizontally in a nest of drawers or vertically in a filing cabinet to suit, either just placed in the drawer or in special suspended files in a fitting supplied for the purpose by makers of steel cabinets. Files should be clearly marked, in a position easily seen, with the name of the job, and if kept in alphabetical order one can be quickly found.

The giving of reference initials to letters sent means little in a small office, where all letters are opened and dealt with by the principal. In the case of a large office the reference will indicate which principal or assistant is dealing with the job and is therefore a convenience when sorting incoming letters. It may be found an advantage to give a serial number to each job, which being put on all letters simplifies filing. The relative register provides a record of all jobs in the office, of assistance, for example, in ensuring that the charging of a fee is not forgotten. It is advisable for all correspondence relating to a particular job to be passed to the senior assistant dealing with the job to see and initial before it is filed. He in his turn must see that anybody working under him whom it affects is informed.

In order to facilitate filing, two separate jobs should not be referred to in the same letter: two separate letters should be written (they can be enclosed together). The copy of each letter will then be traceable in its own file. If a letter referring to two jobs should be received, it should be filed with one of them, and a slip, stating where the letter has been filed, should be put with the other, preferably with a description of what it is about.

DIARIES.—There are those who think that there is a great difference between saying a thing and putting it in writing. The production of a letter is certainly among the best forms of evidence, but a diary entry of conversation made at the time approaches it very closely. The principal should keep a diary in which conversations of importance are recorded, though as an alternative he may make a written memorandum dated and initialled to go to the letter file. Particularly should notes be made of any conversation as to terms of employment, promises of dates for delivery of drawings or bill, or other such items which might later be called in question. If there is doubt it is advisable to write a letter confirming the verbal statements made, so that the other party is quite sure of the position.

A diary will also be required by the principal to record appointments made; probably a small pocket diary is the most convenient form, duplicated, perhaps, by a desk pad to which the office staff can refer for any arrangements to be made in his absence.

The more senior members of the staff should have a diary provided for recording particulars of their meetings with contractors, &c. They could also make a fuller note in it of what they were doing each day than appears in their time record (see page 219).

PRESERVATION OF DOCUMENTS.—Besides letters, each job will have a batch of papers of various sorts belonging to it. In a quantities job there will be dimensions, abstract, draft bill, taker-off's notes, estimates on which p.c. sums are based, architect's specification or notes, &c. As the building progresses there will be dimension books, daywork sheets, interim certificate papers, labour and material fluctuation documents, &c. All these papers belonging to the same job should be kept together, and a steel cabinet with folding doors, a vertical division and shelves of a size to take foolscap documents comfortably probably provides the best method of storage. The doors can have a boldly stencilled label affixed opposite each shelf with the name of the job, and any paper is then quickly found. If preferred, the dimension books can be kept separately on suitable shelves, being numbered on the back edge and indexed for quick reference. The steel cabinet, however, provides a certain amount of protection against damage by a slight fire. Papers such as dimensions, abstract or draft bill before duplication are best kept in a safe as providing better resistance to fire, but an ordinary safe is not fireproof in a really serious fire, which may make it red hot and ruin its contents.

In the case of small jobs a satisfactory alternative to a pigeon hole in a cabinet is a box file large enough to take foolscap papers comfortably. This may be of the normal cardboard pattern with case or in the form of a steel box with hinged lid, and will hold all the papers for the job. Another alternative is a cardboard box with lid which can be specially made to any size required, at quite reasonable cost if 50 or so are ordered from a cardboard box maker.

Arrangements will have to be made for storage of certain documents of finished jobs. Priced bills of quantities can be moved to a different shelf, and material documents, e.g. dimensions, abstract, estimates, &c. can be done up in a parcel, given a reference number, entered in an index book and put away. In very small jobs the drawings can be included in the parcel, but larger drawings can be rolled up, wrapped and

156

labelled, either with the name of the job or with a number like the parcels, and stacked in suitable storage space. Open batten racking, deep enough to take rolls of drawings end-ways and with similar divisions at intervals, is as satisfactory as anything. If the rolls are put away alphabetically, each roll being marked with name of job at its outer end, a batch can be quickly looked through for a particular job.

CATALOGUES AND LEAFLETS.—A collection of leaflets, catalogues and reference books will accumulate with time. Leaflets about any particular product under consideration are usually willingly supplied by manufacturers, but the present-day expense of production of the larger catalogues naturally restricts their issue. Some firms produce their leaflets on various products in such a form that they can be kept together in a folder. Catalogues which are in the nature of books can be kept on shelves or in a book-case, but the filing of the smaller leaflets is a problem. Leaflets can be kept in box files with spring clips inside, serially numbered and each containing the leaflets of a particular group of materials, e.g. Ceiling and Wall Boards, Paints and Distempers, &c. Every leaflet when first received is entered in an index book and marked with the reference number of the box file into which it is put; the leaflet is marked with the same number (so that when taken out for reference it can go straight back) and dated. Such a system seems to work satisfactorily, but it is important to destroy obsolete information when new leaflets about the same material are received. There is also a reluctance to part with leaflets about materials referred to 25 years ago and not heard of since!

An alternative, and perhaps better, method is to arrange the box files alphabetically, dividing the alphabet as is found convenient. Each leaflet is then indexed under the names of the product, proprietary brand (if any) and maker, the index giving the alphabet letter (usually initial letter of the maker's name) under which it is filed.

SfB CLASSIFICATION.—The enormous increase in both type and variety of building materials and components in recent years has tended to swamp out filing systems and has brought the realisation that a more detailed and accurate system of filing technical information must be devised. The R.I.B.A. have taken the lead by adopting and recommending to their members the SfB system, and have published a manual setting out its full detail.[4] This system originated in Sweden some years ago (the letters SfB are derived from the name of the Swedish committee concerned[5]). The classification is divided into three,

[4] SfB/UDC Filing Manual: R.I.B.A.
[5] Samarbetskommittén för Byggnadsfrågor.

functional elements, construction, and materials, and it is linked with the Universal Decimal Classification.[6]

In view of the adoption of this system by many offices, manufacturers and merchants are often marketing their literature with the SfB reference to facilitate its filing. There is, moreover, more than one commercial undertaking which will provide a service of supplying these information leaflets, and even provide containers to keep them in, arrange for supervision of their installation and advise on difficulties. One must, however, remember that these concerns charge a fee to the firms whose literature they circulate (as well as to the office receiving it). Their literature is, therefore, not all-embracing: there will be firms who do not need the publicity, being already well known and able to rely on enquiry being made of them direct by architect or surveyor for his needs.

Like any new administrative change, adoption of the SfB system of filing is bound to be difficult at first, particularly where literature has formerly been classified under the merchant's name. The SfB classification gives no guide as to such names, and the preparation of a separate index of names would be a big undertaking.

The system can, of course, be easily expanded. Further containers can be added as necessary and files moved along from one container to another. To make the collection as complete as possible, it is essential that all catalogues and literature of that nature should be in their proper place in the series, whether supplied for this particular purpose or not. This must mean a certain irregularity, perhaps thick catalogues mixed with leaflets, or necessarily outside the containers. The important thing, as in all filing, is "a place for everything and everything in its place."

REFERENCE BOOKS.—The foundation of a reference library will probably be the surveyor's text-books of his student days (if these were not hired!). The Journals of his Institution, probably supplied with an annual index, should be kept for reference, as most important events in the Industry are either recorded or quoted with a reference given, which can in turn be looked up. The publication of new or revised text-books on the principal subjects met with in the office should be watched, and new books bought when thought necessary, bearing in mind the importance of both principal and staff keeping up to date. They may also be useful for members of the staff working for examinations, but record should be kept of those borrowed, otherwise when one is wanted for reference nobody knows where it is.

Such publications as the British Standards Institution Handbook No. 3 are valuable for specifying. This gives a summary of the principal British Standards for building materials (particularly those required for Housing). In some cases it may be advisable to obtain the full British Standard, e.g. B.S. 4, Parts 1 & 2, which give all the standard rolled steel sections with their properties (unless the surveyor has the handbook of

[6] B.S. 1000: B.S.I.

158

one of the steel manufacturers which gives this information). B.S. 990 for standard metal windows gives a schedule of exact glass sizes, very useful for taking-off. A list of all Building Standards can be obtained free from the British Standards Institution, and a reference to the number of the appropriate Standard will often save a long-winded description. Subscribing members of the B.S.I. receive special terms for their purchases. In the larger offices a subscription and perhaps a standing order for new building publications will be found worthwhile.

Akin to British Standards are Codes of Practice. Whereas the Standards refer to materials, the Codes of Practice refer rather to workmanship, and again can sometimes save long descriptions. The Codes of Practice, originally drafted by Government-appointed Committees, are published by the British Standards Institution, and, as in the case of Standards, a list can be obtained.

An English Dictionary should be in every office, the size and character depending on individual choice. A small handy size dictionary should also be available for use of the typist.

A ready-reckoner is useful for the pricing of daywork sheets and the like, where the same rate, e.g. 46½p per hour, is constantly repeated. For normal pricing out of bills it saves no time and only leads to inactivity of the mind, which needs exercise to maintain its efficiency just as does the body.

A file should be kept of the various forms of contract in use as reference to them may be necessary at short notice. There are also various official publications which are useful, e.g. some of the Statutory Instruments published by H.M.S.O. A standing order can be given with H.M.S.O. for publications on building. Though the resulting documents may not all be of interest to the quantity surveyor, an order minimises the chances of something of interest being missed.

A few further reference books or leaflets likely to be needed in most offices may be named

Working Rules (local edition) of the Building Industry
Plant hire rates
Lorry hire rates

the local Builders' Federation.

Working rules, &c., for specialist trades or civil engineering will probably be obtained when occasion arises.

If employed by a Public Authority there may be circulars from time to time from the authority giving various instructions and rulings. These should be kept together.

Much as one may deprecate the use of price-books, they are valuable if not followed too rigidly, and one or more such publications should be in the surveyor's library. The periodical price lists in the technical journals are useful, if they are cut out and filed. The Ministry of Works Standard Schedule of Prices was prepared for a particular war-time purpose and is now obsolete, though interesting to show the method of preparation of a schedule. The D.O.E. Schedule of Rates, a much more comprehensive document, has been revised in recent years and is another example of a schedule, again primarily prepared for a special purpose—the maintenance of government buildings.

DUPLICATING.—Except in the case of those public authorities which make their own arrangements for duplicating bills of quantities, the surveyor will be responsible for placing the order and paying the cost, recoverable in his account to his client as an out-of-pocket expense. The usual choice is between litho or small offset printing as carried out by most printers today, or reproduction on a rotary stencil duplicator which can be done by any typewriting office. For more important contracts letterpress printing might be adopted, but its cost is not usually justified and even for covers it seems an unnecessary expense. Whatever process is adopted, it is important that the firm entrusted with the work should be experienced in the specialised requirements of setting out, &c. and recognise the principal technical terms. Stencil duplicating has the advantage that the work can be spread more amongst small firms, though lack of understanding of technical terms with the more inexperienced firms results in much correction in the proof. Moreover, with this process the impression is apt to be variable, so that figures occasionally may not be clear.

The surveyor must not forget that duplicating firms have difficulties to contend with just as he has. Being under constant pressure in the matter of time they find it difficult, like the surveyor, to spread the work evenly. Under present conditions it is almost essential to book a date for duplicating well in advance, though, if he should strike a slack period he may be able to arrange at short notice. The surveyor must realise that a date booked must be kept to or warning given as far in advance as possible of any postponement. Because the draft bill is sent two days late, the surveyor cannot be sure that the finished bill will not be delayed more than two days. He may have upset a tightly fitting programme and others must be served. Neglect to realise this shows a lack of consideration which the surveyor himself, if so treated, would resent. Duplicating firms often go to a lot of trouble to meet the requirements (and perhaps fads!) of surveyors and some appreciation of this is their due.

It is important that drafts should be properly edited from the printer's angle, e.g. such things as position of headings and whether in capitals or not should be clear. That writing should be legible goes without saying, remembering that the typist is not technical and cannot know whether, say, core or cove is meant. There is a temptation to edit in proof as it is so much easier to see, but corrections take time: though the duplicating firm will usually make reasonable corrections without charge, there is a limit and if drastic alterations are made a charge must be expected.

The order for duplicating should be given in writing and it is most important that this should set out clearly the number of copies respectively of bill, form of tender and envelope, and, if delivery is to more than one office, how many of each are to go to each destination.

Further copies can be made from the same stencils or plates within a limited time: the period during which this can be done should be ascertained from the firm concerned.

When the surveyor is pressed for time the duplicating firm can help by sending out bills direct to tendering firms. If this is done, instructions must be clear as to documents to be enclosed, and arrangements must be made to see that the firm has any drawings, &c. suitably sorted for enclosure. The cost of such despatch with postages should be regarded as a surveyor's expense and not charged to the client. The same applies to the extra cost due to the duplicating firm being asked to type straight from "cut and shuffle" sheets (the surveyor's cost of writing a draft bill being saved).

Some quantity surveyors do the duplicating of bills of quantities in their own office, but those who do so are practically running a separate business. Duplicating of bills with the large number of pages and sometimes large number of copies requires space—at least one room for the purpose with strong and large tables as well as the duplicator. Stocks of paper and other "consumable stores" must be maintained. In a business of any size at least one person, probably several, would be kept occupied full time in typing stencils and doing the duplicating. Moreover, it takes a very experienced staff to attain the standard of the specialist.

RECORDS OF BUILDING COSTS.—A certain amount of keeping of records is essential in any office, though there is a tendency to delay preparing them because they are not directly productive. Such tendencies should be guarded against as, if records are not made when the information is fresh, they have a habit of never getting done. It is good practice to make a cost analysis of every tender received as a matter of course and such analyses form excellent cost records. The apparent inability of the building industry as a whole to prepare and agree a standard list of elements is disappointing. Each office will have its own ideas as to which particular list is preferred and it may well be that different jobs for different clients require a variety in the forms to be used. When the building is complete the final cost can also be recorded, although it is not usual to recalculate the cost analysis. Supplementary information can be given which may be of assistance in future comparisons, e.g. notes as to construction and finishes, &c. In compiling these records it is important to maintain a constant basis. For instance "external work" such as roads, paths and lay-out of grounds can well be kept out of the price, also any site clearance or preparatory alteration work. Where such deductions are made it is as well to record both the total tender figure and the figure on which the rates are calculated, i.e. after the deductions have been made. Works of alteration do not lend themselves so well to records of this sort, but, on the basis that a record is kept of all jobs, some information can be recorded.

CONTRACT COST RECORDS.—It may be found useful to keep a running summary of cost of a building contract as a job goes on. As each variation ordered is known, an approximation is made of its value and adjustment made accordingly. If such a record is kept, a ready answer can be given to architect or building owner who wants to know how the cost stands. On the other hand, this information can be given for a particular job at two or three days' notice when asked for, without the expenditure of all the time required in keeping the cost of every job up to date.

WAGES RATES RECORD.—It will be found of use to have in the office a table of wage rates with the dates and amounts of all changes entered. The rates recorded would be those of the area in which the office is situated, or any other areas with which the surveyor may be concerned. If preferred, the record could be complete for all areas. Besides the general rate of building tradesman and labourer there are separate rates for heating engineer's men and mates, electrician's men and mates, which change at different times. It is useful when dealing with an account, perhaps a couple of years after work is done, to be able to check that the proper rate at a certain time was so-and-so.

MATERIAL PRICE RECORD.—The best way of keeping a record of material prices is probably to file any price list or quotation with the catalogue or leaflet of that material. It is doubtful whether there is much value in keeping a special record book of materials prices, as the labour in keeping it up is considerable, and the rates must usually depend on place of delivery, quantity of order, &c. Where copies of invoices are supplied to the surveyor which need not be returned, these can be filed, and might come in useful if he thinks "Yes, we had some of that on such and such a job." Original invoices cannot, of course, be retained. Officially announced changes in materials prices are published in the technical press, and it will be found useful to have these announcements cut out and filed in proper sequence, preferably with an index. There are monthly published price lists of materials in two sections, National and

Regional,[7] the prices of some materials being generally applicable, others varying according to locality. The prices in these lists are mostly for small quantities, but they are useful for checking pricing of daywork sheets and the like.

MEASURED RATES RECORD.—The keeping of a record of this is not usually worth the labour. The surveyor will have copies of the priced bills for each contract, which can readily be referred to. It is more reliable to build up a price from the data in each case, at any rate for the most important items.

STAFF TIME RECORD.—It is essential that there should be a complete record of the allocation of the time of the staff. A specimen form of record is included in Appendix 1.[8] This may be required as a basis on which to build up an account for fees for services which are to be charged for on a time basis. Each member of the staff should keep a diary in which he can record not only his time on each job, but his movements, meetings and other matters concerned with his work. That the entries shall be made daily is essential, and assistants should get into the habit of entering up their diary before leaving the office. To put it off till the next day will probably mean that they have forgotten some of the detail. It is useful if, besides giving a time allocation of his work, the assistant notes what type of work he was doing, e.g. taking-off, writing specification, measuring variations, &c. This need not be transferred to the time record sheet, but, if noted in the diary, would be available if wanted.

PROGRESS CHARTS.—The keeping of charts showing the work in the office and its progress is excellent in theory, but again, being apparently unproductive, is apt to be neglected. It is doubtful whether the time expended in preparing it and keeping it up to date gives sufficient return to make it worth while. It is mostly quicker to ask whoever is dealing with the job how it is getting on. Such charts do, however, help in planning future work by showing commitments ahead (if a quantity surveyor can ever be said to be committed until the drawings are in his office). They may be a guide to a decision whether additional staff should be looked for or some should be dropped ("redundant" seems to be the word today).

The form of a progress chart would be similar to that used for building works,[9] different jobs taking the place of the stages in a building contract.

TELEPHONE DIARY.—A record should be kept of all incoming and

[7] Building Materials Market Research Ltd., 149 Preston Road, Brighton 6.
[8] Page 219.
[9] See *The Architect in Practice* (Willis & George), Appendix I.

outgoing calls, as it is often useful to look up the date when somebody rang up or was telephoned. It also provides identification for the staff, when the telephone bill comes, of private long distance calls made by them, which have to be paid for. Since the introduction of S.T.D. (Subscriber Trunk Dialling), it is almost impossible to check the telephone account, as charges are based on the readings of a meter. A check meter can be supplied to the subscriber on payment of a charge for it.

INFORMATION SERVICES.—It is very important that the quantity surveyor should keep up to date in all matters affecting his work. The necessary information can be gathered from a number of sources, but there are organised services which supply it.

The Journals of Professional Institutions, besides containing articles on current developments, usually have a section recording new publications which may be of interest, including such items as British Standards, Statutory Instruments, &c. Subscriptions to the B.S.I. will bring a monthly list of all new and revised British Standards and Codes of Practice. There is also a monthly list of all Government publications published by H.M.S.O.

The Regional Builders' federations have a service for their members giving full details of changes in wages and other emoluments of workmen, working hours, regulations affecting building work (such as safety precautions) and other information useful to the quantity surveyor. They usually allow surveyors to subscribe to the service.

The R.I.C.S., besides the cost information services referred to on page 17, issues monthly for subscription by members "Abstracts and Reviews". These give abstracts and references to articles and other publications of interest. Although they cover all branches of surveying, quantity surveying is naturally well represented.

16

FINANCE

CAPITAL.—Until that day comes when all earnings are paid in advance, capital will always be necessary. Even the builder's labourer must be a capitalist in a small way to finance himself till the end of his week's work, although in these days he often draws "subs", i.e. payments on account, before his wages are due. As salaries are paid weekly or monthly and fees are not paid till the relative work is finished (and sometimes many months after that), there is a need to be provided with ready cash to pay the salaries, rent and other expenses, as well as to draw something from which to pay the butcher and baker at home. A surveyor starting in business must find that capital somehow, either from his own cash, by mortgage of his house or securities, the assistance of relations with cash or guarantee or the good offices of his bank manager, who will normally acquiesce if security is available, but who may otherwise not present the same smiling countenance. If a suggestion on the last matter may be made, it is that boldness and confidence, when backed by honesty, will pay.

In a properly run business capital is, of course, always represented by assets. The money is not borrowed to spend, but to use. Starting with, say £5,000 capital, after six months there may be only £500 in the bank, the position being as follows:

DISPOSAL OF CASH	£	INCOME AND ASSETS	£
Furniture	1,000	Fees received	1,000
Salaries...................	1,500	Fees due...................	1,500
Drawings	1,000	Work in hand—proportion	
Rent and other expenses	1,000	of fees due	2,000
		Value of furniture	1,000
	£4,500		
In bank	500		
	£5,500		£5,500

In other words the original £5,000 has increased to about £5,500 (subject to depreciation of furniture, which will be dealt with later), and some income has been drawn meanwhile as well. As fees are paid the bank balance will be increased, but further payments of salaries, &c. will drain it again. The case is rather like the problems that used to be in arithmetic examinations about a bath being filled at so many gallons and being emptied at so many gallons per hour. The surveyor must for his own comfort see that there is plenty of water in the bath, and that it doesn't run away when he isn't looking.

The amount of capital required must, of course, depend on the prospective volume of work and consequent size of staff. For preparation of bills of quantities payment is due on completion of the work, but one must await tenders to calculate the amount of the fee before rendering the account. If after tenders are in there is delay in accepting one, sending in the account will probably also be deferred. When tenders must be submitted to a Ministry for approval or there are other reasons for long delay, a request for settlement or for a payment on account could be made and is usually readily met. A good deal, therefore, depends on the circumstances.

In the case of variation accounts payment is delayed considerably. Much work may be done in the early stages of a building contract, for which payment will not be received until the variation account is agreed and submitted to the client. The proportion in value of such fees should not be very high ("should be" unfortunately is not the same as "is") and credit is part of what the surveyor is paid for. However, in exceptional cases of very large contracts special arrangements can probably be made. Since in the normal way the client sees nothing of the variation account till the end of the contract, he has no check on the amount of any interim payment for which the surveyor may ask.

Fees for making valuations for certificates could be charged on the practical completion of the building contract, when the last chargeable valuation will have been done. In the case of large contracts an account for these could be rendered at the end of each year or half-year.

Starting from scratch, £5,000 should be enough to start a small business if care is taken to build up capital and not to draw extravagantly.

PURCHASE OF A BUSINESS.—A problem often arises on the death of a quantity surveyor as to the disposal of his business. Subject to what is said later of the establishment of goodwill by partnership, there is normally very little goodwill attached to a quantity surveyor's business. In other words, the surveyor's business is a personal one, unlike a button factory, where a successor can simply take over the order book, keep the name and be assured of a continuation of orders, provided he gives satisfaction. The quantity surveyor's clients will often have a second string to whom they will turn, taking no notice of the nominee of executors. It is, therefore, impossible to fix a fair price for the acquisition of a business. There is one equitable solution, viz. for the surveyor acquiring the business to say, "I cannot agree to pay a lump sum; the prospect is too uncertain. If, however, any of Mr. X's clients come to me I will pay you 10% of the gross fees received for their work within 3 years (or whatever period may be agreed)." Such an arrangement should be satisfactory as giving a fair return to both parties according to results; it would, of course, be quite apart from any payment for assets acquired, such as furniture, stationery, lease of offices, &c. The debts due to the deceased would be collected by the executors, who would also pay out liabilities incurred. A suitable arrangement would have to be made for the division of work in hand.

Whether on taking over a business the name should be continued is a matter for decision in each case. There are many firms of Messrs. A & B or C & D where there is no A, B, C or D (and in some cases has not been for many years). Owing to the personal nature of the quantity surveyor's business, the name is not generally of great importance.

SALARIES.—It is difficult to be very definite on the subject of salaries, as so much depends on the ability and experience of the individual. Salaries will increase with experience, as greater experience saves time—the work is done quicker and more accurately and other people's time is not taken up in answering questions. The really experienced taker-off, who can take complete charge and manage a job, will earn a high salary, comparable with that paid in many of the other professions.

With the pressure of work which the surveyor generally has to meet, he will often find that he needs overtime work from his staff, for which, of course, he will have to make extra payment. An hourly rate will be fixed for each assistant, rather above the rate which would be *pro rata* with his salary, and payment made, probably monthly, according to the record of the assistant's time sheet (see Appendix 1[1]). The working of overtime helps to speed up completion of a job, and is, therefore, worth its cost to the employer, and the extra money is often very welcome to the assistant. On the other hand, one cannot burn the candle at both ends, and, if it is overdone and results in a breakdown in health, both employer and employee suffer. Only actual working time is usually charged for overtime, not extra time when an assistant leaves home early or gets back late because he is going to a job some distance away. He is expected to regard that—within reason—as part of his terms of employment. Overtime is not usually paid in the public service.

The "chars," either takers-off or workers-up, who used to go round from office to office on a purely temporary basis, paid by the hour, are not so often met with today. They are very useful as a temporary addition to the staff when work presses, even though they are paid more highly than permanent staff. The convenience of being able to take on a

[1] Page 219.

man whom one knows and can rely on and give him up after a week or a month, is worth the extra cost. These temporary assistants naturally have the risk of unemployment to cover, and in times of slump are of course, the first to suffer, but they have the compensation whilst in work of an income a good deal higher than their fellow-workers on the surveyor's permanent staff. There is ample scope there for the suitable man who does not mind a little risk (and nothing is achieved without risk). Such work forms a convenient stepping stone to private practice as intervals can be arranged to suit any work of one's own.

REDUNDANCY PAYMENTS ACT 1965.—Under this Act as from 6th December 1965 an employer is required to make lump-sum compensation payments to employees aged 20 or over, who have at least two years' continuous service with him and who are dismissed because of redundancy or, in certain circumstances, laid off or kept on short time for a substantial period. He will be able to claim rebates of part of these payments from a Redundancy Fund financed by a supplement on the employer's weekly National Insurance Contributions.

Readers should refer to the Act for details of the Scheme.

DEDUCTIONS FROM SALARIES.—Up to April 1975 two deductions to be made by the employer were compulsory, where applicable: National Insurance Contributions and Income Tax. The former was made by stamping cards weekly with a stamp representing the appropriate contribution, a fixed part of which had to be deducted from the salary of the employee. Since 6th April 1975 the flat rate stamp contribution has been dispensed with and a new earnings-related basic scheme contribution, collected along with tax under the P.A.Y.E. procedure, has taken its place. The graduated pension scheme was also wound up from the same date. These changes were provided for in the Social Security Act, 1973, and the Labour government of February 1974 announced that it would implement them although it rejected those parts of the Act dealing with occupational pension schemes and the reserve pension scheme. The government also announced (7th May, 1974) that the basic scheme contribution rates would be the subject of further legislation.

Deduction of income tax is made in accordance with code numbers allotted to each individual when the Tax Office has ascertained the allowances due to him. Tables are issued to the employer setting out for each code number and each week of the year how much salary is free of tax and what tax instalment is payable on the balance in each week. Tables on a similar basis are also available for salaries paid monthly. Tax deducted is remitted to the Collector monthly. The cards are finally totalled at the end of the financial year, a certificate given in the prescribed form to each employee showing how much tax he has paid through his employer, and any further adjustment is a matter between the employee and the Inspector of Taxes.

Each member of the staff should with his pay be given a statement showing how it is made up (a specimen is given in Appendix 1[2]). This may be either on a pay envelope or on a separate sheet and will correspond with the entries in the Salaries' Book.[3]

FEES.—The fees payable for the services of a quantity surveyor are fairly well defined by the official scales of the Royal Institution of Chartered Surveyors and other professional Institutions. More closely graduated scales are in use in some cases by Government Departments and Public Authorities, where the services required are rather different from those in the case of private clients, and where, in view of the regularity of work for members of the panel of such bodies, some reduction towards what might be termed "wholesale prices" is properly made.

For some services, e.g. preparation of schedules, specifications, reports, &c., fees are usually based on the time involved. The scale of the R.I.C.S. provides for an additional of 125% on the cost of professional and technical salaries and wages to cover all overheads and profit. The cost of secretarial staff is not chargeable, but is part of the overheads covered by the percentage (except when the cost of typed copies of documents is chargeable, when a separate charge will be made for these). Where the principal does part of the technical work (as distinct from supervision) his time doing this is charged in the prime cost as that of a senior assistant.

For litigation and arbitration the R.I.C.S. scale provides no fixed rates, since so much depends on the nature of the work and the standing of the surveyor concerned. Fees for such work should, if possible, be agreed beforehand, or the surveyor may find that he is expected to accept the taxed costs.[4]

It should be emphasised that unlike those of the R.I.B.A. the R.I.C.S. Scales of Professional Charges are non-mandatory. A chartered surveyor is free to negotiate any fees that he likes provided always that he does not do so in competition.[5]

EXPENSES.—Most scales of fees provide for the recovery of certain expenses of the surveyor. These may be specifically referred to as

---

[2] Page 221.

[3] Page 221.

[4] Taxation of costs is the fixing of charges by the Court on application of one of the parties to enable the amount of the Court's award of costs to be determined. Such taxation will not overrule any prior agreement made between surveyor and client, being only enforceable between the parties to the action.

[5] See page 138.

travelling and subsistence expenses, lithography, &c. or the general term "out of pocket expenses" may be used.

The duplicating of copies of bills of quantities, specifications, &c. is recognised as an expense not covered by the normal fees. The surveyor will add this cost in his account, charging it net without any profit or without taking any discount. On the other hand, in the case of a report, schedule of dilapidations, &c. the fair copy of the document is expected to be covered by the fee, in just the same way as is the typing of a letter. If several copies were asked for there would be justification in charging for typing.

All fares paid in travelling in connection with a job are normally chargeable to it. First class railway fares are admissible for a principal or senior assistant.

Subsistence expenses are chargeable by the surveyor if he is away for a night on business in connection with a job. These may be either at a fixed rate per night, as is the case in the scales of Government Departments, or the surveyor may charge his hotel bill, excluding such items as his conscience will tell him are his personal liability. Subsistence expenses are not usually chargeable when the surveyor is only away for the day, but he may be prepared to meet expenses of his staff, e.g. on lunches in excess of their normal limits, which may be made necessary by their travels on business. It may happen that the surveyor or his staff in visiting distant jobs make a very long day of it to save time, rather than spend a night away. In such case it would seem reasonable to charge to the client such items as breakfast or dinner on the train, in view of the fact that he is saved a night's hotel bill.

Assistants should render a memo of expenses charged, giving name of job, date of journey and any sub-division of the charge, as it sometimes happens that only part is chargeable to the client. These memos can either be presented for payment from petty cash, or they can be attached to a monthly statement for payment with salary.

Postages, telephone calls and other office expenses are part of the surveyor's overheads and not chargeable to the client, but exception may be required by special circumstances, if, for instance, an excessive number of long-distance telephone calls was necessary.

OFFICE COST BOOKS.—The office cost books referred to in Chapter 13 may consist of two books, suggested specimen pages for which are given in Appendix 1.[6] One book would have pages allotted for each member of the staff, their time and proportion for each month being allocated to each job. The totals from this book would then be transferred to an analysis book in which each job has a separate column. From this a running total cost of a job to the end of the previous month would always be available.

[6] See page 222.

BOOKS OF ACCOUNT.—Though the subject of Book-keeping has been dropped from the R.I.C.S. examination syllabus, it is a practical form of economics as important to the quantity surveyor in practice as much of the theory that has to be studied (if not more so). The prospective principal should make a point of studying an elementary book on the subject, to enable him to keep his accounts properly. He would be well advised, when opening his books, to consult the accountant whom he will employ for his annual audit, obtaining, perhaps, a little practical tuition and advice on his difficulties.

Text-books on the subject are apt to concern themselves with the accounts of trading firms and their purchases and sales rather than with those of a professional man. It is proposed, therefore, to say something of the books required by a quantity surveyor and the method of keeping them.[7]

(a) THE CASH BOOK.—This is a copy of the bank account written up from the cheque book and the paying-in slips, every entry having a corresponding entry in one of the ledgers. Periodically—once a month or so—the bank pass sheets should be obtained and checked with the cash book, so that any discrepancy can be corrected.

(b) THE PERSONAL LEDGER.—This contains all the "personal" accounts. A separate account is opened for each client, to which fees and expenses are debited and payments received credited. There are also accounts for those to whom the surveyor will owe money, e.g. stationers, lithographers and other firms from whom he regularly purchases. This ledger is, therefore, the equivalent of Bought Ledger and Sold Ledger of a trading firm. It could be divided into two ledgers—one for those who are generally debtors and one for those who are generally creditors, but in a surveyor's business the creditors are usually few in number whereas the client of every job in hand (and probably some finished!) is generally a debtor, so that their accounts heavily outnumber the creditors' accounts.

(c) THE PRIVATE OR IMPERSONAL LEDGER.—This ledger contains the impersonal accounts. Such items as rent, cleaning, furniture and equipment, telephone, salaries, &c. will all have separate accounts in this ledger, and there will also be a fees account and a capital account.

(d) THE PETTY CASH ACCOUNT.—The petty cash account will be kept by the secretary or a junior assistant. It is one of the ledger

[7] Pages 223 and 224.

171

accounts, but for convenience it is usually kept in an analysed form with a number of columns having such heads as "Stamps," "Stationery," "Sundries" (such as expenses not chargeable to clients, odd purchases, &c.). (See specimen page in Appendix 1.[8]) Periodically, say once a quarter, the columns are totalled and the totals entered in the corresponding ledger account, so making the double entry. An exception is made of expenses chargeable to clients, which it is advisable should be entered immediately in the client's ledger account: they will be entered in detail in the right-hand column of the book and posted direct to the appropriate clients' ledger accounts. These postings complete the double entry, so the total of this column will not be posted anywhere. These expenses will be supported by petty cash vouchers submitted by the persons who have incurred them. The petty cash account not being kept by the same person as the general accounts, a system may be arranged by which the assistant's memo of expenses or other voucher on every such petty cash entry is passed to whoever is responsible for keeping the main accounts. These vouchers will after entry be marked with the ledger folio reference and be returned for referencing in the petty cash book. Alternatively, the petty cash book can be passed at regular intervals, say once a week, for posting of the ledger entries.

The above are the ledger accounts in which the double entry is made. In addition there are books of original entry.

(a) FEES BOOK OR DAY BOOK.—In this are entered as charged the fees for each job, which at the same time are entered in the client's account in the personal ledger, to which expenses will have been already charged. It is, in fact, a sub-division of the fees account in the private ledger. Periodically, again say quarterly, the entries will be totalled and the total transferred to the Fees account. In connection with this book it is advisable to keep a list of jobs in hand, the fees for which have not been entered. This must be kept up to date by crossing out the name of the job when its fee is entered and adding the names of new jobs as they arise. This list will be a reminder when reviewing the position, either to send out accounts or to make a valuation of work not charged. If the job register suggested above[9] is kept, this will serve the purpose.

(b) EXPENSES BOOK.—It is wise to keep an expenses book, in which

[8] For specimens see pages 224 and 225.
[9] Page 155.

can be jotted down the principal's expenses in travelling, odd purchases, &c. These in turn can be credited periodically to a Personal Expenses account, at the same time being debited to the client's account, or, if not so chargeable, to stationery, sundries, or whatever might be appropriate. If a car is kept a car mileage book can be kept and dealt with the same way.

(c) POSTAGE BOOK.—Instead of each letter sent out being entered in the petty cash book, a separate postage book is kept. Periodically stamps will be bought, charged to petty cash and shown in the postage book as stamps received. The various postages will be entered against this with the date and name of the addressee, and the balance at any time between one side and the other should be represented by stamps in stock. A suitable form of postage book can be bought from the large stationers. It serves an additional purpose as evidence of despatch of a letter (subject, of course, to the possibility of posting in a pocket).

VOUCHERS.—Related to books of account are vouchers which record the detail of transactions. These comprise:—

(a) RECEIPTS—which should be filed as received in a file by themselves. Receipts referring to petty cash payments will be in a separate file kept with the petty cash book. Where assistants' travelling expenses, &c. are paid out of petty cash, the memos giving particulars will be kept with petty cash receipts or in a separate file.

(b) INVOICES.—These are received from creditors, e.g. lithographers, stationers, &c., and should be put in a "pending" folder until such time as books are being entered up. The necessary double entry will be made, e.g. debiting a client and crediting the lithographer, or debiting "stationery" and crediting the stationer's account. The invoices should then be filed, so that they can be turned up when reference is required. In a small business they will be kept in one file, but with a larger business there could be separate files for each firm or each category.

(c) BANK PASS SHEETS.—These will be obtained from the bank from time to time as a check on the keeping of the cash book and filed in the leather folder usually supplied by the bank for the purpose.

(d) ACCOUNTS RENDERED.—A carbon copy of all accounts

rendered should be kept in a file. These will give the detail of entries made in the fees book, which need only show the total fee.

KEEPING THE BOOKS.—In a small office the books will be kept by the principal, though in larger offices the keeping of the personal ledger could be delegated to a secretary, with slips recording entries to be made in the private ledger passed as was described above for the petty cash vouchers. No doubt there are practices sufficiently large to give full time work to an accountant, but that would be unusual. Every entry will not be made immediately it arises, but time will be set aside once a week or once a fortnight to bring the books up to date.

The following procedure is suggested:—
- (a) Bring cash book up to date from cheque book and paying-in book counterfoils. Then go through these entries in the cash book and make the second entry and reference it. If a rule is made to reference as the second entry is made, it will reduce the possibility of the second entry being forgotten altogether. Where analysis columns are in use for repetitive items, the second entry will consist of the total of each such column at the end of a convenient period, e.g. monthly, quarterly or annually.
- (b) Write up Petty Cash book from vouchers, etc. Items in the miscellaneous column should be posted to the nominal or private ledger, other postings will be of the total of each analysis column at the end of an accounting period as with the main (Bank) cash book. Petty cash vouchers should be numbered and filed to correspond with the entries in the Petty Cash book.
- (c) Go through the list of jobs in hand and enter any fees settled in the Fees Book, making the second entry in the client's ledger account.
- (d) Exceptional transactions.—A note will have been made of any unusual transaction at the time of its occurrence and a slip put in the "pending" folder until books are next written up. For instance, a letter may come in as a result of which it is agreed that an overcharge has been made. The relative record slip now coming forward, the amount would be credited to the client's account and debited to fees (if the error was on the fee).
- (e) A separate column or columns may be incorporated in the Fees Journal to record V.A.T. on outputs, but most firms will require an additional book to record V.A.T. on inputs. If a Bought Journal (or Expenses Journal) is in operation, however, the necessary information for V.A.T. purposes could be obtained by providing additional columns.

The V.A.T. account, which should be kept in the nominal or private ledger, will be built up from monthly totals of the V.A.T. columns in the books of original entry. In the case of inputs, the V.A.T. will comprise the totals of the V.A.T. figures obtained from the Day books and Petty cash book(s).

Some firms may use one of the printed Input and Output Registers obtainable from commercial stationers in loose or bound form. In this event, it is often the case that such books are additional to, and completely separate from, the ordinary double entry books, being maintained purely for the requirements of the Customs and Excise. The firm's professional accountant or auditor can often advise on ways in which V.A.T. information may be provided without too much duplication of labour by integrating the V.A.T. records partly or wholly with the normal double-entry records.

MAKING UP ANNUAL ACCOUNTS.—Once a year accounts must be totalled up and balanced. A profit and loss account and balance sheet must be prepared and specimens of such accounts are included in Appendix 1.[10] It will probably be found that the final statement does not balance, but a search for the error might be a prolonged affair. It is best, therefore, to leave such error to be found on audit, when the whole of the entries made are followed through and mathematics are checked. A slip in a cast, omission to make the second part of a double entry or other cause of the error will then be found.

One of the subjects to be considered in making up annual accounts is depreciation. A surveyor starting in practice may spend £1,000 on furniture, which appears in his accounts as an asset at that figure. He should aim to write off the original cost of the asset over its anticipated useful life either by a "straight line" or "reducing balance" method and he will therefore credit "Furniture and Equipment" account with a sum for depreciation and debit a special depreciation account, the balance of which will be an expense charged to the profit and loss account. Though depreciation may not be allowed in this form for income-tax purposes, it is advisable to show it year by year so that the balance sheet may reflect the true position of the business.

AUDIT.—It is advisable to have accounts audited by a qualified accountant. Accounts so certified carry more weight with the Inspector of Taxes, who will have to make assessment of tax payable, than the mere statement of the principal. The accountant is also available for advice if in difficulty with the income tax authorities and, if necessary, to carry on negotiations with them. Moreover, in the case of a partnership, the accountant is somebody impartial who can be entrusted with interpretation of the financial terms of the agreement.

[10] Page 226.

175

17
PARTNERSHIP

MEANING OF PARTNERSHIP.—Where two or more persons enter into partnership they are jointly and severally responsible for the acts of the partnership. Further, they are each liable to the full extent of their personal wealth for the debts of the business. There is no limit to their liability, as in the case of the directors of a limited company, to whom failure may only mean loss of their shares in the company, perhaps a very small matter. Each partner binds all his other partners by his acts done in the course of business. He does not, of course, bind them to responsibility for his private transactions. If he goes to a stationer's shop and orders note-paper, his order binds his firm to pay, but if he goes to a florist and orders flowers for his wife the florist cannot claim payment from his firm or from the other partners individually (unless, of course, they were barrow boys dealing in flowers).

WHEN DOES A PARTNERSHIP EXIST?—Partnership is usually established by a written partnership agreement, about which something will be said later, but evidence of existence of an agreement is not necessary to convey the existence of the partnership to third parties. They can see from the firm's note-paper, bearing the name of the firm and probably the names of the individual partners. A limited company (unless specially exempted) must have "Ltd." added to its title and the names on its note-paper will be referred to as "Directors." Owing to the personal nature of a professional business, such businesses are not incorporated as limited companies. In many cases, however, a partnership is evidenced merely by one of the partners holding himself out as such. If he says I am Mr. Apple of Apple & Blackberry, quantity surveyors, he holds himself out as being a partner and legally accepts the responsibility of partnership.

REASONS FOR PARTNERSHIP.—Why, one may say, should an individual agree to be responsible for the acts of somebody else: what compensating advantages are there?
1. If a business expands there comes a time then the principal cannot have a full and proper knowledge of every job, nor be able to give it that supervision by an experienced man which is necessary. He is faced with a choice. Either he must have a senior salaried assistant able to take the supervision out of his

hands, or he must find another man to share the ownership and management of the business with him on terms not necessarily equal but satisfactory to both parties. There have been, of course, many large businesses run by a single man, but bearing in mind that the quantity surveyor is expected to apply his own technical experience and give his personal attention to his clients and not be merely the head of an administrative machine, the quantity surveyor's office cannot be run like a button factory. The addition of a partner divides the responsibility for management, and as the business increases further partners can be added. Partnership can of course be combined with the employment of a responsible manager or senior assistant, who can relieve the partners of a good deal of the work. Such a man can, in fact, be a partner in all but name, taking a share in profits by way of bonus, at the partners' discretion instead of under agreement, but not having the responsibility of a principal.

2. Economy in expenditure can be effected by the pooling of accommodation, equipment or staff by partners. Whereas one principal might not have enough work to employ three assistants, two jointly might be able to do so. The two partners and staff of three might be accommodated in two rooms, whereas as separate businesses they would need four. Of course, both staff and accommodation can be shared without any partnership existing. Each principal would have his own work, the time of the staff being recorded and their salaries allocated accordingly.

3. The search for capital may lead to a search for a partner, but to take a partner solely or principally for this purpose is likely to be dangerous. There is no truer saying than that "the man who pays the piper calls the tune," and one can only say "Beware!"

4. A partner may be able to introduce more work to a business which is short of it.

5. The taking of a partner establishes a goodwill value in a business. As has been explained, a quantity surveyor in practice alone has hardly any goodwill attached to his business. If, however, he has a partner, in the event of death or retirement current contracts with the firm will be automatically continued by the partner. It can usually be arranged for long-term agreements to be made with both partners, and therefore a certain amount of the business will continue. Moreover, the partner will have been introduced in the deceased's lifetime to the clients, who may make him their "second string" and naturally carry on with the surviving partner. This preparation for continuation of the business has a substantial financial advantage for the retiring partner or the deceased-to-be. The incoming partner will either

be prepared to pay for the assurance of future business when he enters the partnership, or he will agree to make a lump sum payment on death or retirement of the senior partner as consideration.

Against the advantages of partnership must be weighed a certain loss of independence which is inevitable. In practice by oneself one may make decisions which, when contemplated in partnership, bring (or should bring) the thought "Am I fair to my partner?" The conscientious man, taking a day off to follow some interest of his own, may well feel that his time is no longer his own, but that he has a responsibility to his partner to employ it fully in the interests of the firm. The only answer is a mutual understanding and a readiness to "give and take."

SELECTION OF A PARTNER.—It is obviously an advantage for partners to have similar views on the technical side, and it is essential for them to have complete confidence in each other in every way. It is, therefore, most common for a firm to take in its junior partners from its own staff, whose capabilities and suitability can have been judged during their period of service as assistants. To advertise for a partner has obvious dangers—one might be lucky, but the risk is considerable. A period of trial in such a case is essential, though a few months' experiment cannot give the same knowledge of each other as several years of working in the same office.

If the new partner is introduced to facilitate continuation of the business, his age must naturally be such that he can continue active work for some time after retirement of his senior. A (aged 50) might take a partner B of, say, 35. In 10 or 15 years' time A, perhaps, retires and B looks for a young successor, and so on. Where the new partner is taken merely on account of expansion of business, the age difference has not the same importance.

TERMS OF PARTNERSHIP.—The practitioner who has built up his own business and takes a partner naturally expects some return for his efforts, the result of which he is sharing. He may get an immediate return through the new partner buying a share in the business, i.e. making a payment for goodwill, or he may get a deferred return through some arrangement for lump sum payment or pension on retirement. Apart from this he will probably take more than a half share of the profits. The proportion in which profits are divided will depend on the income of the business, and should be so arranged that the new partner receives substantially more than the senior assistant and has a prospect of further improving his income on expansion of the business.

SALARIED PARTNERS.—Some firms, as an attraction to senior members of their staff, and, perhaps, as a step to full partnership, have

179

what are known as "salaried partners." Such partners are paid a fixed salary, with or without a small share of profits, and have the full responsibilities of partnership. The advantage to them is that, though they have a fixed salary, to the outside world they have the same authority as full partners. Their name appears on the note-paper (though some firms seem to print a short rule to separate the sheep from the goats!). They may or may not have capital in the business. If such partners were given a share in the profits they would have access to the accounts, but otherwise this would not be necessary, though it might be advisable. The advantage to the full partners is that valuable members of the staff come under agreement for a specified period instead of being free to leave at a month's notice. This tie may, on the other hand, deter an assistant from accepting such a partnership, unless he sees a better prospect than he can find elsewhere.

ASSOCIATES.—Some offices give a reference on their notepaper to "Associates". This term seems to imply that the persons in question have the status of principals but not of partners. Possibly they are senior assistants to whom the principals want to give some credit for their share in the work of the office (this would be particularly applicable to architects, where design is very much an individual matter). Not being partners, they have not the responsibility of partners and quite possibly are paid by salary.

CONSULTANTS.—Also on the note-paper may appear names designated as "Consultants". Their position is very similar to that of Associates, but they are, so to speak, "above the line" (perhaps retired partners) instead of "below". Such consultants would probably be paid by a kind of retaining fee with a share of profits.

THE PARTNERSHIP AGREEMENT.—The partnership agreement should be drawn up by a solicitor, but the main terms will be settled between the partners who should consider the following points:—
  1. Name of the firm.
  2. Place of business.
  3. Bankers to the firm.
  4. Accountant to the firm.
  5. Period of the partnership, i.e. a fixed period or indefinite.
  6. Capital to be provided by each partner.
  7. Division of profits.
  8. Drawings (probably a fixed monthly amount).
  9. Any terms as to consideration to be paid to the senior partner(s).

There are various standard clauses on such matters as limitation of private work, provisions in the case of personal bankruptcy, arbitration,

&c. which will be inserted by the solicitor, but should be carefully examined to see that their content is understood and agreed.

In fixing the amount of drawings it must be remembered that the firm is assessed for and charged with income tax on its profits, which must be apportioned as partners' drawings. The periodical cash drawings of the partners must therefore allow for this. The senior partners would be well advised to consult their accountant on the proposed terms.

The terms of the partnership are entirely a matter for mutual agreement between the partners. A partnership for an indefinite period (in the absence of any particular provision as to the length of notice required) may be terminated by any partner at any time by notice to the others.[1] If the partnership is for a fixed period, it will be terminated at the end of that period, though there may be particular provisions for its earlier termination under notice of a specified period being given. All partnerships are terminated by death, and can be terminated by mutual consent. Where there is ground for dissolution (e.g. where one partner has committed a serious breach of the partnership agreement) the partnership can be determined by recourse to law.

CERTIFICATE OF REGISTRATION.—It should be noted that if the firm's name does not consist of the names of all the partners it is necessary to comply with the requirements of the Registration of Business Names Act 1916. A certificate of registration must be obtained and exhibited in a conspicuous position in the principal place of business, and the names of all the partners must appear on all business letters on which the name of the firm appears. Application forms for the certificate can be obtained from the Registrar of Business Names.[2]

ACTS OF THE PARTNERSHIP.—The acts of the partnership will be expressed in just the same way as those of an individual. Where an individual's verbal agreement is binding, so will be that of any one of the partners. Formal written agreements will probably be made with the partners jointly and severally, the agreement being signed by each of the partners. Ordinary correspondence, however, will have only one signature. This can either be the name of the firm, e.g. "Smith, Brown & Jones," written in manuscript in the hand of one of the partners, or the individual signature of one of the partners with a typewritten prefix "Smith, Brown & Jones." The latter gives, perhaps, a more personal character to the letter, at the same time indicating which partner is dealing with the matter. Routine letters can be signed in the absence of a partner in the same way with the signature or even initials of an assistant or secretary instead of that of one of the partners, but the office copy

[1] Partnership Act 1890, secs. 26 and 32.
[2] At Companies House, 55 City Road, London E.C.1, from whom *Notes for Guidance* and the necessary form can be obtained.

should be left for initialling by the partner concerned at the first opportunity.

It is, of course, important that exact instructions are given to the firm's bank as to the signature or signatures which will appear on cheques, as they will only pay cheques drawn in accordance with the instructions given them. The endorsement of cheques will usually be by the signature of one of the partners with the firm's name prefixed, for which a rubber stamp is useful.

18
PUBLIC SERVICE

GROWTH OF CONSTRUCTION WORK BY PUBLIC AUTHORITIES.—The foregoing chapters have been written largely from the viewpoint of the private practitioner, though references have been given to the Government form of contract as well as the Standard form wherever possible. The same general principles apply to both private practice and the public service, with the obvious exception of the financial responsibility of the principal and the differences in the character and requirements of the respective clients.

For many years the amount of building work for which public authorities are responsible has been growing and in 1973 this covered nearly fifty per cent of the national building output.

Most quantity surveyors, at some stage in their careers, are likely to find themselves working for a public authority whether in private practice or in the public service. It is, therefore, the purpose of this chapter to describe some of the more general characteristics of such authorities and how they affect quantity surveyors in both private and public offices.

Because public authorities are spending public money, they have elaborate (and often cumbersome) methods of administrative and financial control and it is these, together with the size of the authorities, which affect the surveyor's practice. Individual authorities and their quantity surveying departments vary greatly and it is only possible to provide a general description.

SCOPE OF PUBLIC SERVICE.—The public service includes employment in Government Departments, Local Authorities and several statutory bodies.

In Government Service a distinction can be made between the "construction" and the "controlling" function. The largest department concerned with both functions is the Department of the Environment, whose construction arm, the Property Services Agency is responsible for the design, construction and maintenance of buildings and civil engineering projects for most Government Departments. The central department of the D.O.E. deals with house building by Local Authorities and "sponsors" the construction industry in government. The Department of Health and Social Security controls the building activities of the Area Health Authorities, the Department of Education and Science controls the building of schools by Local Authorities, the Department of Transport controls road building and the Home Office has a small construction section.

The large volume of work constructed and controlled by the Department of the Environment involves quantity surveying staffs of about 900 and includes projects varying in size from the very large to quite minor works, as well as large maintenance and repair programmes. There is also great variety in the nature of the work due to the different building requirements of Government.

The function of controlling the building programmes of other public authorities requires the services of only small numbers of quantity surveyors since they are not generally involved in the detailed design and supervision of building projects but mainly with costs and standards and the examination and approval of estimates and tenders.

Local Authorities' offices vary considerably in size according to the areas governed. The government of London, the largest and the most complex urban area, is administered by the Greater London Council, the City of London and 12 Inner and 20 Outer London Boroughs. These authorities came into being on 1st April 1965 as the result of the London Government Act, 1963, under which the whole of Middlesex and portions of the other surrounding counties have been added to the old County of London to form Greater London. The responsibility for the various services has been so allocated between the Greater London Council and the London Boroughs to achieve some degree of decentralisation, but the effect of this has been decreased by the necessity for some of the functions of the old London County Council to be continued by the Greater London Council for an interim period. The quantity surveyors of the Greater London Council are concerned with the building requirements for housing, recreational facilities, fire and ambulance stations, sewage and refuse disposal and roads in the Greater London area, educational buildings for the 12 Inner London Boroughs and, on behalf of other authorities, the housing, factories and town centres of many expanding towns. The London Boroughs have architectural departments to undertake the building responsibilities arising from the various services they provide. These include housing and, in the case of the 20 Outer London Boroughs, schools. The average population of these Boroughs is about 250,000 and many areas in them require redevelopment.

Next come the Counties, Districts and Metropolitan Councils whose building requirements are mainly concerned with housing, schools, police housing, and old people's homes.

Statutory bodies include national undertakings such as the National Coal Board, British Rail, Area Health Authorities, Milk Marketing Board, Central Electricity Generating Board and the United Kingdom

Atomic Energy Authority, as well as Government sponsored Corporations. The number of the latter is growing; recent additions were the British Airport Authority and the Post Office. The nature of the work undertaken is naturally confined to the requirements of the particular organisation and in many cases civil engineering forms a large part of their work.

NATIONAL BUILDING AGENCY.—In a special category is the National Building Agency which was commissioned by a Government White Paper in 1964[1] to promote increased productivity and new techniques both in traditional and industrialised building. The Agency has no power to engage in direct building and it has no direct link with any authority, private developer, contractor or manufacturer. It seeks to achieve its object by offering its services to both public and private sectors of the industry as a consultant. Quantity surveyors in the Agency are engaged in the study of new systems, devising new forms of contract, bills of quantities and procedure to suit industrialised building and studying the economic aspects of manufacture, purchase and use of components and materials.

ORGANISATION.—The organisation of public offices varies considerably, for instance the construction work of the P.S.A. is controlled by a line management structure which includes posts which are open to surveyors and other professions. The design and construction of projects and planning of programmes is organised in relation to the type of client, e.g. the Directorate of Post Office Services deals with Post Office work, the Directorate of Defence Services deals with work for the armed services. The maintenance and minor works for all clients and some larger projects are allocated on a geographical basis to Regional Directorates (in the United Kingdom and overseas) who may also be allocated the post-contract work on some of the projects initiated in the London Directorates. In contrast, the offices of the National Coal Board and British Rail are sub-divided into autonomous divisions each with its own Chief Quantity Surveyor. Local Authority offices, being concerned with smaller areas, are generally centralised.

Within each large office, the public service tends to reflect the organisation of the very large private firm and staffs are subdivided by function. That is to say, there are sometimes separate staffs for estimating, taking-off, working-up, site measurement and settlement of final accounts. It is held by some that it is more efficient to divide the staff into groups, each group being responsible for a number of jobs through all their stages. It would be difficult either to prove or disprove this contention but the arguments for specialisation evidently carry

[1] *A National Building Agency:* Cmnd. 22283, H.M.S.O. And see R.I.C.S. Journal, May 1965, page 617.

more conviction as most large offices are organised in this way. For smaller offices specialisation has fewer advantages and the staff are generally concerned with all of the surveying functions carried out in the office.

The range of quantity surveying functions undertaken by public service offices varies according to policy, volume of work and staff available. The function most commonly assigned to the private practitioner is the preparation of bills of quantities, but any or all of the functions may be so assigned whether for a proportion or for all the building projects. For example, in the Department of the Environment and the Greater London Council a high proportion of the estimating, cost planning, valuations and final accounts are done by the Department and Council Surveyors, but, whereas the Department prepares only a small proportion of the bills of quantities it requires with its own staff, the proportion prepared by the Greater London Council's own staff is large. At the other end of the scale the Surveyors in some offices act as co-ordinators of the activities of private surveyors to whom all work is sent.

PRIVATE PRACTICE PANELS.—The difficulty of the private practitioner in spreading his work evenly is solved in the public service by engaging only a proportion of the staff required to deal with the total requirements of the particular office. The remainder of the work is issued to private firms.

Some public offices use private firms almost exclusively, so that private practitioners are employed regularly, in others they are only employed in cases of extreme pressure when their own staffs cannot cope with the volume of work. The formation of a panel of private practitioners gives an elasticity to an organisation: the nucleus of established staff is fully employed and in time of slump reduction of staff is avoided by decreasing the work issued to private firms.

The professional services required by public offices also varies. Some offices, due to policy or to relieve the pressure on their own staffs, require firms to prepare bills of quantities only, retaining the adjustment of accounts in their own hands. Others require firms to provide full professional services from the original estimate to the settlement of the final account.

CONDITIONS OF EMPLOYMENT.—In private offices details of a surveyor's remuneration are a matter arranged between the surveyor and his employer. In public offices a surveyor's salary is dependent on the grade of his appointment, and details of the salary scales are public knowledge. Each grade has a minimum and maximum with regular annual increments and in many authorities there is provision for frequent reassessment of salaries to take account of changes in responsibility, additional experience and qualifications. Alterations or improvements of the pay and grading structure are the subject of negotiations between representatives of a staff organisation and the employer's or "official" side. For this the Greater London Council has its own Staff Association, in most other Local Authorities the negotiating body is the National Association of Local Government Officers (N.A.L.G.O.) and in the Civil Service it is the Institution of Professional Civil Servants. These bodies look after the interests of professions other than surveyors. Most appointments and promotions in the public service necessitate formal interviews before an examining board.

Appointments in the public service carry pension benefits. In Local Authority offices and most nationalised bodies every member of the staff is entitled[2] to superannuation for which a percentage is deducted from his salary. On moving to another local authority a surveyor's superannuation benefits are automatically transferred. They may also be transferred on moving to the Civil Service if he is appointed to an established post within 12 months.

In the Civil Service established (or permanent) staff are eligible for pension benefit and appointment to an established post can only be made by the Civil Service Commissioners who are independent of all Government Departments. No deduction is made from salaries.

Pensions in the Public Service, generally, are based on length of service and the average salary during the three years prior to retirement. The retiring age in the Civil Service and in Local Authorities varies by grade, in the P.S.A. for instance people leave at 60, 63 or 65 depending on the grade they have reached.

Established staff in Government Departments are expected to be willing to move to appointments anywhere in the United Kingdom if the needs of the Department require it, those in the Department of the Environment being liable for two to three-year tours of duty overseas.

In Local Government service it is common for staff to move from one authority to another. Since authorities vary in size and importance the grading of their officers also varies. The chief and senior quantity surveyors to a large authority will be in higher grades than the chiefs and seniors in minor ones. It is natural, therefore, that there should be constant movement among local authority staffs in their desire to improve their positions.

Although some movement takes place from time to time, there is relatively little movement between Departments in the Civil Service.

DUTIES.—The work done by the surveyor in public service is technically the same as that of a surveyor in private practice. He

---

[2] Subject to the conditions of entry to the fund, which include requirements regarding health and period of service.

prepares approximate estimates, cost plans, bills of quantities, valuations for certificates, measures variations and agrees accounts with the contractor.

In "controlling" Government Departments the surveyor's work is restricted to the examination of estimates prepared by surveyors for subordinate authorities, and of the tenders subsequently received with a view to the Department's approval being given.

In recent years, surveyors both in "controlling" and building Departments have undertaken an additional and highly important task, the setting of cost limits arrived at in collaboration with administrative and architectural colleagues and other professions.

One hears so much of filling in forms that it has become a regular music hall joke. However, forms are essential in any large organisation or an organisation dealing with a large number of other organisations. They help to ensure that the information necessary to make decisions or to record progress is fully and accurately conveyed. One has only to think of the Department of the Environment dealing with about 1,500 local authorities, as well as having its very large staff distributed throughout the British Isles and abroad, to realise the chaos which would exist if it were left to each Local Authority or subordinate surveyor to decide what information they thought the Department should have.

Even in the smaller offices in private practice where the principal can remain in constant touch with detail, some forms are essential and others desirable, e.g. time records for the staff, records of building costs, forms for certificate valuations, &c.

BUILDING CONTRACTS.—The P.S.A. of the Department of the Environment has a Contracts Directorate which is responsible for ensuring that government contracting policy is carried out. The staff consists of non-professional Civil Servants who carry out the client's functions in much the same way as the Clerk to the Council of a Local Authority.

Most Local Authorities and statutory bodies use the Standard form of contract or one based on that form. Government work, however, is carried out under the GC/Works/1 form, which may be used for both building and civil engineering work. Under the GC/Works/1 form of contract, the quantity surveyor has much the same duties as he has under the Standard form.

No matter how elaborate or comprehensive a building contract is thought to be, there are frequently unforeseen circumstances which require individual judgment and the client's approval. When dealing with an individual private client it is easy for the surveyor to discuss the matter with him to recommend a course of action. Since the client has only himself to please and he is not likely to be creating a precedent for

188

himself, he is likely to make a quick and usually reasonable decision. With government, and to a lesser extent, local authority work, the quantity surveyor's recommendation (whether it be a private firm or staff surveyor) has to be referred to a Contracts Directorate or a Committee. Because they are spending other people's money (yours and ours), because they are subject to independent auditors and because they may be called upon publicly to account for apparently unusual expenditure, the quantity surveyor must expect others to examine his recommendations in considerable detail which he may have to endure with much patience. Whereas the individual client may be ready to meet a payment which is justifiable on moral grounds, officers in public service who exercise the client's functions will be reluctant to depart from the strict interpretation of the contract, irrespective of the surveyor's recommendation. When they do unbend, the payment is invariably described as *ex gratia* to avoid creating a precedent.

PUBLIC SERVICE AS A CLIENT.—Such differences as exist between practice for a private client and for a public body largely result from the safeguards which are required in spending public money. Because of this, administrative controls are set up to consider, examine and approve building projects and their estimated costs. This creates a requirement for professional people, including surveyors, to submit proposals in a prescribed manner. Sometimes they also have to perform duties which would not be required by private clients.

When it comes to accepting tenders, honouring certificates and paying final accounts, methods of financial control are required to make sure that every payment is properly authorised, is within the amount approved and that there is no possibility of fraud or wilful negligence.

The administrative and financial controls are operated by administrative staff and accountants who have no training and little knowledge of quantity surveying or building contracts, beyond what they gradually acquire through experience. Yet they find themselves answerable to Committees and District Auditors in local government or in central government to the Treasury, Select Committee on Estimates, Exchequer and Audit, the Public Accounts Committee and finally Parliament itself. It is not to be wondered at that what seems a straightforward case to the surveyor often takes a long time to reach settlement. The system of controlling public expenditure, particularly in Government service, is over 100 years old and some administrators and economists think that fundamental changes are now due. Whatever the procedure, the surveyor must provide the information, advice and help considered necessary in the interests of the public.

Two requirements of the public service as a client particularly affect the surveyor—and no distinction is made between the surveyor in private practice or in public service.

When a project is financed from public funds a specified sum is allotted for the purpose. The sum must not be exceeded and the surveyor is expected to assist the Architect or Engineer in keeping the cost of the project within the allotted sum. If additional money is required, a case has to be fully substantiated and approval obtained before the Authority is committed to the additional expenditure. This is important on Government contracts, particularly when successive Chancellors keep trying to reduce expenditure. With private clients, although the surveyor tries to warn them of additional expenditure, if only in a general way, it is not unknown to have to explain a list of extras at the end of the job.

The second requirement which touches the surveyor closely is the audit. Most public offices, other than Government Departments, have their accounts audited twice; once internally by members of the Finance officer's staff and again externally by independent auditors. The officers who carry out the audit are mostly accountants, but others without financial or quantity surveying training are also employed. Their task is to ensure that the financial provisions of the contract have been faithfully carried out, that all payments have been properly made and that any allowances have been recovered. In addition they must be on the watch for negligence and fraud. Because of these responsibilities it is necessary for the quantity surveyor to prepare the final account in strict conformity with the conditions of the contract and in minute detail. He has not the same latitude as with the private client, and cannot always use the "give-and-take" methods of balancing trifling or obvious self-cancelling variations. Only an experienced quantity surveyor can judge the fairness of "give-and-take" methods and the auditor cannot be expected to have this skill. Since public money is being spent and each account and payment must be not only correct but seen to be correct, there seems no alternative under the present financial system to the more thorough checking and minute scrutiny of accounts than is usual with the private client.

COMPARISON WITH PRIVATE PRACTICE.—The surveyor in public service has not the worry of running a practice—finding capital and offices, employing staff, ensuring a flow of work and avoiding losses. His appointment is normally secure and he can look forward to a steady income and a well-earned pension. His prospects of promotion to a well paid post are good, although the ultimate reward may not compare with that of a private surveyor with his own practice. On the other hand, he is not so much his own master, his hours are more rigid, he will not receive bonuses and only rarely be paid for overtime work. In Government service he may be liable to transfer to another locality—even abroad—and in consequence his domestic life can be upset.

Though the variety of work in some public offices may be limited, there is some satisfaction in being concerned in a continuous programme of national or local public works and, though the "client" may be always the same, at least the surveyor has a foreknowledge of his requirements. In the larger offices the work is varied but if the staff is specialised the surveyor may be confined to a limited range of duties, which may tend after a while to make him feel he needs different experience. There is, of course, the same possibility in the larger private practices.

The surveyor's great responsibility in the public service is that of controlling the expenditure of public money, money placed at the disposal of his Department by people who, unlike private clients, are quite unknown to him, and who have no option but to rely on him to spend their money wisely and economically.

APPENDIX 1
FORMS & PRECEDENTS

1. LIST OF DRAWINGS

SOUTHTOWN SCHOOL
LIST OF DRAWINGS

Date

No.	Scale.	Subject.
SS/ 1	I : 1000	Block plan.
3	I : 100	General plan.
4	I : 100	Sections and Elevations.
5	I : 20	Classrooms.
6	I : 20	Cloaks and Lavatories.
7	I : 20	Assembly Hall.
8	I : 20	Heating Chamber.
11	F.S.	Doors.
12	I : 50	Metal windows with Schedule.

Date

15	I : 200	Drainage.
17	I : 20	Fittings to Classroom Stores.

2. QUERIES FOR ARCHITECT

SOUTHTOWN SCHOOL
QUERIES

Date

Query.	Reply.
1. Finish to floor of Entrance Hall specified wood block, coloured as tile.	
2. Should not dimension between piers on North wall be 5·08 not 5·03? (to fit the over-all 56·85).	
3. D.p.c. not mentioned in the Spec. notes. ? lead-cored felt.	
4. Should brick facing to concrete beams be tied back?	

&c. &c.

193

3. RUNNING INDEX TO DIMENSIONS AND PROGRESS CHART

<u>Dims. cols.</u>   Abstracted.*

1–56	Foundations.	√
57–120	Brickwork.	√
121–156	Facings.	√
157–184	Floor Construction.	
185–272	Roofs.	
273–400	Internal Finish.	

&c. &c.

* For a Progress Chart for cut and shuffle work, see *Elements of Quantity Surveying* 7th Edition pages 204-5.

4. FORM OF TENDER

FORM OF TENDER*

Tender for Southtown Church of England Primary School.
To L. M. N. Esq. F.R.I.B.A.

SIR,

I/We having read the conditions of contract and bills of quantities delivered to me/us and having examined the drawings referred to therein do hereby offer to execute and complete the whole of the works described for the sum of £ . . . . and within . . . . weeks from date of possession and I/we undertake in the event of your acceptance to execute with you a form of contract embodying all the conditions and terms contained in this offer.

I/We agree that should obvious errors in pricing or errors in arithmetic be discovered before acceptance of this offer in the priced bill of quantities submitted by me/us these errors be corrected in accordance with Alternative I contained in Section 6 of the "Code of Procedure for Single Stage Selective Tendering 1977"

This tender remains open for consideration for . . . weeks.

Dated this . . day of . . 19

Name   . . . .

Address   . . . .

* Based on the form suggested in *A Code of Procedure for Single Stage Selective Tendering*, Appendix C: N.J.C.C.

5. SPECIMEN ENQUIRY FOR SANITARY FITTINGS

<u>Sanitary Fittings</u>
<u>required at</u>
<u>Southtown Church of England Primary School</u>
<u>for</u>
<u>The Blankchester Diocesan Board of Finance</u>

L.M.N. Esq., F.R.I.B.A.,	*R. S. & T.*,
Chartered Architect,	*Chartered Quantity Surveyors,*
21, High Street,	*Bank House,*
Southtown.	*Northtown.*

Date

Item   £

I   The sanitary fittings supplier will be required to enter into a sub-contract with the General Contractor on terms consistent with those of the main contract (Standard Form. Private Edition (with quantities) 1980 edition).

2   This estimate shall be subject to 5% cash discount to the General Contractor in accordance with Clause 36 of the Contract.

3   Any variations in price under the terms of the Contract will be net and not subject to discount.

4   White glazed fireclay low level W.C suite etc.   } Nr. 16

&c.
&c.

£

. . . .

. 19

Alternatively the J.C.T. Standard Form of Tender for Nominated supplies can be used.

6. SPECIMEN SUB-CONTRACT BILL
   FOR WOOD BLOCK FLOORING

Bill of Quantities
for
Wood Block Flooring
at
Southtown Church of England Primary School
for
The Blankchester Diocesan Board of Finance

L.M.N. Esq., F.R.I.B.A.,   *R. S. & T.*,
Chartered Architect   *Chartered Quantity Surveyors,*
21, High Street,   *Blank House,*
Southtown.   *Northtown.*

Date

Item   £

1   The flooring contractor will be required to enter into a
    sub-contract with the General Contractor on terms
    consistent with those of the main contract (Standard
    Form Private Edition (with quantities) 1980 edition.

2   The blanks in the Appendix to the contract will be filled in
    as follows:-

    Clauses

    17.2   Defects Liability Period—6 months.
    22A   Percentage to cover Professional fees—10%.
    23.1   Date for Possession—14 days after signing
            contract.
    1.3   Date for Completion—As stated on form of
            tender.
    24.2   Liquidated and Ascertained Damages—£25
            per week.
    28   Period of delay—1 month.
    30   Period of Interim Certificates—Monthly.
            Period of Honouring Certificates—14 days
            after presentation.
            Percentage of Certified Value Retained—3%.
            Period of Final Measurement—6 months.

                    Contd.   £

Item	Contd.

3   This estimate shall be subject to 2½% cash discount to the General Contractor in accordance with Clause 35 of the Contract.

4   Any variation in price under the terms of the Contract will be net and not subject to discount. In the event of the acceptance of this estimate the Flooring Contractor will be required to submit basic price lists of labour and materials for agreement before a sub-contract is entered into.

5   The Flooring Contractor shall include in his price for any additional cost of returning to site to complete the cleaning off and polishing of his floors.

6   The General Contractor will be responsible for unloading and distributing the flooring materials to the various floors.

7   The General Contractor will also be responsible for providing artificial lighting if required, power for floor polishing machines, latrines, messing and welfare facilities, the provision of lock-up stores for materials, plant and tools and for clearing away rubbish arising from the Flooring Contractor's work.

8   The flooring shall be 25 mm nominal Sapele block flooring laid herring bone pattern and bedded in an approved mastic on cement screed (by General Contractor).

9   The flooring shall comply with B.S. 1187 and shall be laid in accordance with B.S.C.P. 201.

10   Prices for flooring shall include for cleaning off on completion to a fine surface ready to receive polish and polishing with two coats of approved wax polish.

11   25mm Flooring as described.   m² 150

&c.
&c.

£

....

....

...............................19

Alternatively the J.C.T. Standard Form of Nominated Sub-contract Tender and Agreement will be used.

7. **SPECIMEN SCHEDULE OF P.C. AND PROVISIONAL SUMS**

SOUTHTOWN PRIMARY SCHOOL
SCHEDULE OF P.C. AND PROVISIONAL SUMS

Item	Source of Information, Quotation, &c.	£	Amount included	Date	Bill Item No.
Nominated Sub-Contractors.					
Wood Block Flooring.	Messrs. Flooring Ltd.'s quotation ABC/J.D. dated ...... based on Q.S. sub-contract bill.	2,153.30			
	Add for mathematical mistakes in quotation.	15.05			
&c.		2,168.35	£2,200		34
Nominated Suppliers.					
Sanitary Fittings.	Simple Sanitary Co. Ltd. estimate JA4163 dated	852.20	890		48
&c.					
Statutory Undertakings.					
Water Connection.	Southtown Water Board letter ABC/DEF dated......		£200		56
&c.					
Provisional Sums.					
Contingencies.	Spec. notes Item 18.		£2,000		69
Planting and Sowing.	Query No. 60.		£250		70
&c.					

R, S & T.
Chartered Quantity Surveyors,
Bank House,
Northtown.

8. LETTER OF PRELIMINARY ENQUIRY FOR INVITATION TO TENDER*

Date

DEAR SIRS,

Proposed New Primary School, Southtown

We are authorised to prepare a preliminary list of tenders for the construction of the works described below.

Will you please indicate whether you wish to be invited to submit a tender for these works. Your acceptance will imply your agreement to submit a wholly *bona fide* tender in accordance with the principles laid down in the "Code of Procedure for Single Stage Selective Tendering 1977" and not to divulge your tender price to any person or body before the time for submission of tenders. Once the contract has been let, the architect undertakes to supply all tenderers with a list of the firms who tendered, and lists of the tender prices.

You are requested to reply by *date*. We are instructed to advise you that your inability to accept will in no way prejudice your opportunities for tendering for further work under the direction of the architect: neither will your inclusion in the preliminary list at this stage guarantee that you will subsequently receive a formal invitation to tender for these works.

Yours faithfully,

Particulars

a. Job: Southtown Church of England Primary School.
b. Building owner: Blankchester Diocesan Board of Finance.
c. Architect: L.M.N. Esq. F.R.I.B.A.
d. Quantity surveyor: R.S. & T. F.F.R.I.C.S.
e. Consultants with supervisory duties: — None.
f. Location of site: (site plan enclosed).
g. General description of works: New Primary School.
h. Approximate cost range £x to £y.
i. Standard Form of Contract: Clause 40 Formula adjustment of fluctuations will apply.
j. Anticipated date for possession: *Date*.
k. Period for completion of works: 52 weeks.
l. Approximate date for dispatch of all tender documents: *Date*.
m. Tender period: 4 weeks.

* Based on the form suggested in *A Code of Procedure for Single Stage Selective Tendering* Appendix A: N.J.C.C. See page 39.

9. LETTER OF FORMAL INVITATION TO TENDER*

Date

DEAR SIRS,

New School, Southtown.

Following your acceptance of the invitation to tender for the above, we now enclose the following:

a. two copies of the bill of quantities;

b. general arrangement drawings indicating the general character and shape and disposition of the works;

c. two copies of the form of tender;

d. an addressed envelope for the return of the tender, and instructions relating thereto.

Will you please also note:

1. working drawings and details may be inspected at the architects office during normal working hours.

2. the site is open for inspection.

3. tendering procedure will be in accordance with the principles of the "Code of Procedure for Single Stage Selective Tendering 1977".

4. examination and correction of priced bill (Section 6 of the Code), Alternative I will apply.

5. the Employers do not bind themselves to accept the lowest or any tender and will not pay any expenses incurred in connection therewith.

The completed form of tender is to be sealed in the endorsed envelope provided and delivered or sent by post to reach . . . not later than 12.00 noon on Friday the *date*.

Will you please acknowledge receipt of this letter and enclosures and confirm that you are able to submit a tender in accordance with these instructions.

Yours faithfully.

R. S. & T.

* Based on the form suggested in *A Code of Procedure for Single Stage Selective Tendering* Appendix B: N.J.C.C.

10. SUMMARY CORRECTED

SUMMARY	£
Preliminary Items	18,662.00
P.C. and Provisional Sums	55,408.00
Substructure	17,479.06
Concrete Work	8,131.16 ~~8,031.16~~
Brickwork and Blockwork	19,083.69
Roofing	4,789.88
Woodwork	18,103.97
Metalwork	4,392.36 ~~4,394.36~~
Plumbing Services	1,884.28 ~~1,848.28~~
Plasterwork and Finishings	8,616.01
Glazing	1,036.77
Painting	4,302.74
Drainage	3,728.98
External Works	16,445.98
	£182,064.48 ~~£181,930.68~~
Water and Insurance 3·5%	6,367.57
	£188,432.25 ~~£188,298.25~~

Tender submitted £188,250.00

In the above Summary alterations have been made correcting clerical errors &c. assumed to have been found in the priced bill. The increased total means that all rates (except p.c. and provisional sums, which the contractor has no power to reduce) will be subject to a percentage rebate. To find this, extract of p.c. and provisional sums will first be made as follows:-

201

	£
Provisional Sums	10,000
Mechanical Services	14,850
Electrical Services	8,223
Wood Flooring	2,200
External Staircase	4,050
Metal Windows	6,500
Water Mains	200
Ironmongery	550
Sanitary Fittings	890
Daywork	2,610
	£50,073

The rebate to be expressed as a percentage is

		£
Errors	182,064	
	181,930	
		134
Rebate in tender	188,298	
	188,250	
		48
		£182

(This total equals the total difference between £188,432 and £188,250).

The percentage is worked out as follows:

	£
Corrected total without insurance, etc.	182,064
Less p.c. and provisional sums	50,073
	£131,991

$$\text{Percentage} = \frac{182}{131,991} \times \frac{100}{1} = 0.14\%$$

In the variation account, therefore, all rates will be subject to addition of 3.50% for water and insurances, and all except p.c. and provisional sums and accounts set against these will also be subject to a rebate of 0.14%. The water and insurance percentage can be converted into a percentage on the contractor's own work instead of on the whole total as appears in this example, and in that case the two percentages can be combined into a single percentage. As, however, in this case the contractor has expressed water and insurances as a percentage of the whole they are so treated.

202

11. CIRCULAR LETTER TO CONTRACTORS
(CORRECTIONS TO THE BILL OF QUANTITIES)

Date

DEAR SIRS,

New School, Southtown.

Will you please make the following corrections in the bill of quantities:-

Item 246. For "16 m³" read "66 m³".

356. For "m²" read "m".

Please acknowledge receipt of this letter.

Yours faithfully,
R, S & T.

12. SURVEYOR'S CHARGES FOR PREPARATION OF BILL OF QUANTITIES

Date

The Blankchester Diocesan Board of Finance
TO
R, S & T.

Southtown School.		£
To preparing bill of quantities for the above new School calculated on the amount of the lowest tender, £188,250.00		
R.I.C.S. Scale, Category B	£	
On the first £120,000.00	2,430.00	
1.10% £68,250.00	750.75	3,180.75
To preparing specification as agreed		250.00
To cost of duplicating bills of quantities and specification		418.00
To travelling expenses		23.50
		£3,872.25
V.A.T. at 15.00% on £3,684.00*		552.60
		£4,424.85

The current R.I.C.S. Scale requires a rebate on educational projects and also permits a surcharge of 12½% as agreed by the former Prices Commission, both of which should be applied.

* The printing of the specification, being a complete document is VAT free and is therefore excluded from the calculation.

13. METHOD OF PREPARING CERTIFICATE VALUATION

Certificate No. 2.

Date

		£	£
Bill No.1 Preliminaries.			
Sheds.		100	
Plant.		250	
Telephone.		20	
Watching.		100	470

No.2 Excavation.		£		
All excn.		3,050		
less provisional (not done)		125		
			2,925	
Hardcore			100	
				3,025

No.3 Concrete Work.		
All foundations.	1,425	
Basement floor.	150	
Site concrete $^2/_3$.	223	
Reinforced bed to terrace.	110	
Wire fabric to do.	25	
Lintels.	65	
Precast thresholds.	10	
		2,008

No. 4. Brickwork.				
All foundations (except provl.).			2,175	
D.P.C.			100	
56.50 m reduced	£2.20	125		
1300 m h.b. casing	£1.05	1,365		
130 m h.b. ptn.	£100	130		
			1,620	
Sundry labours, &c.			100	
Facings 600 m at 40p			240	
Slab ptns. 100 m at 50p			50	
				4,285

No. 5. Asphalt Work.		
Basement tanking, &c. complete		373

No.6 Masonry.		
Templates.		10

		Contd.	£10,171

204

	Contd.	
	£	£10,171

Bill No. 8. Woodwork.

Wood-wool slabs } 333 m at 75p }	250	
Fascias.	60	
Door frames built in.	25	
		335

No. 11 Plasterer.

Screeds for roofing.		100
		£10,606

Sub-contractors

Messrs. G & H Engineering	4,000	
I & J Electrical	1,500	
K & L. Metal Windows.	1,000	
	6,500	
Profit & attendance, as bill 3%	195	
		6,695
		£17,301
Add Water & Insurances } 3·50%. }		606
	£	£17,907
Less rebate	10,606	
	195	
0.14% on	£10,801	15
		17,892
Less retention 3%.		537
		£17,355

Unfixed Materials on Site.

As detailed list	1,500	
Less retention 3%.	45	
		1,455
		£18,810

Price Adjustment.

Labour increase as detailed.		535
		£19,345
Previous valuations.		10,000
Balance		£9,345
	say £9,350	

Valuation

No: 2

Date   x

QS Reference   RS/143/2

Quantity Surveyor. of	R.S.&T. Chartered Quantity Surveyors Bank House, Northtown.
Architect/E.Q. of	L.M.N. Esq., F.R.I.B.A. Chartered Architect 21, High Street Southtown.
Employer of	Blankchester Diocesan Board of Finance Church House Blankchester.
Contractor of	X.Y.Z. Ltd., 55 High Street Blankchester.
Works at	Southtown Church of England Primary School. Newfields Southtown.

‡We have made, under the terms of the Contract, an interim valuation as at   y

† and I/we report as follows:—

Gross valuation   [including nominated sub-contractors' values from
attached statement   *]

Less retention—either £ 3 % of £ 19,397

—or [from attached statement *]

Less previously CERTIFIED

	£	
	£	
	£ 19,350	
	£ 10,000	
	£ 9,350	

Balance (in words) Nine Thousand three hundred and fifty pounds

Contract sum £ 188,250

Signature:

Quantity Surveyor.

Notes:

(i) All the above amounts are exclusive of V.A.T.

(ii) The balance stated is subject to any statutory deductions which the Employer may be obliged to make under the provisions of the Finance (No. 2) Act 1975 where the Employer is classed as a "contractor" for the purposes of the Act.

(iii) It is assumed that the Architect (S.O. will:—

    (a) satisfy himself that there is no further work or material which is not in accordance with the Contract.

    (b) unless otherwise agreed, notify Nominated sub-contractors of payments due to them.

    (c) satisfy himself, if he wishes, that previous payments to Nominated sub-contractors have been discharged.

(iv) The Certificate of payment should be issued within seven days of the date indicated thus†.

(v) Action by the Contractor should be taken only on the basis of figures contained in the Certificate of payment.

© 1977 RICS

* Delete as appropriate.

n.j.a.

15. STATEMENT OF NOMINATED SUB-CONTRACTORS' AMOUNTS

This form is A4 size and the last line appearing here is at the bottom of the form.

Quantity Surveyor	R.S. & T. Chartered Quantity Surveyors Bank House, Northtown
Works known as situate at	Southtown Church of England Primary School Newfields, Southtown

Statement of amounts included in respect of

Nominated Sub-contractors

The following amounts have been included in the calculation of this valuation in respect of work materials or goods, executed or supplied by the nominated sub-contractor(s) listed below.

The sums stated are the gross amounts due to the named nominated sub-contractor(s). No account has been taken of any retentions which the contractor might withhold under the terms of the sub-contract(s), or of any discounts for cash to which the contractor might be entitled if setting the accounts within 14 days of the receipt of the architect's certificate or of a duplicate copy.

Payment of nominated suppliers is not conditional upon the issue of a certificate.

Nominated sub-contractor		Gross total to date £	Certified previously £	Balance £
G.H. & Co. Ltd.	Engineering	4,000	2,800	1,200
I.J. & Co. Ltd.	Electrical	1,500	–	1,500
K.L. & Son Ltd.	Metal Windows	1,000	–	1,000

Signature   Quantity Surveyor   © 1973 RICS

16. NOTIFICATION TO NOMINATED SUB-CONTRACTORS

The R.I.B.A. contract provides for this notice to be given by the Architect, but the Quantity Surveyor may be required to give such notice, or, at any rate, to fill in the form (see page 62).

Notification

Architect's name*
and address

to nominated
sub-contractor

to nominated sub-contractor
concerning amount included
in certificate

I/We inform you that under the terms of the Contract for the

works known as

Serial no.

situate at

Date of issue

a certificate has been issued for presentation to the employer

Date of valuation

The contractor

Instalment no.

of

has been directed that in the said certificate an amount is due to you as follows

Gross total to date	Certified previously	Balance included in certificate
£	£	£

Signed _____ Architect*

*Issue of this form under the
name of a person who is not
registered as an architect may
constitute an offence under the
Architects Registration Acts.

The sum stated is the gross amount due. No account has been taken of any retentions which the contractor might withhold under the terms of the sub-contract or of any discounts for cash to which the contractor might be entitled if settling the account within 14 days of the receipt of the architect's certificate or of a duplicate copy thereof.

17. FORM OF ARCHITECT'S INSTRUCTION

Architect's name *
and address

Works

situate at

To contractor

Under the terms of the Contract

dated

**Architect's
Instruction**

Instruction no.

Date

I/We issue the following instructions. Where applicable the contract sum
will be adjusted in accordance with the terms of the relevant Condition.

For office use: Approx costs

Instructions

£ omit   £ add

*Issue of this form under the
name of a person who is not
registered as an architect may
constitute an offence under the
Architects Registration Acts.

Office reference

Signed_____Architect*

Notes

Amount of contract sum £
± Approximate value of previous instructions £ _____
£
± Approximate value of this instruction £ _____
Approximate adjusted total £ _____

To Contractor ☐   Copies to Employer ☐   Quantity surveyor ☐   Clerk of works ☐   Structural consultant ☐

Heating consultant ☐   Electrical consultant ☐   ☐   ☐   Architect's file ☐

© 1967 RIBA

18. FORM OF ARCHITECT'S CERTIFICATE

Architect's name *
and address:

**Interim
certificate**

Serial No: 0566626

Employer's name
and address:

Issue date:
Valuation date:
Instalment No:
Job reference:

Contractor's name
and address:

① I/We certify that in accordance with
Clause 30 of the Standard Form of Building Contract, 1963 Edition,

under the Contract

dated: in the sum of £

for the Works:

situate at:

interim payment as detailed below is due from the Employer to the Contractor

Total value . . . . £
*includes the value of works by nominated sub-contractors as detailed on
direction form no.   dated*

Less retention . . . . £
*after deducting any retentions released previously or herewith
(as detailed on the attached statement of retention ②)*

Balance (cumulative total amount certified for payment) . . . . £

Less cumulative total amount previously certified for payment . . . . . . £

Amount due for payment on this certificate . . . . £

(in words)

All the above amounts are exclusive of VAT

*Issue of this form under the
name of a person who is not
registered as an architect may
constitute an offence under the
Architects Registration Acts.*

Signed_____Architect *

Contractor's provisional assessment of total of amounts included in above
certificate on which VAT will be chargeable   £   (a)   %

This is not a Tax Invoice

Notes: ① Where the form of contract is the Agreement for Minor Building Works 1968, delete this line and insert
'Clause 10 of the Agreement for Minor Building Works first issued 1968'.
② Delete words in parentheses if not applicable.
③ This form may be used for the purposes of releasing retention on practical completion, on partial possesion
or on making good defects. When used for this purpose and no statement of retention is issued, insert here
appropriate wording from the following:
'including release on practical completion/partial possession/making good defects'.

ᶜ RIBA Publications Ltd. 1977

19. LETTERS TO CONTRACTORS FIXING APPOINTMENT TO MEASURE VARIATIONS

A. NO APPOINTMENT FIXED

Messrs. X, Y & Z.   *Date*

DEAR SIRS,

Southtown School.

We should like to take the opportunity of beginning the measurement of variations on the above contract, and suggest doing so on Tuesday week, *date*. We should be glad to know if your representative could meet us on the site at, say, 10 a.m. on that day. If not convenient, perhaps you would suggest another day in that week.

Yours faithfully,
R, S & T

B. APPOINTMENT ARRANGED VERBALLY

Messrs. X, Y & Z.   *Date*

DEAR SIRS,

Southtown School.

As arranged on the telephone we propose to begin measurement of variations on the above contract next Tuesday week, *date* and understand that your representative will meet us on the site at 10 a.m.

Yours faithfully,
R, S & T

20. LETTER ASKING FOR INVOICES, &c.

Messrs. X, Y & Z.   *Date*

DEAR SIRS,

Southtown School.

We should be glad to have as soon as possible the following further information to enable us to complete the draft variation account:-
1. Invoices against p.c. and provisional sums as list attached.
2. Daywork sheets covering work in Instructions 16 and 17.
3. Price adjustment (Labour) sheets since *date*.
4. Invoices for sheet lead used. This item on the schedule of basic prices has been omitted from your statement.

Yours faithfully,
R, S & T.

21. LETTER ENCLOSING DRAFT VARIATION ACCOUNT

Messrs. X, Y & Z. *Date*

DEAR SIRS,

Southtown School.

We are enclosing draft variation account in connection with the above and should be glad if when you have looked through it you will arrange an appointment here to go through any points you have to raise.

You will note that a blank has been left on page 12 for the daywork sheets referred to in our letter of *date* which are still awaited.

Yours faithfully,

R, S & T.

22. SUMMARY OF THE VARIATION ACCOUNT

Item	No.			Summary.		Omissions.		Additions.
						£		£
		1		Foundations.		1,573.47		1,683.07
		2		Drains.		153.16		261.36
		3		Reinforced Concrete } Construction.		7,724.80		7,910.15
		4		Roof Coverings.		1,093.60		1,081.50
		5		Metal Windows.		3,264.79		3,214.34
		6		Floor Finishings.		625.14		591.55
		7		Ironmongery.		273.96		312.05
		8		Heating and Hot } Water Services.		4,729.55		5,021.23
		9		Electrical Work.		1,295.10		1,314.10
		10		Sanitary Fittings.		566.50		554.05
		11		Contingency Provision.		1,500.00		–
		12		Reduced size of Cloakrooms.		329.37		21.20
		13		Reduced length of Centre Wing.		153.12		11.47
		14		Garden Store.		10.80		95.63
		15		Plastering to Classrooms.		42.08		236.35
		16		Doors to Assembly Hall } Entrance.		56.55		134.46
		17		Fittings.		233.20		376.55
		18		Entrance Road.		462.47		612.16
				Add Water and Insurances } 3.50%.	£	24,087.66 843.07	£	23,431.22 820.09
				Less rebate (see attached) Omission 24,649.71 Less not subject 19,900.00	£	24,930.73	£	24,251.31
				0.14% £4,749.71 Additions 23,977.95 Less not subject 18,675.88		6.65		–
				0.14% £5,302.07		–		7.42
				Contd.	£	24,937.38	£	24,258.73

	Omissions.	Additions.
Price Adjustment Formula	£ 24,937.38	£ 24,258.73
Contd.	–	3,745.08
	£ 24,937.38	£ 28,003.81
		24,937.38
Net Addition		
Carried to Statement.		£ 3,066.43

STATEMENT.

	£
Amount of Contract.	188,250.00
Net Addition as above.	3,066.43
	£ 191,316.43

Calculation of Rebate.
Items not subject to rebate.

	Omissions.	Additions.
	£	£
Item No. 3	7,500.00	7,594.10
4	1,000.00	995.71
5	3,000.00	2,934.89
6	400.00	412.60
7	250.00	269.62
8	4,500.00	4,712.10
9	1,200.00	1,210.03
10	550.00	546.83
11	1,500.00	–
	£ 19,900.00	£ 18,675.88

23. LETTER ENCLOSING FINALLY CORRECTED VARIATION ACCOUNT

Messrs. X, Y & Z.   *Date*

DEAR SIRS,

Southtown School.

We are now enclosing variation account, in which we have incorporated the amendments made at our recent meeting, showing a total of .... We should be glad if you will sign page 54 confirming your agreement to this figure subject to audit and return to us, so that we can submit it to the Architect for approval.

Yours faithfully,
R, S & T.

24. STATEMENT OF ACCOUNT FOR CLIENT

(A simplified form easily understood by the non-technical man which can accompany the full variation account)

SOUTHTOWN SCHOOL.
Analysed Statement of Account

Date

		£	£
	Amount of Contract.		188,250.00
	<u>Additional Works.</u>		
1.	Plastering to Classrooms.	194.27*	
2.	Waterproofing of Ducts.	110.16	
3.	Enlarged platform to Assembly Hall.	50.14	
4.	Block floor in lieu of tiles to Entrance Hall.	79.17	
5.	Sliding Screen in lieu of wall between Classrooms 2 and 3.	63.14	
6.	Hardwood in lieu of softwood doors to Assembly Hall entrance.	77.91	
7.	Additional shelving to Classroom Stores.	22.50	
8.	Cupboard fitting in Head Master's Room.	19.17	
9.	Concrete in lieu of tarmacadam entrance road.	149.68	
10.	Entrance notice boards.	16.11	
			782.25
	(This can be extended *ad lib.* with any additional items required.)	Contd. £	189,032.25

---

* The adjustment for insurances and rebate has not been shown here. To be strictly accurate it should be calculated on each item. It can, however, come in the omnibus item 5 of Omissions.

			£
	Contd.		189,032.25

Less Omissions.

			£	
1.	Reduced length of centre wing }		141.63	
2.	Acoustic tiling to Assembly Hall.		100.34	
3.	Reduction in Cloakroom and Lavatory accommodation. }		308.07	
4.	Blackboards (supplied by School Authorities) }		65.10	
5.	Net Omission from adjustment of provisional sums and sundry variations. }		845.76*	

		1,460.90
		£ 187,571.35
Add V.O.P. as Price Adjustment Formula		3,745.08
		£ 191,316.43
By payments on account.		189,500.00
Balance	£	1,816.43

*   This item is the difference remaining after all the items detailed have been added or deducted. If it can be an omission all the better. It is arrived at by working backwards from the final total.

25. LETTER TO ARCHITECT ENCLOSING VARIATION ACCOUNT

L.M.N. Esq.   *Date*

DEAR SIR,

Southtown School.

We are now enclosing the Variation Account on the above contract from which you will see the total is £191,316.43. We are also enclosing an analysed statement, which may be of assistance in explaining the main adjustments to the Committee. We shall be pleased to call and go through the account with you if you will telephone us and arrange a time.

Yours faithfully,
R, S & T.

26. SURVEYOR'S CHARGES FOR VARIATION ACCOUNT

Date

The Blankchester Diocesan Board of Finance
TO
R, S & T.

Southtown School.

To making up account of variations on contract and
agreeing with contractors.

		£	£
1.50% on Omissions.		24,937.38	
Less amounts not requiring measurement as statement attached.		22,025.47	
	1.50% on	2,911.91	43.68
2.50% on Additions.		24,258.73	
Less amounts not requiring measurement.		16,480.00	
	2.50% on	£7,778.73	194.47
0.50% on remaining Additions, on £16,480.00			82.40
To check price adjustment calculations	2.50% on	£3,745.08	43.63

To taking particulars and advising on the amounts
of interim certificates.

		£	£	
	0.50% on	60,000.00	300.00	
	0.40% on	129,500.00	518.00	818.00
		189,500.00		

To cost of typing copies of Variation Account as agreed	82.70
To travelling expenses.	87.16
To subsistence expenses—6 nights at £20.00 per night as agreed.*	120.00
	£1,522.04
V.A.T. 15.00%	228.31
	£1,750.35

* Alternatively, the amount of the hotel bills.

Note: The R.I.C.S. scale of fees provides an alternative lump sum fee for post-contract
services, based on the final cost and again the 12½% surcharge will apply.

217

APPENDIX 1

Items on which no charge is made.

		Omissions £	Additions £
Item No.	1	1,573.47	– †
	3	*7,725.00	7,622.00†
	4	*1,030.00	– ‡
	5	*3,090.00	2,987.00†
	6	*412.00	– ‡
	7	*257.50	– ‡
	8	*4,635.00	4,738.00†
	9	*1,236.00	1,133.00†
	10	*566.50	– ‡
	11	1,500.00	–
		£22,025.47	£16,480.00

* Provisional sums plus 3% added for profit and attendance.
† Lump sum estimates plus do. (excluding daywork or other items requiring checking).
‡ Assumed re-measured.
   Water and Insurances, and rebate have not been adjusted on these items.

218

27. STAFF TIME RECORDS

(Monthly sheet for each member of the staff).

J. G. JONES

Month 19

	Southtown School	N.W. Hospital	London Bakery	Westborough Housing I	Westborough Housing II						
1											
2	7½										
3	7½										
4	6½	1									
5	7½										
6			7½								
7											
8											
9	7½										
10	3			4½							
11	3+2*			4½							
12	7½										
13	7½+1										
14											
15											
16	7½+2										
17	6				1½						
18					7½						
19	7½										
20	7½										
21	+3										
22											
23		7½									
24											Away ill.
25											
26	7½										
27	3				4½						
28											
29											
30					7½+2						
31					7½+2						
	96½+8	8½	7½	9	21+2 =	142½+	10				

* 2 hours' overtime are indicated by +2. The sheet total will show the total overtime to be paid for.

219

28. SPECIMEN PAGE OF SALARIES BOOK

	Salary	Overtime		Total Gross	Income Tax§	National Insurance		Total Net	Employer's N.I.
		Date							
J. G. J.	220.00	–		220.00	48.25	14.30		157.45	29.70
C. W. R.	118.00	22.60		140.60	28.00	9.14		103.46	18.98
R. W. N.	112.00	–		112.00	27.50	7.28		77.22	15.12
						30.72		338.13	63.80
								30.72	
								307.41 *	
								63.80 †	
								371.21 ‡	
		Date							
J. G. J.									
C. W. R.									
R. W. N.									

* Total posted to "Salaries" Account.
† Total posted to "Employer's Insurance Contributions" Account.
‡ Total of cheque to include money for insurance stamps.
§ The amount in this column is not included in the cheque, but is paid monthly to the Collector of Taxes.

29. SPECIMEN SALARY STATEMENT

Week ending *Date*

Miss C. W. Reynolds

			£
Salary			38.00
Overtime	3 hrs at £2.00		6.00
			44.00
Income Tax		6.25	
National Insurance			
6.50% on £44.00		2.86	
			9.11
			34.89
Expenses			–
			£34.89

30. EXTRACT FROM A SALARIES ANALYSIS BOOK

A. B. SMITH

	Flat rate £1.41			Overtime rate £1.48	
Name of job	Normal Hrs.	O/t	Total cost of Normal Hours	Total cost of Overtime	Total cost of all time
			£	£	£
B.T.	70½	15½	99.40	22.94	122.34
M.G.	14		19.74		19.74
S.H.	18		25.38		25.38
S.G.	59½	8½	83.90	12.58	96.48
C.B.P.	2		2.82		2.82
Time off	1		1.41		1.41
	165	24	£232.65	£35.52	£268.17

A similar summary for the next month would follow.

221

31. EXTRACT FROM A JOB COST ANALYSIS BOOK

The initials at the top represent the jobs, those at the side the members of the staff.

	S.G.	M.G.	B.T.	D.I.	D.T.C.	B.H.	C.B.P.	S.H.	Time off
	£	£	£	£	£	£	£	£	£
Year									
Month									
	103.04	120.07	54.36	160.10	29.18	11.06	–	–	–
Month									
X.Y.Z.	34.33	–	–	–	45.08	–	–	–	–
W.V.U.	–	–	17.16	45.11	11.38	–	–	–	–
A.B.S.	23.85	4.81	30.43	–	–	–	0.65	6.19	4.35
D.E.F.	6.19	1.55	3.13	2.18	–	–	0.50	–	–
	167.41	126.43	105.08	207.39	85.64	11.06	1.15	6.19	4.35

A similar analysis for the next month would follow with totals carried on, except where ruled off (as under S.G. above) to indicate that the job is finished.

Separate columns can be made for study or examination time, illness, sundries (i.e. work not related to a particular job). These would all give a guide as to the amount of such variable overheads.

32. SPECIMEN PAGE OF FEES BOOK

				£
Year		Contd.	£	4,623.03
Date	Z. Stores.			
	Variation a/c as detailed.		F26	896.14
Date	14, Narrow Street.			
	Report on premises.		F30	150.00
Date	D.V.G. *v.* H.			
	Attendance in Court.		F31	350.00
Date	Westborough Housing I.			
	Fee for bill of quantities.		F25	2,800.00
		To Fees Account	101	£8,819.17
				£
Date	G's Factory.			
	Valuation for certificate.		F35	70.00

33. SPECIMEN PAGE OF PETTY CASH BOOK

Receipts			Payments	Stamps	Stationery	Travelling not Chargeable	Cleaner	Sundries	Office Equipment	Running Balance	Ledger
Year		Brot fwd	13.15	2.39	2.36	1.17	6.00	1.23		6.85	
20.00											
Month	19	Envelopes	0.23		0.23					6.62	,
	21	Bus J.G.J. Hoxton	0.03			0.03				6.59	
	21	Cash								26.59	
20.00											
	24	Fares Birmingham J.G.J.	6.16							20.43	F11 6.16
	24	30 m tape	5.05						5.05	15.38	
	25	Cleaning materials	0.50				0.50			14.88	
	28	Stamp a/c	10.50	10.50						4.38	
	28	Calculator batteries	0.75					0.75		3.63	
	31	Cash								23.63	
20.00											
	31	Cleaning materials	0.50				0.50			23.13	
	31	Fares and subsistence J.G.J. B'ham	7.48							15.65	F11 7.48
	31	Paper	3.50		3.50					12.15	
60.00			47.85	12.89	6.09	1.20	7.00	1.98	5.05		13.64
								1.98			
								12.89			
					4 6		1 5	1.20	2 1		
								16.07			
								3.4			
Month	1	Balance									
12.15											

The "Ledger" column is for items to be posted immediately to a client's account and reference is given to the Personal (or Fees) ledger with the prefix F to distinguish such references from those to the Private ledger which would be without prefix.

A running balance column showing balance after each entry is convenient but not essential.

When totalled at the end of the quarter check should be made as follows:-

Receipts total minus payments total = last running balance figure.

Expense total add up horizontally = the total of "Payments" column.

The totals of Stamps, Travelling, and Sundries are added together to be posted as one total, £16.07, to Sundries ledger account.

The totals posted are marked with the reference to the Private ledger.

34. SPECIMEN PAGE OF CASH BOOK

Year		Brot. fwd.			£ 1,416.56	Year		Brot.	fwd.		£ 129.07
Date	11 Mains Rd			F11	10.50	Month	Salaries	18	818.03	F32	
						10	Insurances	25	20.62		
											838.65
											19.23
						18	Duplicat-			F32	10.60
							ing Ltd.				
						18	Drawings			121	25.00

35. SPECIMEN PAGE OF PERSONAL LEDGER

Northtown Hospital

Year				£	Year			£
Month	9	Petty Cash	P.c.	0.51				
	10	Pers. Exs.	94	0.79				
Year								
Month	28	Duplicating						
		Ltd.	F32	85.46				
Month	14	Fees.	101	1,123.75				
	24	Do.	101	105.00	Month	31	Balance.	1,315.51
				£1,315.51				£1,315.51
Year								
Month	1	To Balance		1,119.26				

36. SPECIMEN PAGE OF PRIVATE LEDGER

Stationery.

Year		Brot. fwd.		£ 34.46	Year				£
Month	10	X, Y & Co.	F11	3.07					
	14	Pers. Exs.	94	0.16					
	31	Petty Cash.	P.c.	4.39	Month	31	To a/c	P & L 91	42.08
				£42.08					£42.08

37. SPECIMEN PROFIT & LOSS ACCOUNT

Profit and Loss Account for year ending *date*

		£			£
To Rent.	1	2,120.00	By gross fees.	101	30,045.44
Cleaning.	5	137.30			
Heating and Lighting	9	225.46			
Telephone	15	320.11			
Salaries.	19	12,972.25			
National Insurance.	25	827.21			
Fire Insurance, &c.	29	22.78			
Stationery.	35	342.08			
Postage and Sundries.	41	239.10			
Accountant's Fees	45	97.35			
Institution Subscriptions	51	108.40			
* Depreciation on Furniture	59	225.10			
Balance Net Profit		12,408.30			
		£30,045.44			£30,045.44

* Not chargeable for income tax purposes. Wear and tear of furniture, fixtures and fittings may be claimed, or alternatively renewals when incurred; a motor car used for business purposes may also be the subject of a wear and tear allowance at the appropriate rate.

An individual in practice by himself is assumed: there is therefore no object in showing interest on capital. In a partnership interest on capital of each partner would be charged in the Profit & Loss Account before arriving at the profit to be divided. Interest on capital charged in this way is, like depreciation, not an expense for purposes of income tax. It must be included in the profit returned.

38. SPECIMEN BALANCE SHEET

Balance Sheet at *date*

	£	£		£	£
Sundry Creditors.		52.09	Office Furniture.	1,300.00	
			Additions for the year.	125.10	
Capital at *date*.	1,972.07				
Add Profit for the year.	12,408.30				
	14,380.37			1,425.10	
Less Drawings.	4,211.03	10,169.34	Less Depreciation.	125.10	1,300.00
			Sundry Debtors.		4,021.23
			Do. for work in hand.		3,750.00
			Cash at Bank.		1,146.05
			Do. in hand.		4.15
		£10,221.43			£10,221.43

APPENDIX 2
BIBLIOGRAPHY

Specification

B.S. Handbook No.3	B.S.I.
Sectional List of Building Standards including Codes of Practice	,,
British Standards, as required	,,
Codes of Practice, as required	,,
Specification Writing (Willis)	Crosby Lockwood Staples
Specification Notes (Aqua Group)	,, ,,
Constructional Bye-laws (for London practice)	G.L.C.
The Building Regulations 1965 (S.I. 1965, No. 1373)	H.M.S.O.
Do. Amendments (S.Is. 1966, No. 1144; 1967, No. 1645; 1969, No. 639)	,,
Do. Technical Memoranda and Index	,,
Guide to the Building Regulations 1965	,,
National Building Specification	N.B.S. Ltd.

Quantities

The Standard Method of Measurement of Building Works, 6th Edition*	R.I.C.S.
Code for the Measurement of Building Work in Small Dwelling Houses*	,,
Standard Phraseology for Bills of Quantities (Fletcher & Moore) 4 vols.	George Godwin Ltd.
Elements of Quantity Surveying (Willis)	Crosby Lockwood Staples
An Example in Quantity Surveying (Willis)	,, ,,
More Advanced Quantity Surveying (Willis)	,, ,,
Do. Supplement: Two Metric Examples	,, ,,
Group Measurement of Building Works (Holes)	,, ,,
Junior Principles of Quantity Surveying (Wood)	Estates Gazette
Principles of Quantity Surveying (Wood)	,, ,,
Measurement of Building Work (Wainwright & Whitrod)	Hutchinson Technical
Preambles for Bills of Quantities	G.L.C.
Preparation of an Operational Bill	Building Research Station

Estimating and Pricing

Building (weekly)	The Builder
The Architects' Journal (in an issue about the end of each quarter)	Architectural Press
Spon's Architects' and Builders' Price Book	Spon
Spon's Mechanical and Electrical Services Price Book	
Laxton's Building Price Book	Kelly's Directories
Schedule of Rates for Building Works	H.M.S.O.
Do. Metric Edition	,,
Rates Schedules for Weekly and Casual Hire of Road Vehicles	Road Haulage Association

Cost Planning of Buildings (Ferry)	Crosby Lockwood
Cost Control in Building Design (R & D Management Handbook 4)	H.M.S.O.
The Cost of Building—Variations from 1914 to date	The Builder

Building Contracts

Standard Form of Building Contract for use with quantities	J.C.T.
Do. without quantities	,,
Do. with quantities Local Authorities Edition	,,
Do. without quantities do.	,,
Do. with approximate quantities	,,
Do. with approximate quantities Local Authorities Edition	,,
Standard Form of Nominated Sub-contract	,,
Tender and Agreement	,,
Standard Form for Nomination of a sub-contractor	,,
Guide to the Standard Form of Building Contract 1980 edition	,,
Practice Notes on Standard Form of Building Contract	,,
Form of Agreement for Minor Building Works	,,
Fixed Fee Form of Prime Cost Contract	,,
Standard Form of Valuation	R.I.C.S.
Copy Valuation Form	,,
Standard Form of Statement of Nominated Sub-contractors' Amounts	,,
Standard Form of Statement of Retention	,,
Definition of Prime Cost of Daywork under a Building Contract	,,
Do. of Daywork of a Jobbing or Maintenance Nature	,,
Do. of Daywork for Heating &c. Contracts	,,
Do. of Daywork for Electrical Contracts	,,
Schedule of Basic Plant Charges	,,
General Conditions of Government Contracts for Building & Civil Engineering Works (Form GC/Works/I)	H.M.S.O.
The Placing and Management of Building Contracts	,,
Code of Procedure for Selective Tendering	N.J.C.C.
Preparing to Build (R & D Management Handbook 1)	H.M.S.O.
Selective Tendering for Local Authorities (R & D Management Handbook 2)	,,
The Chartered Quantity Surveyor and "Package Contracts"	R.I.C.S.
Contract Administration (Aqua Group)	Crosby Lockwood Staples
Hudson on Building Contracts	Sweet & Maxwell
The Law Relating to Building and Engineering Contracts (Creswell & Davies)	Pitman
The Standard Form of Building Contract (Walker-Smith & Close)	Knight
Law and Practice of Building Contracts (Keating)	Sweet & Maxwell
Building Contracts and Practice (Emden & Gill)	Butterworth

General

Guide to the Use of the Metric System in the Construction Industry (PD 6031)	B.S.I.
Building by Local Authorities (Layton)	Allen & Unwin
National Working Rules for the Building Industry	N.J.C.B.I.

BIBLIOGRAPHY

Annual Holidays with Pay	Building & Civil Engineering Holidays Scheme Management Ltd.
National Agreement as to Working Rules and Conditions in the Heating, Ventilating and Domestic Engineering Industry	Joint Conciliation Committee of the Industry
Industrial Agreements and National Working Rules for the Electrical Contracting Industry	National Federated Electrical Association
Royal Institution of Chartered Surveyors—List of Members	Skinners Directories Ltd.
The Services of the Chartered Quantity Surveyor	R.I.C.S.
Schedule of Professional Charges for Quantity Surveying Services	,,

Scale No.36 (Building Works – Inclusive scale: 1 March 1972)

Scale No.37 (Building Works Itemised scale: 1 July 1939 amended 1 July 1971)

Scale No.38 (civil engineering works: 1 July 1965 amended 1 July 1971)

Scale 41: Charges for QS services in connection with local authority houses or bungalows (12 March 1969)

Scale 42: Charges for QS services in connection with flat dwelling for local authorities (1 Dec 1977)

Scale 43: Charges for QS service in connection with site layout works for Housing Schemes (1945)

Scale 44: Charges for QS services in connection with improvements to existing housing and environmental improvement works (1 Feb 1973)

Scale 45: Charges for QS services in connection with housing schemes for housing societies (agreement with the Housing Corporation) (1 Oct 1968: amended 1 June 1971 and 1 August 1974)

Scale 46: Charges for QS services in connection with loss assessment of damage to buildings from fire, etc. (1 Sept 1972)

Index to Q.S. Scales

Form of Agreement for Appointment of Quantity Surveyor	,,
Notice Forms A to G for use under the London Building Act (for London practice)	R.I.B.A.
R.I.B.A. Directory	,,
The Architect in Practice (Willis & George)	Crosby Lockwood Staples
Pre-contract Practice (Aqua Group)	,, ,,
Construction (Health & Welfare) Regulations (S.I. 1966, No. 95)	H.M.S.O.
Do. (General Provisions) Regulations (S.I. 1961, No. 1580)	,,
Do. (Lifting Operations) Regulations (S.I. 1961, No. 1581)	,,
Do. (Working Places) Regulations (S.I. 1966, No.94)	,,
Guide to the Construction Regulations	N.F.B.T.E.
Government Publications. Sectional List No.61 (Publications on Building)	H.M.S.O.
Offices, Shops & Railway Premises Act 1963	,,
Do. A General Guide	,,
A Concise Building Encyclopaedia (Corkhill)	Pitman
The Concise Oxford Dictionary	Oxford U.P.
Modern English Usage (Fowler)	,,
Complete Plain Words (Gowers)	H.M.S.O.

Titles and Forms of Address	Black

Civil and Structural Engineering Work

Civil Engineering Procedure	Institution of Civil Engineers
*I.C.E. Conditions of Contract	Institution of Civil Engineers
Civil Engineering Standard Method of Measurement	
*Working Rule Agreement	Civil Engineering Construction Conciliation Board
Handbook (annually)—incorporates the publications marked * above	,,
A Manual of Specifications and Quantities for Civil Engineers (Johnson & King)	English Universities Press
Building and Public Works Administration, Estimating and Costing	Newnes Books
Estimating for Building and Civil Engineering Works	,, ,,
Civil Engineering Quantities (Seeley)	Macmillan

Law (*see also* **Building Contracts** *on page* 228)

Elements of English Law (Geldart)	Oxford U.P.
The Book of English Law (Jenks)	Murray
Principles of the English Law of Contract (Anson)	Oxford U.P.
London Building Acts (Amendment) Act 1939 (for London practice)	H.M.S.O.
Arbitration Act 1950-1979	H.M.S.O.
Arbitrations and Awards (Lawrence & Williams)	Estates Gazette
The Architect as Arbitrator	R.I.B.A.
Formula Method of Price Adjustment for Building Contracts	CALUS.

Periodicals & Leaflets

ESTIMATING

Building Cost Information Service (for members by subcription), R.I.C.S.
Elemental Bills: The Builder, October 26th, 1956; R.I.C.S. Journal, May 1956, p.605, April 1957, p. 542 and July 1957, p.16.
Cost Analysis: R.I.C.S. Journal, May 1957, p. 602, June 1959, p.693.
Cost Research: R.I.C.S. Journal, August 1957, p. 90.
The Economic Control of Building Development: R.I.C.S. Journal, May 1958, p.613.
The Role of the Quantity Surveyor during the Design Stage: R.I.C.S. Journal, July 1959, p.20.
Cost Planning: R.I.C.S. Journal, September 1959, p.149, November 1959, p.236.
Cost Research & the Quantity Surveyor: The Builder: September 11th 1959, p.197.
Cost Planning: Architects' Journal Information Library, February 7th—May 9th, 1962.
Cost Information: R.I.C.S. Journal, April 1962, p.510.
The Cost Check: R.I.C.S. Journal, July 1962, p.35.
The Housing Cost Yardstick: R.I.C.S. Journal, February 1968, p.391.
Cost Planning: R.I.C.S. Journal, May 1966, p.587.
Notes on Activity Bills: I.Q.S. Journal, September/October 1966, p.31.
The Bill of Approximate Quantities: I.Q.S. Journal, July/August 1966, p.3.

CONTRACTS

Civil Engineering Contract Conditions: The Builder, March 12th 1965, p.587.
Making the Contract: R.I.C.S. Journal, June 1966, p.647.
The Position of Subcontractors under the R.I.B.A. Contract: R.I.C.S. Journal, January 1969, p.339.
Insolvency and the Building Contract: R.I.C.S. Journal, December 1967, p.283 and January 1968, p.348.

BIBLIOGRAPHY

The Fixed Fee Form of Prime Cost Contract: R.I.C.S. Journal, April 1967, p.531.
Delays and Extensions of Time under the R.I.B.A. Contract: R.I.C.S. Journal, September 1966, p.149.
R.I.B.A. Contract (July 1971) Insurances: I.Q.S. Journal, May/June 1972 p.138.
The Chartered Quantity Surveyor and Package Deal Contracts: R.I.C.S., Q.S. Quarterly, December 1973, p.34.

SPECIFICATION
Specification and Bills of Quantities: Their Use and Inter-Relation: R.I.C.S. Journal, December 1954, p.441.
B.S.I. News: to subscribing members.

CERTIFICATE VALUATIONS AND VARIATION ACCOUNTS
Variation Accounts: I.Q.S. Journal, November/December 1955, p.111.
Interim Valuations for Certificate Purposes: R.I.C.S. Journal, March 1956, p.498.
Nominated Sub-contractors: Competitive Tenders and Final Accounts: I.Q.S. Journal, March/April 1957, p.217.
Standard Form of Q.S. Valuation: R.I.C.S. Journal, May 1968, p.567.

GENERAL
Rules of Conduct of the R.I.C.S. with *Note for Chartered Quantity Surveyors*: R.I.C.S.
Directions to Chartered Quantity Surveyors on Advertisements and other Public Announcements: R.I.C.S.
Future Practice & Procedure in Quantity Surveying: R.I.C.S. Journal, December 1960, p.313 and January 1961, p.376.
Can the Bill of Quantities be Improved? The Builder, March 16th 1962, p.565.
The Function and Uses of the Bill of Quantities: R.I.C.S. Journal, December 1962, p.320.
The Operational Bill: R.I.C.S. Journal, February 1963, p.429. Reprinted in Building Research Station Current Papers, Design Series 1.
The Critical Path Method: The Builder, June 14th and 21st 1963, pp. 1203 & 1269, and R.I.C.S. Journal, January 1964, p.339.
Professional Practice & Procedure for Quantity Surveyors: R.I.C.S. Journal, October 1963, p.179.
Producing Bills of Quantities by Computer: R.I.C.S. Journal, November 1963, p.239.
Introduction to Operational Bills: I.Q.S. Journal, September/October 1964, p.27. Reprinted in Building Research Station Current Papers, Design Series 32.
Bills of Quantities by Computer: The Builder, February 19th 1965, p. 403.
The Aims and Objectives of the National Building Agency: R.I.C.S. Journal, May 1965, p.617.
Operational Bills in Practice: R.I.C.S. Journal, April 1965, p.550.
Contractor-designed Projects: R.I.C.S. Journal, August 1965, p.81.
The Use of Computers by Quantity Surveyors: R.I.C.S. Journal, October 1965, p.181.
Partnerships: R.I.C.S. Journal, October 1965, p.187 and January 1966 (Correspondence).
Metrication and the Quantity Surveyor: R.I.C.S. Journal, March 1968, p.450.
The Quantity Surveyor and the Computer: I.Q.S. Journal, May/June 1966, p.133.
Bills of Quantities for Electrical Installations: R.I.C.S. Journal, December 1968, p.271.
The Quantity Surveyor and Engineering Services: R.I.C.S. Journal, March 1967, p.467; May 1967, p.600; August 1967, p.92.
Quantity Surveying Aspects of Coding and Data Coordination: R.I.C.S. Journal, May 1969, p.542.
Educational Training Supplement: R.I.C.S. Journal, May 1969, p.547.
Serial Contracting: R.I.C.S. Journal, May 1969, p.554.
Bills of Quantities by Computer: R.I.C.S. Journal, September 1969, p.113.
Public Accountability of the Quantity Surveyor: R.I.C.S. Journal, March 1970, p.403.
Adjustment of Preliminaries: R.I.C.S. Journal, June 1970, p.109.
Cost Benefit Analysis: R.I.C.S. Journal, September 1970, p.147.
Bills of Quantities for Engineering Services: R.I.C.S. Journal, October 1971, p.188.
Building Maintenance Cost Information Service: R.I.C.S. Journal, February 1972, p.408.
The Building Cost Information Service: R.I.C.S. Journal, March 1972, p.460.
V.A.T. and the Chartered Surveyor: R.I.C.S. Journal, November 1972, p.204.
What a Client Expects from a Quantity Surveyor: R.I.C.S. Journal, February 1973, p.357.

V.A.T. Notes for Quantity Surveyors in Private Practice: R.I.C.S. Journal, March 1973, p.419.

V.A.T. Question Time for Quantity Surveyors: RI.C.S. Journal, April 1973, p.453; May 1973, p.494.

Firm Price Tenders: a New Approach: R.I.C.S., Q.S. Quarterly, December 1973, p.31.

New Price Adjustment Formula: I.Q.S. Journal, May/June 1974, p.140.

P.S.A. schedule of Rates: R.I.C.S. Journal, Q.S. Quarterly, December 1976, p.28.

Construction Project Control: R.I.C.S. Journal, C.Q.S., January 1979, p.10.

SUNDRY NOTES

Review of Contract Settlements by Local Authorities' Financial Officers: R.I.C.S. Journal, February 1952, p.519.

Separation of provisional sums for statutory work: R.I.C.S. Journal, April 1952, p.675.

Chartered Quantity Surveyors and Consortia: R.I.C.S. Journal, September 1960, p.108, February 1962, p. 405 and February 1963, p.434.

INDEX

The names of law cases are given in italics

Accommodation, office, 145
Account, books of, 171, 223-5
Accounts
  annual, 175, 226
  for fees, *see* Fees
Adjoining owners, 6, 84, 86
Agent (or contractor), 14, 93
Agreements, legal requirements in,
  104, 105
"All-in" contracts, 3
Alterations in taking-off, 33
Alternative materials, 21
Appointment of quantity surveyor,
  25, 104, 105, 124, 131
Apprenticeship of operatives, 97, 98
Approximate estimates, *see*
  Estimates
Arbitration, 7, 84, 129
Arbitrators, Institute of, 85
Architect, relations with, 9, 91, 106
Architect's Instructions, 67, 68, 125,
  210
Architects, registration of, 91
Arenson v. Casson Beckman Rutley
  & Co., 113, 114
Associates in a firm, 180
Audit
  of office accounts, 175
  of variation accounts, 80
Authorities controlling building, 11,
  13

Bankruptcy,
  of contractor, 65, 108, 118, 128
  of employer, 108
  of surveyor, 118
Banwell, Report, 43, 228
Basic rates for materials, *see*
  Schedule of basic rates of
  materials

Bickerton & Sons v. N.W.
  Metropolitan Hospital Board,
  126
Bill of quantities
  accurate, 1
  approximate, 1, 21
  contract copy of, 55
  copyright in, 118
  corrections in, 41, 201
  despatch of, 38, 42, 200
  divisions of, 18
  duplicating of, 38, 40, 160
  editing of, 38
  elemental, 18, 32
  errors in, 41, 111, 203
  errors of pricing in, 45, 47, 55, 122,
    201
  for specialists' work, 35
  issue of, 41, 200
  operational 32, 232
  prices in, confidential, 55
Bill of variations, 77, 212, 213
Billing, organisation of, 35
Binding office documents, 57
Blair v. Osborne & Tomkins, 119
Book-keeping, 170-75, 202-26
Branch offices, 132
British Standards Institution, 99,
  158, 227
Builder
  office organisation of the, 92
  relations with the, 11
  representation of a, 83, 142
Builders' federation, 94
Builder's office, 92
Builder's site staff, 93
Builder's surveyor, 12
Builder's yard and shops, 92
Building Centre Ltd, The, 29, 95
Building industry

Continued – Building industry
   composition of, 91
   National Joint Council for, 95
   working rules of, 95, 229
Building inspector, 11
Building owner
   financial stability of, 108
   relations with, 9, 104, 131
   risks of, 123
Building Regulations, 227 (*and see*
   Construction Regulations)
   (Safety, Health and Welfare), 98,
   229
Building Research Establishment,
   100
Business cards, 153
Business Names, Registration of,
   181

Capital, 165
Case law, 103
Cash discount, 36, 46, 126
Catalogues, 157
Certificate valuations
   accuracy of, 59
   dates for, 59
   form for, 206-207
   interference with, 123
   materials unfixed in, 62, 124
   measurement for, 59
   on bankruptcy of contractor, 128
   preliminary bill in, 61
   price adjustments in, 62
   records of, 64
   responsibility for, 123
   retention sum in, 63-5
   specimen, 64, 206-208
   sub-contractors in, 61, 207-208
"Chartered Quantity Surveyor, The
   Services of the", 1
Civil Engineering Construction
   Conciliation Board for Great
   Britain, 100
Civil Engineering Contractors
   Federation of, 5, 100
   work, 4, 100, 231
Civil Engineering Work, 4
Civil Engineers, Institution of, 4, 5,
   100, 231

Claims by contractor, 77
Clerk of Works, duties of, 14, 68
Client of quantity surveyor, 9, 131
Codes of Practice, 100, 159, 227
Consortium, 4
Construction Regulations, 98, 229
Consultants
   in a firm, 180
   need for and relations with, 10, 91
Consultative committees, 100
Consulting Engineers, Association
   of, 100
Contract copy of the bill, 55
   GC/Works/1 form of, xi, 43, 46-8
   I.C.E. form of, 44, 240
   Standard forms of, xi, 44-6, 48, 49,
   228
Contractor, *see* Builder
Contracts
   "all-in", 3
   books on, 228
   firm price, 49
   Joint Tribunal, 49, 99
   negotiated, 55
   prime cost, 3, 48, 228
   with corporations, 105
   without quantities, 1, 25, 80, 88
Controlling authorities, 11, 13
Co-operation in the industry, 98
Copyright in bill of quantities, 118
Corporations, contracts with, 105
Corrections in bill of quantities, 41,
   201
Correspondence
   despatch and filing of, 154
   examples of, 194, 199, 200, 203,
   212-13, 216
   writing of, 153
Cost analysis, 18, 162
   control, 17, 21, 65, 162, 228, 232
   planning, 17, 21
   records of building, 18
Costing in the quantity surveyor's
   office, 139, 171, 221, 222
Costs, comparative, 17, 22
Cubing for approximate estimates,
   20
"Cut and shuffle", 31, 136

Dawnays v. F.G. Minter Ltd, 123

Daywork, 69
Death
of the building owner, 117
of the surveyor, 117
Department of Education and
Science, 183
Department of Health and Social
Security, 178, 180
Department of the Environment, 21,
183, 184, 186
Design and build contracts, 83
Despatch of bills, 38, 44, 200
Diaries, 155
Dilapidations, schedule of, 7, 86
Dimension sheets
index to, 33, 194
numbering of, 33
Disputes, 7, 81, 83
District Surveyor in London, 11
Documents
preservation of, 156
property in, 118
study of, 26
surveyor's office copies of, 57, 111
Donoghue v. Stevenson, 112, 113
Drawings
issue of, 41
marking of, 27
numbering on, 33
taking over, 26, 193
Duplicating bills, 38, 41, 160
Dutton v. Louth Corporation, 122

Editing bills, 38
Elemental bills, 18, 32
Employer, see Building owner
Employers' liability insurance, 150
Engineering and Allied Employers'
National Federation, 100
Engineering works, 11 (and see Civil
or Structural Engineering)
Envelopes for tenders, 39
Errors in bill of quantities, 41, 67,
111, 203
contractor's pricing, 45, 47, 53
Esso Petroleum v. Mardon, 113
Estimates
approximate, 18; by approximate
quantities, 21; by cubing, 19; by
elements, 20; by floor area, 18;

per unit, 20; reliability of, 22;
storey enclosure system of, 20
of nominated sub-contractors, 35,
76
records of, 18, 161
European Economic Community, 25
Expansion of surveyor's business,
132
Expenses, charging of, 169, 172
Extra payments to operatives, 97

Fees
accounts for, 56, 138, 203, 217
amount of, 108, 138, 169, 229
payment of, 107, 108, 166
sharing of, 139
Filing
catalogues, 157
documents, 157
letters, 154
Finance
public, 189
quantity surveyor's, 165
Fire damage assessment, 7, 87
Fire insurance, etc. (surveyor's
own), 149
Fire insurance valuations, 88
Firm price contracts, 49
Fixed fee contracts, 48
Floor areas
calculation of, for estimates, 19
records of, 161
Foreman
general, 14, 93
working, 14
Forest Products Research Station,
101
Forms in facsimile
R.I.B.A. Architect's Certificate,
211
R.I.B.A. Architect's Instruction
(Variation order), 220
R.I.B.A. Notification to
sub-contractors, 209
R.I.C.S. Amounts included for
nominated sub-contractors, 208
R.I.C.S. Certificate Valuation,
206-207

Gifts, accepting of, 143

G.K.N. Foundations v. Wandsworth L.B.C., 124
M.J. Gleeson Ltd v. London Borough of Hillingdon, 66
Gold v. Patman & Fotheringham, 121
Grading of districts, 96
Greater London Council, 9, 184

Hardy v. Walmsley Lewis, 115
Health Authorities, 183, 184
Heavy Engineering Work, 6
Hedley Byrne & Co. v. Heller & Co., 112
Hill v. South Staffordshire Railway, 126
Holidays with pay schemes, 97, 229

Income Tax, 168
Indemnity policy, 150
Index to dimension sheets, 33, 194
Information services, 18, 164
Inland Revenue Department, 80
Inman v. Lubliner, 110
Inner London Boroughs, 9, 184
Insurances by surveyor (fire, etc., employer's liability, indemnity), 149
Insurances under building contract, 45, 47, 49, 121

Joint Consultative Committees of Architects, Quantity Surveyors and Builders, 49, 99
Joint Contracts Tribunal, 49, 99

Ker v. Allan & Sons, 116

Lamprell v. Billericay Union, 125
Law, books on, 231
Letter-writing, 153, 199, 200, 203, 212, 213, 214, 216
Liaison committees, 99
London, *see* Greater London Council, Inner London Boroughs
London Building Acts (Amendment) Act 1939, 6, 84
London School Board v. Northcroft, 111, 114, 119

Luncheon vouchers, 135

Manufacturers, trade associations of, 95
Materials
  alternative, 22
  basic rates of, 37, 54, 74
  prices of, 74, 75, 162
  proprietary, 29
  unfixed included in certificate valuations, 62, 124
Measured rates record, 163
Mechanisation in the office, 136
Merchants, relations with, 13
Midland Bank Trust Co. v. Hett Stubbs & Kemp, 113
Modern Engineering Ltd v. Gilbert Ash, 124
Moneypenny v. Hartland, 115
Monopolies Commission, 109
Moon v. Witney Union, 105, 108
Mutual Life Ltd v. Evatt, 113
Myers v. Sarl, 125

National Building Agency, 185
National Consultative Council of the Building and Civil Engineering Industries, 100
National Consultative Machinery, 99
National Federation of Building Trades Employers, 94, 100
National Insurance, 168, 220, 221
National Joint Consultative Committee, 49, 100
National Joint Council for the Building Industry, 95, 97
National Working Rules, 95, 159, 229
Negligence, 111
Negotiated contracts, 58
North v. Bassett, 107
Note-paper, 151
Numbering
  dimension sheets, 33
  items in the bill, 37
  rooms, etc., on drawings, 33

Office accommodation, 145
Office cleaning, 149

Office costs, 139, 170, 221, 222
Office equipment, 148
Office furnishing, 147
Office heating and lighting, 149
Office insurance, 149
Office stationery, 151, 153
Office telephone, 149
Offices, Shops & Railway Premises
    Act 1963, 146
Operational bills, 32, 243
Overseas work, 6
Overtime, 72, 167, 191, 219

P.A.Y.E., 168, 220, 221
"Package-deal", 3
Paper sizes, British Standard, 151
Partners
  salaried, 180
  selection of, 179
Partnership
  acts of the, 181
  meaning of, 177
  reasons for, 177
  terms of, 179
Party wall awards, 7, 84, (and see
    Adjoining owners)
P.C. sums, see Provisional and p.c.
    sums
Pension schemes, 135
Periodicals, articles, etc., in, 232
Petty cash account, 171, 173, 224
Postages, 172, 173
Practice, definition of, xi
Practice Notes, 46
Preambles, 35
Preliminary bill, 35
Price adjustment (labour), 73, 75
Price adjustment (materials), 53, 55,
    67, 74, 75
Price books, 29, 163, 228
Priced bill
  confidential, 55
  examination of, 52
  return of, 40
Prices
  approximate; by cubing, 19; by
    elements, 20; by floor area, 18;
  estimating alternative, 21
  per unit, 20
  schedule of, 2, 44

Prime cost, definition of, 48, 72
Prime cost contracts, 3, 48, 228
Printing bills, 37, 40, 160
Procedure, definition of, xi
Profit sharing, 141
Progress charts, 84, 163, 194
Proofs of bill, 40
Proprietary materials, 29
Provisional and p.c. sums, 36, 48, 60,
    67, 76, 198
Provisional quantities, 71
Public service
  building contracts in, xi, 43, 46, 49,
    188
  compared with private practice,
    190
  duties in, 187
  employment in, 186
  financial control in, 190
  organisation of, 184
  private practice for, 186, 188
  scope of, 183
Purchase of a business, 166

Quantities
  books on, 227
  not part of the contract, 25, 80, 89
Quantity Surveyor
  appointment of, 25, 105, 106, 123,
    131
  work of, 1, 131, 138
Queries for the architect, 28, 193

Receipt of tenders, 51
Records of hidden work, 14, 69
Records, office
  building costs, 18, 162
  job costs, 139, 170, 221
  materials prices, 162
  measured rates, 163
  personal diaries, 155
  progress charts, 163
  staff time, 163, 219
  wages rates, 162
Reduction bills, 54
Redundancy Payments Act 1965,
    168
Reference books, 158, 227
Registration
  of architects, 91

Continued – Registration
of business names, 181
Remeasurement, 126
Reports, 89, 115, 116
Retention sum, 46, 47, 63
R.I.B.A. publications, 209-11,
227-32
Richardson and Waghorn v. Beales,
106
R.I.C.S. publications, 206-208,
227-32
Rulings of paper, British Standard,
37, 151

Salaries, 134, 167, 220, 221
*Saunders and Collard v. Broadstairs
Local Board*, 115
Schedule
of basic rates of materials, 37, 54,
56, 74
of p.c. and provisional sums, 198
of prices, 2
War Department, 2, 44
Schedules
of allocation, 38
of condition, 86
of dilapidations, 7, 86
use of specification, 28
Scope of the book, xi
"Services of the Chartered Quantity
Surveyor, The", 1
SfB classification, 157
Sickness benefit, 134
Sincock v. Bangs, 116
Site meetings, 68
Specialist bills, 35
Specification
books on, 231
preparation of, 88, 55
references to, 35
Staff
expenses of, 134, 221
quantity surveyor's, 133
salaries of, 133, 167, 220, 221
temporary, 163, 168
time records of, 163, 219
training of, 135
Stages, building erected in, 31, 45, 65
Stamping of agreements, 105

"Standard Method of Measurement
of Building Works, The", 99,
227
"Standard Method of Measurement
of Civil Engineering Quantities,
The", 4, 230
Standards, British, *see* British
Standards Institution
Stationery, 151, 153
Statutory authorities, 13, 184
Storage of documents, 156
Stovin-Bradford v. Volpoint Ltd, 119
Structural engineering work, 5, 8,
100, 230
Structural Engineers, Institution of,
100
Sub-contractors
certificate valuations for, 61, 207,
208, 209
estimates of, 35, 36, 196
legal position of, 126
need for, 12
nomination, accounts of, 76
retention on, 63
terms of, 45, 47
work of, omitted and paid direct,
126
Summary of the bill of quantities,
corrections in, 53, 201, 202
Suppliers, nominated, 36, 46, 47, 64,
195
Surveyor
Contractor's, 12
under building contract, 1, 104,
124
Sutcliffe v. Thackrah, 114

Taking-off
alterations in, 33
for elemental bills, 37
organisation of, 29
trade-by-trade, 31
Taxation of costs, 169
Telephone, 149, 163
Tender
forms of, 39, 194
invitations to, 39, 199
Tendering, Code of Procedure for
Selective, 39, 53, 99, 194, 199

Tenders
  delivery of, 39, 51
  effect of, 121
  errors in, 122
  publication of, 52
  receipt of, 51
  reporting of, 51
Thompson Horsley Bridge Ltd v. Wellingborough Steel and Construction Ltd, 124
Tout and Finch Ltd. Re, 128
Trade associations of manufacturers, 95
Trade names, 29
Trade Representatives, 15
Trade unions of operatives, 94, 100

Universal decimal classification, 157

Valuations, *see* Certificate valuations, Fire damage assessment, Fire insurance valuations
Variation accounts, 67-82, 220, 222, 228
Variation orders, 67, 68, 124, 220
Variations
  admission of, 67
  billing of, 77
  itemising of, 71
  measurement of, 68, 69-72, 122, 123, 212-14
  pricing of, 77-9
Vouchers, 173

Wages of operatives, 96, 162
Watson and Carter v. Cooper, 118
Welfare, 98
Wilkinson ex p. Fowler. Re, 127
Work of the quantity surveyor, 1, 131, 138
Working rules, 96, 159, 229

Young v. Smith, 108

ML m00

This book is to be returned on or before
the last date stamped below.